THIRD EDITION

CONSERVING NATURAL RESOURCES

Principles and Practice in a Democracy

SHIRLEY WALTER ALLEN, M.F.

Professor Emeritus of Forestry

JUSTIN WILKINSON LEONARD, Ph.D.

Professor of Natural Resources

School of Natural Resources
The University of Michigan

McGRAW-HILL BOOK COMPANY

New York   St. Louis
San Francisco   Toronto
London   Sydney

Conserving Natural Resources

Library of Congress Catalog Card Number 65–28230

01081

34567890   MP   732106987

Title page photograph: View on Hiwassee Lake, TVA
(Courtesy Tennessee Valley Authority)

CONSERVING NATURAL RESOURCES

PREFACE

Since *Conserving Natural Resources: Principles and Practice in a Democracy* was first published in 1955, it has been used by numerous colleges and universities as a textbook. Experience indicates that both revision and a change in format are warranted. Consequently the original seven chapters have been divided into fourteen with the hope that greater usefulness as a teaching text may result. A coauthor has been enlisted, whose close cooperation in the revision has been maintained.

The authors realize that no one, or even two, writers can hope to cover the whole field of the conservation of natural resources with the authority demanded by many teachers. They believe, however, that there is much to be said for a unified text rather than the more frequent symposium type in which many authors contribute separate, possibly profound, but often poorly related, chapters. They believe that the unity sought in the previous editions has been maintained.

The authors believe also that emphasis on the policies and procedures characteristic of a democracy is important. The rights of the individual and the corporation in such a nation, where cooperation with government reaches a respected status, demand consideration.

The help of many agencies and individuals must be sought in treating so broad a subject as conserving natural resources, and the friendly assistance of the following Federal agencies deserves special mention: the Soil Conservation Service and the Forest Service in the Department of Agriculture; the Bureau of Land Management, the National Park Service, the Office of Saline Water, the Fish and Wildlife Service, the Bureau of Mines, the Bureau of Outdoor Recreation, the Bureau of Reclamation, and the Geological Survey in the Department of the Interior; the Division of Air Pollution in the Public Health Service of the Department of Health, Education, and Welfare; the Corps of Engineers of the United States Army in the Department of Defense; the Tennessee Valley Authority; and the Saint Lawrence Seaway Development Commission. At the state level, the California Department of Fish and Game and the Michigan Department of Conservation have supplied helpful information and illustrations. The Great Lakes Fisheries Commission, an international body, has supplied useful tabular material.

Certain quotations, tables, and illustrations are used by special permission of the individual or agency supplying them. These include, in addition to those mentioned in the 1959 edition and credited again in this text, Resources for the Future, the National Association of Manufacturers, The Johns Hopkins Press, the McDonnell Aircraft Corporation, and the Massachusetts Audubon Society. We extend our thanks to them.

Other individuals and agencies to whom we are grateful for help are Prof. Archibald B. Cowan for reading and making suggestions on the chapter on wild animals; Prof. Dow V. Baxter for furnishing a number of photographs from his Alaskan travels; Dr. James P. Gilligan for two wilderness photographs; Robert W. Kelley, for suggesting certain changes in the chapter on metals and miscellaneous nonmetallics; the Air Pollution Control District of Los Angeles County for reading and making valuable suggestions on the chapter on atmosphere; the National Coal Association for a number of photographs and other illustrative material and for reading and criticizing the material on coal; the Indiana Coal Producers Association for photographs of strip mining and rehabilitation of strip-mined lands; the American Petroleum Institute for photographs and suggestions; Roy Jarvis for an airplane photograph of the Point Loma desalting plant; and the Consumers Power Company for a photograph of their nuclear power plant at Big Rock Point in Michigan.

Revision copy was skillfully interpreted and typed by Ethel Huntwork and Barbara Robbins.

Valuable assistance in proofreading was given by Sara Howard Allen, wife of the senior author; Fannie A. Leonard, wife of the junior author, assisted in surveys of current literature.

It is our hope that this book not only may serve as a text in teaching but may merit being read and used for reference by the general public in libraries. There is no substitute for an informed public in the effort to accomplish the objectives of conserving natural resources.

Shirley Walter Allen
Justin Wilkinson Leonard

CONTENTS

CONSERVING NATURAL RESOURCES

1 INTRODUCTION

THE NEEDS AND the wants of mankind are brought into clearer perspective with the growth of scientific knowledge and technology. Such developments as the discovery and application of nuclear power, the exploration of outer space, the search for greater knowledge of the resources of oceans, and the control of human disease add to, rather than supplant, what people want out of life and what they need for survival. In these days of automation, there is nothing automatic about satisfying the wants and needs of a growing population, whether they be material or spiritual. In fact this can hardly be done without giving our natural resources some pretty rough treatment. Yet in a democracy where people may have a part in the management of their country, there is plenty of opportunity *to use rationally, build up, and distribute equitably in terms of public benefit those things that people call their natural resources.* This is conservation.

Carrying out such a program requires from the citizens of a democracy continuing effort to understand their natural environment; to respect, and to submit to, police power where restraint in use and exploitation is necessary; to encourage and finance the search for knowledge and development of skills to apply such knowledge in natural-resource management, whether public or private; and, perhaps the most important of all, to accept the idea of trusteeship in behalf of all the people, rather than unrestricted private ownership of any natural resource. There is in such a program no place for *laissez faire,* politics in its evil sense, or failure to use scientific knowledge, forethought, and organization. Many arts, sciences, and procedures are involved.

Rational use of natural resources will seek to avoid *waste,* an oversimplified definition of which is destruction or loss without equivalent gain. Waste can occur both in production and in consumption. *Absolute waste* is destruction without return. A good example of this is the accelerated erosion of soil by wind or water. Another and more severe waste is not only absolute, but *waste plus,* the destruction of other resources in the wasteful management of one. An example would be a forest fire which destroyed game animals as well as trees or depleted the game population by destroying cover. Then there is *relative waste,* in which a disproportionate amount of a natural resource is used to accomplish a given purpose. In consumption, this might be the use of a copper roof for a temporary building. In production, an example might be the washing away of a productive hayfield by hydraulic mining in order to recover a moderate yield of gold from the underlying gravel. Finally there is *organized waste,* where artificial scarcities are produced by deliberately destroying valuable resources or crops or the manufactured goods produced from them in order to maintain prices, make way for a new product, or gain space. Problems of avoiding waste are particularly difficult in a mass-production economy where waste due to styling or contrived obsolescence appears almost necessary if things are to keep moving.

Our record in the management of the natural resources of a great democracy is none too good, but it is improving. Something of this record will be discussed later, but such a treatment will be more intelligible following a look at natural resources as factors of production and in their natural groupings.

NATURAL RESOURCES

Natural resources in a narrow sense are those uncaptured natural stores which are useful to mankind in any way. They are most commonly grouped as waters, soils, forests, grasslands, wild-animal life, and minerals. In so far as they constitute collectively one of the factors of production, the economist speaks of them as "land." When they are manipulated by human powers which in turn are aided by tools and other operating devices, three factors, "land, labor (including enterprise), and capital," swing into action and what the economist calls "production" gets going. Forests become houses, railroad ties, fuel, paper, or pencils; grass and other forage become meat and leather; waters become available for drinking, cooking, cleansing, transporting, and actually make up an important part of the volume of many useful articles and materials; wild-animal life becomes food, fur coats, quarries, photographic targets, trophies, or museum specimens; minerals become household fuels, abrasives, fertilizers, paper clips, automobiles, bulldozers, and jet planes.

The six groups mentioned above may well be arranged for convenience, and they might line up this way:

Inexhaustible natural resources
    The atmosphere
    Water in its cycle
Replaceable and maintainable natural resources
    Water in place
    Soils
    Land in its spatial sense
        For human activities
        For the scene and other amenities
    Forests
    Grasslands and other forage resources
    Wild-animal life
    Human powers[1]
        Those of the body
        Those of the spirit

[1] There is nothing unnatural about human powers, and the term *human powers* makes their consideration here more appropriate than the more common term *human resources*. Either term is different from and broader than *labor* or *enterprise*.

Irreplaceable natural resources
  Minerals
    Metals
    Mineral fuels and lubricants
    Miscellaneous nonfuels, nonmetallics
  Land in natural condition[2]
    Nature-study areas
    Specimen wildernesses

INEXHAUSTIBLE NATURAL RESOURCES

The Atmosphere. There is plenty of air. It is indispensable to life. There are places where it carries distressing impurities. Its moisture content, temperature, and movements in the great mass known as *atmosphere* constitute what is called *climate,* and this makes it important in determining the character of the soil and land in its spatial sense and how it may be used. It is therefore a natural resource which affects profoundly other natural resources. In a local and limited sense it can perhaps be managed, but the fact that it is in continual circulation puts it beyond all but the most superficial efforts in this direction.[3]

Water in Its Cycle. Rainfall, runoff, circulating ground water, rivers, lakes, oceans, and atmospheric moisture constitute an inexhaustible supply of water. It is indispensable to life, but whether or not this moving supply is made to serve mankind adequately is a question of control and management of regional and local supplies. Not infrequently, temporary or permanent local or regional shortages are experienced through waste or through need for special amounts and qualities. Of course, also, the original availability of water as a natural resource depends on climate.

REPLACEABLE NATURAL RESOURCES

Waters in Place. Waters in the particular places where they are needed and can be used may be maintained or augmented in supply through seeing to it that rainfall reaches underground storage, that runoff is retarded by vegetation and is impounded and distributed, and that land use and occupancy do not dissipate or pollute water supplies. Water which we see, use, and consider indispensable, therefore, is replaceable.

Soils. Because most of the food and clothing and much of the shelter required by mankind must come from plants that grow in the soils or from animals that feed on such plants, soils are indispensable to life. They are

---

[2] Maintainable perhaps, but questionably replaceable.
[3] The National Center for Atmospheric Research, established in 1961 by fourteen universities with its budget paid by the National Science Foundation, is undertaking a weather-research program. Its director stresses the danger of attempts at large-scale weather control with our present lack of knowledge.

replaced very slowly in nature but to some extent can be "rebuilt" and maintained in quality and fertility by human effort. "Maintainable" rather than "replaceable" therefore more accurately characterizes soil as a natural resource.

Land in Its Spatial Sense. Land surface is required for human activities, if only enough to stand on. Space occupied by a cornfield or farmstead in 1941 may have been preempted by a vast war plant in 1963 or a jet landing field in 1965. The city of today stands in the marsh or forest of yesterday. Here again, land as space or room is maintainable in the sense that it may be kept in shape to endure intensive human use and prevented from becoming "blighted" for such use. Occasionally its most important use may be to furnish a restful or inspiring scene, but even here its availability for the purpose may depend upon care and protection. The airport, the freeway or turnpike, the subdivision (Fig. 1-1), and the testing grounds for atomic-energy developments are modern examples of space demand.

Forests. Whether left in their natural state or helped out by good management, forests usually renew themselves. They persist through the ages even though they suffer from human encroachment and other abuses. Left to itself, the forest renewal process is often extremely slow. The practice of forestry accelerates the renewal process and the production of the species most needed by mankind. Forests are renewable and maintainable.

Grasslands and other Forage Resources. Both livestock and game animals depend for support on the nation's vast areas of grasslands and

Need for space for human activity is constantly on the increase. Here the city crowds and passes the fairgrounds and farm land. Subdivision for residence will probably take the remaining open land. (Ann Arbor Daily News.)

figure 1-1

edible woody plants. The carrying capacities of these areas have their limits, but if they are not overused, they may produce forage indefinitely. However, they are needed not only for support of livestock and game animals but for human occupancy and use as well. Such uses are often in conflict, but with wise regulation the productive capacity of these areas can be maintained and even increased.

Wild Animal Life. Almost every form of animal life is subject to capture or control by man. Also, the food and habitat upon which these forms depend may be damaged or destroyed by human activities. Certain species have already become extinct, and others are presently endangered. However, science-based regulation of the harvest of periodic increase and protection of range from encroachment give permanence to this resource.

Human Powers. It is obvious that human powers such as strength, dexterity, and the physical skills which may be grouped as powers of the body are necessary to existence. In no less degree, certainly, men's power to reason and to live in peace and justice with their fellow men, which may be grouped as intellectual and moral powers or powers of the spirit, are essential to existence. There is nothing *unnatural* about these powers. They are capable of renewal and maintenance and may well be considered the greatest of all *natural* resources.

IRREPLACEABLE NATURAL RESOURCES

Minerals. The metals, the mineral fuels and lubricants, and the numerous useful nonmetallic, nonfuel resources are truly irreplaceable. They are necessary surely to the present technological stage of human living, and they affect profoundly the convenience and comfort of such living. Only in the most limited sense are the metals maintainable in use. The mineral fuels and lubricants are of course destroyed in use, while the maintainable nonmetals such as the building stones, sands, and clays are comfortably plentiful. Moreover, when ancient buildings are razed, their stone may be available for modern structures.

Land in Natural Condition. In the cultural life of any nation, certain appreciable areas in natural and undisturbed condition may be said to be indispensable for purposes of study and for those inspirational values which can come only from combinations of scenery and solitude—the two things are not the same (Fig. 1-2). Once radically exploited or modified, the original or natural values in such lands cannot be wholly recaptured. Even a great part of a dedicated "wilderness area" can lose, through overuse, certain values which cannot be fully restored.

CONSERVATION ATTITUDES

Original Abundance of Natural Resources. With this background in mind, it is well to consider the attitudes of the settlers who started our

figure 1-2
Land in natural condition. Cougar Lake with House Mountain in background, near Goat Rocks Wild Area, Washington. Mine dumps or a road zigzagging up the face of this mountain or a raised lake level for industrial power would make it impossible to recapture this scene. It is irreplaceable. (Photo by James P. Gilligan.)

democracy and how those attitudes have persisted and influenced the use of natural resources up to the present.

The nation still ranks high in the occurrence of all essential natural stores except for a few of the indispensable metals. Forests of vast extent, fertile soils, inland waters for any important purpose, wild-animal life in

7

abundance, and minerals for the taking greeted the settler and made him feel perhaps that here at last was a land of inexhaustible resources. They might not be arranged just the way he wanted them, for forests stood where he needed arable land for food crops; the crude water-wheel mills for grinding could not always take advantage of falling water where he wished; the game animals for food and skins had to be hunted and trapped; and even the trees he needed were of inconvenient size. When it came to minerals, he had little of the wherewithal to convert them into use. But it was good land and rich, and the settler did what other pioneers throughout the world had done before him. He made lavish use of natural resources to make up for the scarcity of the other two factors of production. Labor in terms of his own puny strength was scarce. Capital in terms of tools, money as a device of exchange, buildings, and transportation equipment were scarce. Under these circumstances it is not strange that natural resources suffered.

Forests gave way over a period of 200 years to farms and pastures until the original area of forest has been reduced from 822 million acres to 647.7 million, plus an additional 16.5 million acres in Alaska. Not all this area today produces usable timber, and local scarcities exist in many places. Use and exploitation were characterized by terrific waste both through failure of reasonably complete utilization of products and through fire as an incident of human activity, often followed by tragic losses from insects and disease.

Water, plentiful at first for all uses, has served one of its greatest purposes, that of transporting human and industrial wastes, to such an increasing extent that the pollution of streams and underground waters has made many of them intolerable for use for any other purpose save transportation and power production. Concentrations of population have overused underground accumulations of water to an alarming degree.

Land cleared so the soil could be used for crops is frequently found in service after 200 years of cropping, but increasing amounts of soil have been lost through water and wind erosion accelerated by ignorance and carelessness in cultivation. Likewise, the nutrient materials essential to plant growth have been removed by crops and by the failure to prevent loss of the actual soil by erosion and failure to return available plant residues, animal manures, and other soil builders.

Not everybody wants to see the country too plentifully supplied with wild-animal life. Even the sportsman is inclined to battle for the maintenance of his favorite quarry only and to advocate the destruction of certain predators which may also have economic or aesthetic importance. But game and fur animals existed in marked abundance in this country and still exist to form the basis of hunting and fishing which support equipment, supply, and servicing businesses running annually into billions of dollars. Furs, too, are taken in great numbers each year, and millions of Americans get thrills from seeing, hearing, and photographing wild creatures all the way from butterflies to mountain lions. Certain of the fisheries are of great commercial importance. But the history of wild-animal life in this country is one of destruction and, in some instances, of extinction.

Minerals are difficult and expensive to recover from the earth, and at first thought this should influence men to use them sparingly, take good care of them, and seek the more ready-at-hand, replaceable, and easily exploited substitutes. But men have a lot of audacity in their make-up, and if convenience, profit, and comfort to the human race can result from reckless and wasteful exploitation of minerals, that is the course their use is likely to take. Policies governing development of mineral resources have contained few safeguards against wasteful methods either at the source or in subsequent development and merchandising. Hence the public often seems to expect to enjoy perpetual availability at low prices.

Human powers pose a persistent problem. In a democracy, particularly, every citizen has the right to expect opportunity to maintain health, to work productively and for a sufficient reward to assure a reasonable living and financial security, and to learn what he needs to know to make him fit into his environment and become increasingly useful to society. And certainly he should expect every encouragement in his pursuit of freedom from fear and want and of freedom of religion and speech. In no form of government do these opportunities and encouragements exist to such an extent as in a democracy. Yet even our own country has need to increase them. Through them come the availability and to some extent the development of human powers in the role of natural resources.

Conservation as a Definite Movement. It is frequently said that the scientists of the country are responsible for the definite movement toward the conservation of natural resources. The thought and leadership of political economists and of certain statesmen, however, have been generous and just as nearly indispensable. Moreover, none of these groups could have been effective without an awakening among the people, although this still is not sufficiently widespread.

"Economy of natural resources" preceded the more popular term "conservation of natural resources" which came into general use in the administration of Theodore Roosevelt, about 1907. The suggestion of the term *conservation* is said to have come from English visitors to the United States who had long used the title "conservator" in managing the land resources of India.

The movement assumed definite shape on a country wide scale with the meeting of a conference of governors called by President Theodore Roosevelt in May, 1908. Here are some of the events that led up to this conference:

1. The various laws governing the disposal of the public domain and their operation including, among others, the Homestead Act of 1862, the mining laws, and the Timber and Stone Act of 1878 (Fig. 1-3)
2. The spectacular lumbering operations which were beginning to alarm observers as the industry plowed through the Lake states from 1870 on
3. Consideration of forest exploitation by the American Association for the Advancement of Science and presentation of memorials to the Congress in 1870 and again in 1890, resulting in the establishment of a Forestry Bureau in the U.S. Department of Agriculture in 1890 and in the legalization and withdrawal from settlement of the first "forest reserves" in 1891
4. Studies and publication of a report by Major J. W. Powell on *Lands*

figure 1-3
More than one-half the total land area of the fifty states has been disposed of to private holders and to the states. (Bureau of Land Management, U.S. Department of the Interior.)

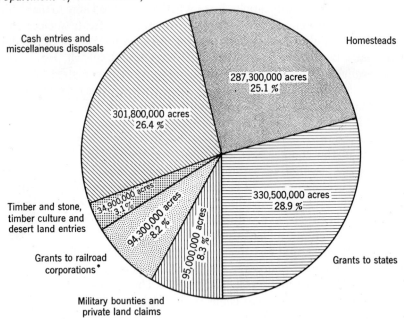

Cash entries and
miscellaneous disposals

Homesteads

287,300,000 acres
25.1 %

301,800,000 acres
26.4 %

Timber and stone,
timber culture and
desert land entries

34,900,000 acres
3.1 %

94,300,000 acres
8.2 %

95,000,000 acres
8.3 %

330,500,000 acres
28.9 %

Grants to railroad
corporations*

Grants to states

Military bounties and
private land claims

*Exclusive of revested area

Total disposals 1,143,800,000 acres

of the Arid Region in 1879 and the establishment of an irrigation division in the United States Geological Survey

5. Recommendations by the National Academy of Science in 1897 strengthening forest-reserve policy and the resulting legislation
6. Long agitation for, and passage of, the Reclamation Act in 1902
7. Rapid growth of population from 1890 on, predictions that the United States would have more than 200 million people by 1950, and a growing fear that the country was not managing its resources wisely to take care of all these people.
8. Appointment of the Inland Waterways Commission by President Theodore Roosevelt in 1907 and its first report emphasizing the interrelated character of water, forest, transportation, and fuel problems

The White House conference of 1908 itself was no usual gathering, and it was the first one to which the governors of all the states had been invited for consideration of any question of national policy. Members of the Senate and the House of Representatives, the judges of the United States Supreme Court, representatives of the important scientific societies, members of the Inland Waterways Commission, and certain prominent citizens at large contributed to an unusual meeting of minds expressed in a "Declaration of Principles." This document left no doubt as to their conviction that some order should come into the use of natural resources.

It should be noted here that this declaration took no account of wild-animal life and apparently gave consideration to human powers only in terms of safety for mine workers. (One speaker at the conference brought up the subject of the natural scene and the importance of conserving it but was listened to, apparently, only with politeness.)

The leadership of two dynamic characters was everywhere seen at this conference: Gifford Pinchot, Chief of the United States Forest Service and Chairman of the Inland Waterways Commission; and President Theodore Roosevelt, whose fighting idealism so frequently led to vigorous action.

Two important and immediate results of the White House conference were: (1) the appointment of a fifty-man National Conservation Commission composed about equally of scientists, businessmen, and statesmen, which reported back to the governors in December, 1908, with an inventory of the country's natural resources; and (2) the appointment of state conservation agencies in forty-one states by governors who had become convinced that such agencies were necessary.

One other very important result, which can hardly be termed immediate, was the use of the inventory, by the President, as a basis for the withdrawal from further settlement and entry (pending private acquisition) of vast areas of the public lands for study, looking to permanent dedication as public mineral, timber, and water-power "reserves." A total of some 200 million acres was thus withdrawn, but not until 1920 were the Mineral Leasing Law and the Federal Power Law enacted to provide for administration of a character similar to that already available for the "forest reserves." Following careful study, some 50 million acres of mineral reserves and more than 148 million acres of forest land and water-power sites were finally reserved permanently out of the above total withdrawals.

The inventory submitted by the National Conservation Commission would not have been possible without the help of skilled scientists and others in the various Federal bureaus, whose services were prompt and of a high order. Subsequent analysis and planning on a creditable scale by the Commission required an initial appropriation of $25,000, which was requested from the Congress by President Taft. The request, however was ignored, and thus passed out of existence the National Conservation Commission, a body which might have become a great natural-resource planning agency appropriate in that particular period of the life of a democracy.

The North American Conservation Conference. In February, 1909, upon call of President Theodore Roosevelt, a conference of North American nations met in Washington with representatives present from Canada, Newfoundland, Mexico, and the United States, to consider natural-resource questions on an international scale. Here, as in the White House conference of governors, conclusions were embodied in a "Declaration of Principles" which was broader and more specific than the one adopted by the earlier conference. Public health, "game preservation . . . and special protection for such birds as are useful to agriculture" were mentioned. Drainage of wetlands and the control of grazing on nonirrigable public lands were recommended. The suggestion of calling a world conference on conservation was approved. The leaders of the world were, therefore, requested by President Theodore Roosevelt in February, 1909, to meet at The Hague to consider world natural-resource problems. He went out of office, however, in March, 1909, and lack of interest on the part of the Taft administration which followed resulted in failure to carry out Roosevelt's plan. That world conference was never held. It is interesting to speculate on what such a meeting at that time might have meant to world cooperation and peace. After 40 years and two terrible world wars, a conference of somewhat different character *was* held at Lake Success in 1949 and known as the United Nations Scientific Conference on the Conservation and Utilization of Resources. This conference was first suggested by President Harry S. Truman in 1946 to the United States representative on the Economic and Social Council of the United Nations. It was a direct outgrowth of the idea which Gifford Pinchot had kept alive until his death the same year. The opportunity of using such a conference for the enlightenment of international statesmen appears to have been overlooked, but somewhat better cooperation among scientific workers of many nations has resulted.

The period from 1909 to 1933, as far as conservation activity is concerned, was characterized by somewhat slow, but steady, progress in the acquisition by the Forest Service of forest lands at the headwaters of navigable streams and elsewhere in the Eastern United States and the establishment of the principle of Federal, state, and private cooperative attack on forest fires, both authorized in the Weeks Law of 1911; by an increasing interest in the protection and development of wild-animal resources; by recognition of, but inadequate provision for the handling of, water-power resources; by the development, under Federal lease and regulation, of mineral resources on public lands; by a slow and steady awakening of certain industries and corporations to the duties and advantages of better natural-resource management; by healthy growth in state conservation agencies; by a recognition of the value and indispensability of the scenic and inspirational resources of the country and a considerable extension of national and state park areas; and by continuing failure to see clearly in human powers the greatest natural resource of all.

Conservation from 1933 to the End of World War II. With the inauguration of President Franklin D. Roosevelt in March, 1933, the plight of large numbers of people who had lost their possessions and jobs during the years after the financial crash of 1929 and the physical disaster of wind erosion dramatized the appropriateness of a great public-works program to furnish employment and to accomplish useful work in managing natural resources. This Roosevelt had not attended the governor's conference at the White House in 1908, but two years later, as a young and newly elected assemblyman in New York, he had been appointed by Governor Dix to the chairmanship of a reputedly "innocuous committee on forest, fish and game" which had straightway improved its reputation through the interest and energy of its chairman. He was also at this time close to Thomas Mott Osborne, who had been appointed Commissioner of Forests, Fish and Game in New York on the doubtful qualification of a great knowledge of penology and the more suitable one of a great desire to learn what conservation of these natural resources was about. Whether or not this association and the struggle of these two men together to master their assignments are reflected in President Franklin D. Roosevelt's program of conservation, a combined interest in conserving human powers and other natural resources at the same time is unmistakable.

The President's first stroke was the establishment of the Civilian Conservation Corps under the authority of an act passed by the Congress on

March 31, 1933, granting broad powers to employ young men for the purpose of conserving natural resources. The "enrollees," many of whom had never had any opportunity for remunerative employment, were organized into companies of 200 under army officers who operated the camps and cooperated with project superintendents, who with their staffs supervised the work on forest protection, construction, forest research, forest planting and care, soil-erosion control, pest control, lake and stream survey and improvement, recreational developments, flood control on Federal public lands and on state, county, and private lands where the Federal government was legally authorized to cooperate. Mobilization was surprisingly swift, more than 1,500 camps of 200 men each being established throughout the country within 3 months (Fig. 1-4).

Records of accomplishments are impressive, as are the records of improved health, skill, and reduction of delinquency among the men enrolled. By 1935 the number of camps had increased to more than 2,600, and many enrollees were currently leaving for employment of their acquired training in industry.

The Civilian Conservation Corps was reauthorized for 3 years in 1937, with more emphasis on vocational training prescribed, and finally closed out as no longer necessary in 1940, having enlisted some 2½ million young men.

Other relief organizations authorized during President Franklin D. Roosevelt's administration included the Works Progress Administration (WPA), which enlisted unemployed people of all ages and classes and

figure 1-4
One of the temporary tent camps of the Civilian Conservation Corps in Michigan. During the 1930s more than 2,000 of these camps were in operation (throughout the country), and almost 300,000 young men were enrolled at one period. (Michigan Department of Conservation.)

which accomplished, along with other types of activity, a considerable amount of work in conserving natural resources. It was considered "smart" during this period to ridicule the WPA, but it should be remembered that some of the best citizens in the country, through no fault of their own, found themselves on its rolls, that it was considerably less demoralizing than the dole, that it did accomplish useful work, and that the necessity for maintaining it is no compliment to our economic system. Then there was the Prairie States Forestry Project, involving the area otherwise known as the "shelterbelt," extending along the 100th meridian from the Canadian boundary in North Dakota through the Panhandle of Texas. This project, started in 1934, developed into a program of farmstead tree planting to obtain protection from hot and cold driving winds which damaged the land, the crops, and the very lives of men and livestock. Here again there is a human-relief angle in the fact that the drought-persecuted people were employed in establishing the belts of trees, fencing them against grazing, and sometimes watering them until they became established. The total accomplishment of this project is impressive in terms of better crop and living conditions.

Establishment of the Soil Conservation Service in the Department of Agriculture through the Soil Conservation Law of 1935 was preceded by the action of President Roosevelt in setting up the Soil Erosion Service in 1933 as an emergency organization in the Department of the Interior. Thus 27 years after the brave pronouncements of the governors at the White House conference of 1908, soil conservation came into its own as a Federal policy. Later, the emergency bureau was transferred to the Department of Agriculture as the Soil Conservation Service, and its work greatly expanded.

Other significant conservation events which occurred during the administration of President Franklin D. Roosevelt include: operation of the somewhat short-lived National Industrial Recovery Act of 1933, under which, in adopting a "Code of Fair Competition," the lumber industry committed itself to the practice of more intensive forestry in its logging operations and continued these practices after the act was declared unconstitutional in 1935; establishment of a National Planning Board in 1933 which was succeeded by the National Resources Board and finally became the National Resources Committee and published in 1934 a second attempt at an inventory of the country's natural resources; establishment of the Resettlement Administration, concerned with allocating marginal and submarginal lands to appropriate nonagricultural uses and to directing and helping people located on these lands to better economic opportunity; establishment of the Tennessee Valley Authority in 1933, which has undertaken the entire readjustment of the economy of a great river valley; strengthening the administration of the Federal Power Commission under the law of 1920 by authorizing in 1935 the appointment of five full-time commissioners instead of passing the job to busy ex-officio cabinet officers; calling the first North American Wildlife Conference at Washington in 1936 to unite the efforts of scientists, sportsmen, trappers, and lovers of wild animals, and which representatives from Canada, Mexico, and every state in the Union attended and at which they achieved a better understanding of the complex problems of conserving wild-animal life; enactment of the Flood Control Act of 1937 which, among other things, recognized the importance of cover in headwater control and brought other bureaus besides the Office of Engineers of the United States Army into the research and alleviation picture; passage of the Guffey Coal Act of 1936, which authorized the industry itself to bring some order into its operations through so-called production control but which failed to be reenacted in 1943; during World War II, the authorization of curtailments of civilian use of many materials during wartime, which dramatized the individual's duty to conserve finished products and, thus, the natural resources involved. The net effect of this was, of course, somewhat offset by tremendously wasteful war uses of natural resources of every kind.

Conservation after World War II. With a hungry world desperately in need of everything from food to shelter, the natural resources of a rich country like the United States were looked to for continuing heavy use.

Soil conservation, river development, the justified opening up of hitherto inaccessible public forests, and a mildly militant realization by the man in the street that shortages in comforts flowing from natural resources *can* occur even in a strong democracy—all these ideas were bound to obtain increasing attention. It was hoped that an agreement on the international management of Great Lakes commercial fisheries would be reached between the United States and Canada, but this dwindled into little more than an agreement to exchange research data. More accurate appraisals of the forest resources of the country were being finished. Corporations and individuals controlling the timber-growing business of the country were making steady, if somewhat slow, progress in putting private timberlands under forest management. State conservation departments were assuming increasing responsibility for managing timber, wild animals, and mineral resources. Conservation materials were beginning to find their way into public-school teaching.

While natural resources as well as mankind took an inevitable beating during World War II and losses were being offset slowly, there were some important gains in the decade following 1950. Probably the most notable of these were the amendment of the Materials Disposal Act of 1947 which called something of a halt to abuse of the mining laws and the reenactment of the Water Pollution Control Law. The latter had been twice extended since 1948 and was finally strengthened and made permanent. A similar law covering air pollution was also enacted.

During this decade also the Congress increased appropriations for the National Park Service and for the recreation and wild-animal-life activities of the Forest Service. Support of the other conservation agencies of the Federal government, such as the Fish and Wildlife Service, the Soil Conservation Service, and the Reclamation Service, was continued. The fact that some of these agencies often appear to operate at cross-purposes does not lessen the significance of the over-all increase in public awareness and congressional support of conservation needs.

The Tree Farm movement, conceived in 1940 and taken over and promoted by the forest-products industries a year later, gathered considerable momentum between 1950 and 1960. This was an attempt to promote better management of privately owned forest lands.

The long debated St. Lawrence Seaway was authorized and, in cooperation with Canada, was completed as far as Lake Erie, and work started on deepening connecting channels farther west.

Two important nation-wide studies were completed between 1950 and 1960; *Resources for Freedom,* a report on the natural-resource situation with projections of future needs by the President's Materials Policy Commission, published in four volumes in 1952; and *Timber Resources for America's Future,* with projections of future needs, by the Forest Service, published in 1955. Both of these studies will be drawn upon in appropriate chapters of this book.

A Third Wave of Conservation Effort? Sincere interest in and recognition of the urgent need for attack on new natural-resource problems is to be credited to President John F. Kennedy, who came into office in 1961. He said in his special message to the Congress on natural resources early in 1961:

> In the resource field, predictions of future use have been consistently understated. But even under conservation projections, we face a future of critical shortages and handicaps. By the year 2000, a United States population of 300 million—nearly doubled in 40 years—will need far greater supplies of farm products, timber, water, minerals, fuels, energy, and opportunities for outdoor recreation. Present projections tell us that our water use will double in the next 20 years; that we are harvesting our supply of high-grade timber more rapidly than the development of new growth; that too much of our fertile topsoil is being washed away; that our minerals are being exhausted at increasing rates; and that the Nation's remaining undeveloped areas of great natural beauty are being rapidly preempted for other uses.

The President in this message issued a call for a White House Conference on Conservation, no doubt having in mind the first conference called in 1908 by President Theodore Roosevelt and hoping that it would spark a third wave of conservation effort such as those led by the two Roosevelts.

This conference was held on May 24 and 25, 1962. It was dominated by Federal and state officials, and while it issued no recommendations or declaration of policy, it constituted a review of the 1962 natural-resource situation and emphasized the action which the President thought should be forthcoming. Secretary of the Interior Stewart L. Udall summarized the President's program as follows:

Exploit science to "create" new resources and enlarge the use of existing resources;

Give new vigor to traditional programs;

Unlock the resources of the sea;

Reserve for their high human uses the remnants of the American wilderness;

Establish a land conservation fund to ensure the acquisition of key conservation lands;

Wage an all-out attack on water and air pollution;

Help cities save open space and plan their growth;

Grow adequate timber supplies for future needs;

Save the remaining shorelines for public use;

Learn to husband fresh water, and seek means of extracting it from the sea;

Plan now the water development of all river basins;

Preserve a viable habitat for waterfowl and wildlife;

Mount a vigorous campaign—with invigorated state and local participation —to enlarge the opportunities for outdoor recreation;

Earmark military reservation lands as an ultimate conservation reserve for Federal, State and local governments;

Establish a Youth Conservation Corps to work in the vineyard on most of these problems; and above all

Share our know-how and conservation ethic with men everywhere.

The Secretary added "This program, as the President fully realizes, calls for a new level of performance by our people, new leadership at all levels of government—and additional sacrifices by our citizens."

Perhaps because the 1962 White House Conference lacked the enthusiasm of the 1908 conference which marked the formal beginnings of the conservation movement, or because there was no depression as in 1933 to dramatize the proposals, this revival of effort experienced a slow start. Up to the time of the assassination of President John F. Kennedy, the Congress appeared to take little interest in the new program, and private enterprise, which had been largely ignored in the conference, had undertaken few new projects.

However, two important laws were enacted in 1963. A Bureau of Outdoor Recreation in the Department of the Interior was established to coordinate the outdoor-recreation resource activities of the several Federal bureaus concerned and to advise the states in this field, and the Clean Air Act of 1963 became a law. Both of these will be further discussed in subsequent chapters.

Toward the last of the sessions of the Eighty-eighth Congress, which ended late in 1964, the lengthy debate on civil rights appeared to have sidetracked consideration of many natural-resource proposals. Before adjournment, however, legislation was acted upon, and with the two acts mentioned above it may well be the basis for a third wave of conservation activity with emphasis on outdoor-recreation resources. Congress established legal status for the wilderness areas as they were recognized in 1964 and authorized the study of further areas proposed for this classification; it created a land and water conservation fund (which would accumulate from other than existing Federal funds) for the acquisition of lands needed for outdoor-recreation use; and it enacted the so-called "poverty law" which provided for a job corps somewhat resembling the CCC (see page 13) and assigned conservation duties to it.

President Lyndon B. Johnson indicated his interest in natural resources by addressing a special message to the Eighty-ninth Congress in February, 1965.

The Attitude of Industry toward Conserving Natural Resources. Industry, upon which the American people depend for much of their investment and employment, for the manufacture and distribution of most of the necessities of life, and, to a great extent, for keeping the economy moving, was slow to get enthused over the conservation program advocated in the day of President Theodore Roosevelt. But industry has come a long way since then, and now it spends millions of dollars each year in the attempt to maintain renewable natural resources, to reduce waste, to correct nuisances necessarily created—such as water and air pollution—and to treat the landscape more kindly.

Industry held a conservation conference of its own in San Francisco on January 31, 1964, sponsored by the National Association of Manufacturers and known as the National Industrial Conservation Conference. The program featured accomplishments by industry in the fields of the multiple use and management of land by the timber and oil industries; the use and reuse of water by the power and pulp industries; and the control of water pollution by the canning, paper, and oil industries. It emphasized the fact that the public knows little of the natural resource problems of industry and how they are met and that many of the necessary waste-disposal precautions are unproductive and costly.

While no declaration of principles was issued by this conference, certain policies adopted by the National Association of Manufacturers in recent years were assumed to be reaffirmed. These are summarized as follows with the Association speaking for industry:[4]

Basic Policy

Conservation and Management of Natural Resources

The basic responsibility for participating in programs of natural resource development must be shared by individuals, voluntary associations, business enterprises, and the various levels of government. However, the fundamental concept of a limited government of specifically delegated powers and responsibilities must be rigorously adhered to in order to achieve the full benefits of this shared responsibility and to avoid government ownership and operation of production facilities in competition with private enterprise.

Industry recognizes fully the tremendous importance of the nation's soil, water, timber, range, mineral, and other interrelated resources to the future safety and prosperity of the United States and to the future supply of industrial raw materials. Likewise, it recognizes the vital importance of the conservation of these natural resources through long-range planning, sound development and wise utilization, and that non-use may be the antithesis of true conservation.

Industry believes continuation of soundly conceived educational programs participated in by individuals, private organizations, and government will help overcome obstacles to better resource development and that federal, state and local cooperation in these programs should be encouraged.

Industry believes that ineffective and ill-advised conservation and use practices, where they exist, as they concern natural resources must be replaced by modern and scientific measures of real and lasting benefit.

Natural watersheds provide the most feasible units for handling the whole complex of renewable natural resource problems. Such watershed improvement programs should be formulated and executed by local government units and local voluntary associations.

Publicly owned lands containing agricultural and industrial resources, water supplies, recreational features, esthetic scenery and other multi-purpose uses, should be managed to encourage all uses to the fullest extent possible.

[4] *Our Native Land,* a pamphlet supplied for public-school use by the National Association of Manufacturers, New York, 1962, p. 29. (Prepared with the help of an advisory committee of seven educators and eight industrial officials and approved by the NAM Educational Aids Advisory Committee of fifteen educators.) Quoted by special permission of the National Association of Manufacturers.

Industry urges that the Congress and state legislatures give prompt and careful attention to a thorough and comprehensive revision, correlation, clarification and improvement of statutes relating to natural resources.

Although there are a number of points of agreement between these basic policies and the principles which the authors have chosen to list on page 21 as those held valid by many other conservation workers, there are sharp differences. The most important of these concerns the ownership and sometimes the management of natural resources in competition with private enterprise by the people as a whole, through their government, versus turning everything over to regulated private enterprise. Public power is not mentioned by name by industry in this statement, but it is highly controversial. Where the Federal government finds itself with power as a by-product of legitimate irrigation or flood-control projects, it *does* service areas which have been unable to obtain power from private enterprise. Federal agencies *do* market this power and sometimes create a demand which keeps them in business, even to the extent of producing power from steam plants. Of course such a business is subsidized, and, moreover, preference in marketing is granted by Federal agencies to municipalities, cooperatives, and others servicing new territory or having financial trouble. The Tennessee Valley Authority and the Bonneville Power Administration in the Northwest have been sharply criticized as competitors with private enterprise.

Principles of Conserving Natural Resources. But whether one agrees with industry or with the broader viewpoint covering the following principles, and whether or not we are to experience a third wave of conservation, there remains the ever-present need for every citizen to understand our natural resources. Certain fundamental principles should be a part of this understanding, and it is well to list them here.

BENEFICIAL USE   Natural resources are for the benefit of society, and any control of such resources places upon the "owner" an obligation to use them beneficially and with minimum waste.

VARIABILITY OF WASTE   What is waste in either production or consumption may vary under numerous conditions where the factors of production are out of balance or adequate physical distribution is impossible, but deliberate waste for purposes of profit only is seldom justified.

SUBSTITUTION   In general, the substitution of replaceable for irreplaceable and plentiful for scarce natural resources, where the former will serve adequately, is sound practice.

HARMONIOUS PROPERTY RELATIONS   Pooling of ownership and operation of adjoining natural-resource properties to any extent practicable and with safeguards against predatory monopoly tend to assure opportunity for most effective conservation.

PROVIDENTIAL FUNCTIONS OF GOVERNMENT   Governments by their very nature must do certain things for their people which private enterprise cannot or will not do because such services are marginal as profit producers. The control and even the operation of many natural resources are activities of this character, and in many situations conservation can be achieved only under public control.

PRODUCTIVE POWERS   The productive powers of natural resources, capital, and human strength and talent are subject to maintenance and increase through positive direction, and *conservation* of natural resources to serve this end is the exact opposite of a *laissez-faire* attitude toward them.

FORECASTING AND PLANNING   Orderly programs of conserving natural resources demand forecasting and planning.

SPIRITUAL VALUES   Undisturbed natural scenes, historical areas, and certain plants and animals which occupy wanted space frequently represent values which should prevail over economic use.

INDIVIDUAL RESPONSIBILITY FOR CONSERVATION   The prized freedom and dignity of the individual in a democracy must be balanced by a high sense of understanding and assumption of responsibility by every citizen if natural resources are to be conserved in a democracy.

BIBLIOGRAPHY

ALLEN, SHIRLEY WALTER, AND GRANT WILLIAM SHARPE: An Introduction to American Forestry, 3d ed., McGraw-Hill Book Company, New York, 1960.

American Forests, monthly magazine of The American Forestry Association, Washington, D.C.

BENNETT, HUGH H.: Soil Conservation, McGraw-Hill Book Company, New York, 1939.

BUTLER, OVID M.: American Conservation in Picture and Story, American Forestry Association, Washington, D.C., 1935.

CALLISON, CHARLES H., ed.: America's Natural Resources, The Ronald Press Company, New York, 1957.

CAMERON, JENKS: The Development of Governmental Forest Control in the United States, The Johns Hopkins Press, Baltimore, 1928.

Conservation of Renewable Natural Resources, Proceedings of Inter-American Conference, Denver, 1948, U.S. Department of State Publication 3382.

COYLE, DAVID CUSHMAN: Conservation, Rutgers University Press, New Brunswick, N.J., 1957.

DEWHURST, J. FREDERIC, AND ASSOCIATES: America's Needs and Resources, The Twentieth Century Fund, New York, 1947.

ELY, RICHARD T., AND ASSOCIATES: The Foundations of Our National Prosperity, The Macmillan Company, New York, 1923.

GABRIELSON, IRA: Wildlife Conservation, The Macmillan Company, New York, 1942.

Our Native Land, National Association of Manufacturers, New York, 1962.

PINCHOT, GIFFORD: Breaking New Ground, Harcourt, Brace & World, Inc., New York, 1947.

Quest for Quality, U.S. Department of the Interior Conservation Yearbook, 1965.

UDALL, STEWART L.: The Quiet Crisis, Holt, Rinehart and Winston, Inc., New York, 1963.

VAN HISE, CHARLES R., AND LOOMIS HAVEMEYER: Conservation of Our Natural Resources, The Macmillan Company, New York, 1930.

WAKE, WILLIAM H.: Conservation: A Many Faceted Diamond, Address at meeting of Pacific Coast Geographers, Los Angeles, Calif., 1963. (Mimeographed.)

2 SOIL: PHYSICAL PROBLEMS

THE LAND AND the soil are not the same thing. Both terms are used loosely and with more than one meaning. "Land" as popularly understood is the broader term and carries the idea of space. "Soil," on the other hand, is the surface layer of the land, formed from decomposed and disintegrated rock combined with organic matter, supporting a biological population of its own, and varying widely in its ability to produce crops under favorable climatic conditions. Soil is but one part of the land and, in this sense, the less stable part. Since soil is subject to transport by erosive forces, it may, at a given time, overlie a substrate which is not its parent material.

The quantity of land is fixed. Table 2-1, which gives the total number of acres in the United States and the major uses of the land as of 1959, indicates some significant trends. Within a 5-year period the amount of cropland in the original forty-eight states was reduced by 21 million acres; yet in the last 50 years better seeds, pest and weed control, and improved farm management and fertilization have increased the average yield per acre by about 65 per cent.[1] In spite of the decrease in the number of acres in cropland, the 1950s and early 1960s have experienced agricultural surpluses. The 129 million acres devoted to special use, e.g., cities, transportation, recreation, etc., show an increase of 24 million acres. With continued increase in our population, this shift from crop use of the land to special noncrop uses will probably continue. This poses the problem of maintaining adequate farm land to meet the needs of an increased population in the face of the increasing demands for living space. Soil conservation programs must conserve the soil for today and must also include long-range plans for tomorrow.

SOILS

Marbut[2] points out as direct characteristics of the soil (1) that it is the surface layer of the unconsolidated rock material and (2) that it differs from the material beneath it and the material from which it was originally derived in color, texture structure, chemical composition, physical constitution, biological composition, number and arrangement of parts, and general morphology. These characteristics, which are the basis for soil classifications, are determined by the inorganic material or the rock from which the soil was formed, the temperature, the rainfall, the topography of the region, the plants and animals in the area, and the time involved in the soil-forming process. Soil formation results in layers or soil horizons. These layers are visible in the walls of natural or artificial excavations, and the kinds of soil are distinguished by the charac-

---

[1] *Resources*, Resources for the Future, Inc., Washington, D.C., February, 1962.

[2] C. F. Marbut, Soils: Their Genesis, Classification and Development, Lecture before the Graduate School of the U.S. Department of Agriculture, February to May, 1928. (Unpublished.)

TABLE 2-1. MAJOR USES OF LAND IN THE UNITED STATES, 1959
(IN MILLIONS OF ACRES)

	48 states	50 states
Agricultural:		
Cropland	457	458
Open pasture and range	630	633
Farmsteads and farm roads and lands	10	10
Total, agricultural	1,097	1,101
Commercial forest land	488	530
Total used for products of the soil	1,585	1,631
Noncommercial forest land*	126	216
Land committed to special uses:		
Urban areas	27	27
Transportation rights of ways and airports	25	25
State-owned institutional sites and other uses	1	1
Areas limited primarily to recreation or wildlife use	47	63
Public installations and facilities	29	31
Total, land committed to special uses	129	147
Miscellaneous land †	62	277
Total surface area	1,902	2,271

SOURCE: Adapted from Bureau of Land Management.
* Excludes approximately 25 million acres of reserved forest land in the forty-eight states and an additional 2 million acres in Alaska and Hawaii, used primarily for parks, wildlife refuges, and wilderness areas. Much of this noncommercial forest land is used for grazing.
† Includes miscellaneous special uses, marshes, open swamp, bare rock, deserts, sand dunes, etc.

teristic properties and arrangement of these horizons. Natural soils differ in an almost infinite variety of ways. The scientific classification of soils recognizes 75,000[3] individual kinds. Each is different from the other in depth, in size and arrangement of particles, in mineral composition, in water-holding capacity, or in other important characteristics. Any useful classification or grouping of soils requires synthesis. Soil scientists strive to predict the behavior of the whole soil as an entity. Each soil characteristic influences other characteristics, and each soil is a unique combination of characteristics with many potentials for interaction.[4] The uses to which soil is put are influenced by the particular combination of characteristics of the soil and the natural vegetative cover as well as by location, temperature, and rainfall. On the other hand, temperature,

[3] Charles E. Kellogg, Soil-use Planning for Individuals and Public Goals, *Bull. of the Atomic Scientists*, November, 1964.
[4] Charles E. Kellogg, Soil Interpretation in the Soil Survey, Soil Conservation Service, U.S. Department of Agriculture, April, 1961.

rainfall, and vegetative cover have been powerful influences in the development from the *parent material of the soil* of what is known as the soil itself.

The breaking down of parent material, or what is thought of as rock, occurs through weathering. This process includes *disintegration,* a physical process which is helped along by such forces as changes in temperature, changes in volume, friction through movement in stream beds and glaciers, and action of waves and winds, and *decomposition,* a chemical process effected by exposure to oxygen, water, and to a very small extent, weak acids in rainwater. Actually, both processes go on at the same time.

Expansion and contraction through heating and cooling occur at differing rates, with various mineral constituents of rocks producing strains which break down the rocks themselves. When water penetrates cracks and depressions, it freezes and expands, thereby exerting a cumulative breaking force. Glaciers not only transport soil material from one location to another but actually pick up rocks and use them as gouging, planing, and abrasive "tools" on the rocks over which they pass. Roots of plants also penetrate cracks in rock, manage to find enough moisture and soil nutrients to keep the plant growing, and sometimes actually split huge rocks apart. These forces and their action are physical, and they produce disintegration of rock into soil materials.

Iron and other minerals which occur in rock readily take on oxygen when exposed to air and moisture in the process of oxidation. In doing so, they increase considerably in volume so that there is a physical change as well as a chemical one, both disintegration and decomposition taking place. Carbonation is a somewhat similar process which may also increase the solubility of minerals. Perhaps the most important decomposition process, however, is hydration, in which water enters into chemical combination with minerals, changing old and producing new compounds, some of which are highly soluble. Dissolving is still another decomposition process.

Disintegration and decomposition of rocks have not now produced soils but *soil materials.* If development were halted here, there would be no soil but only a layer of unconsolidated minerals. The accumulation of these materials, their population with microorganisms, and the incorporation of organic matter into them from the plant and animal wastes must follow. Soil materials may be accumulated residually, or they may be transported by wind, water, gravity, or glaciers from the place where first broken down to the place where further soil formation proceeds.

Man himself can do much to change, improve, and conserve the soil. An ideal soil for plant growth would: (1) have a rooting zone at least

18 inches deep, (2) have a loamy texture (a favorable mixture of sand, silt, and clay particles), (3) have good structure (particles of sand, silt, and clay grouped in granules permitting water to enter easily, roots to penetrate deeply, and air to move in and out freely), (4) contain organic matter and microorganisms and small animals, such as earthworms, that help decompose the organic matter, (5) have an adequate and balanced supply of nutrients, and (6) have proper chemical reaction or acidity for plan growth.[5] Although maps to show the latest system of soil classification are not yet available, Figs. 2-1 and 2-2 give some indication of the character, diversity, and distribution of the nation's soils.

One of the most significant facts in this story of the development of soil from parent material is the slowness with which it proceeds in nature and the relative helplessness of men to hurry it along. Various estimates of the rate of geological soil building run from 1/600 inch a year to 1 foot in 10,000 years. The latter figure amounts to more than 140 long human lifetimes. The human race, therefore, needs to be alert that soil does not wash or blow away, that it does not lose its fertility, and that it gets all the help in actual development that human effort can supply.

PROBLEMS OF CONSERVING THE SOIL

Three great problems challenge the thinking and the energy of those who use the land and the wider circle of people who live from the products of the land. The first is how to control erosion or keep the soil in place, the second is how to maintain the nutrient materials in the soil, and the third (Chap. 3) is how to bring about understanding and action on the part of those who control the soil resources of the country. The first two problems listed above are physical problems and overlap to some extent because soil removal by erosion amounts also to the removal of nutrient materials.

The two physical problems involve learning through observation, research, and inquiry, and actually practicing what is learned on the land itself. The third problem is one of influencing the minds of men and working out procedures, cooperative and other, by which determination to conserve may be translated into action.

Men will understand and act only when they know what brings about loss of soil and its nutrient materials, something of the extent to which such loss is occurring, and what such loss means in terms of their own and other human welfare. Such considerations should therefore be taken up next.

[5] *Soil Conservation at Home,* Soil Conservation Service, U.S. Dept. Agr., *Agr. Inform. Bull.* 244, February, 1963.

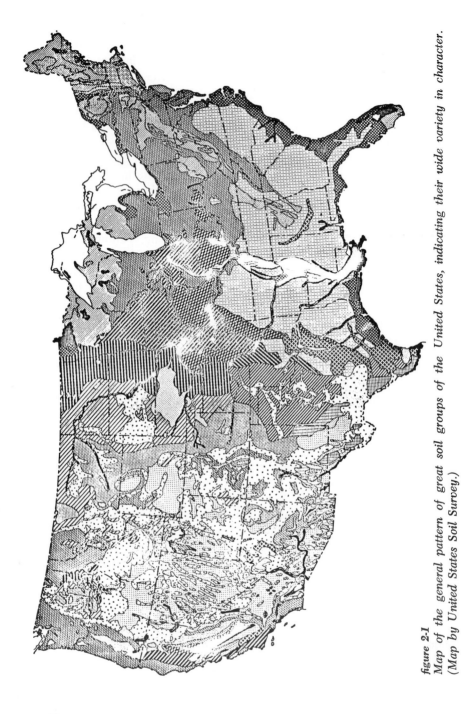

figure 2-1
Map of the general pattern of great soil groups of the United States, indicating their wide variety in character. (Map by United States Soil Survey.)

ZONAL

Great groups of soils with well-developed soil characteristics, reflecting the dominating influence of climate and vegetation. (As shown on the map, many small areas of intrazonal and azonal soils are included.)

PODZOL SOILS — Light-colored leached soils of cool, humid forested regions.

BROWN PODZOLIC SOILS — Brown leached soils of cool-temperate, humid forested regions.

GRAY-BROWN PODZOLIC SOILS — Grayish-brown leached soils of temperate, humid forested regions.

RED AND YELLOW PODZOLIC SOILS — Red or yellow leached soils of warm-temperate to hot, humid forested regions.

PRAIRIE SOILS — Very dark brown soils of cool and temperate, relatively humid grasslands.

REDDISH PRAIRIE SOILS — Dark reddish-brown soils of warm-temperate, relatively humid grasslands.

CHERNOZEM SOILS — Dark-brown to nearly black soils of cool and temperate, subhumid grasslands.

CHESTNUT SOILS — Dark-brown soils of cool and temperate, subhumid to semiarid grasslands.

REDDISH CHESTNUT SOILS — Dark reddish-brown soils of warm-temperate, semiarid regions under mixed shrub and grass vegetation.

BROWN SOILS — Brown soils of cool and temperate, semiarid grasslands.

REDDISH BROWN SOILS — Reddish-brown soils of warm-temperate to hot, semiarid to arid regions, under mixed shrub and grass vegetation.

NONCALCIC BROWN SOILS — Brown or light reddish-brown soils of warm-temperate, semiarid regions, under mixed forest, shrub, and grass vegetation.

SIEROZEM OR GRAY DESERT SOILS — Gray soils of cool to temperate, arid regions, under shrub and grass vegetation.

RED DESERT SOILS — Light reddish-brown soils of warm-temperate to hot, arid regions, under shrub vegetation.

INTRAZONAL

Great groups of soils with more or less well-developed soil characteristics reflecting the dominating influence of some local factor of relief, parent material, or age over the normal effect of climate and vegetation. (Many areas of these soils are included with zonal groups on the map.)

PLANOSOLS — Soils with strongly leached surface horizons over claypans on nearly flat land in cool to warm, humid to subhumid regions, under grass or forest vegetation.

RENDZINA SOILS — Dark grayish-brown to block soils developed from soft limy materials in cool to warm, humid to subhumid regions, mostly under grass vegetation.

SOLONCHAK (1) AND SOLONETZ (2) SOILS
(1) Light-colored soils with high concentration of soluble salts, in subhumid to arid regions, under salt-loving plants.
(2) Dark-colored soils with hard prismatic subsoils, usually strongly alkaline, in subhumid or semiarid regions under grass or shrub vegetation.

WIESENBÖDEN (1), GROUND WATER PODZOL (2), AND HALF-BOG SOILS (3)
(1) Dark-brown to block soils developed with poor drainage under grasses in humid and subhumid regions.
(2) Gray sandy soils with brown cemented sandy subsoils developed under forests from nearly level imperfectly drained sand in humid regions.
(3) Poorly drained, shallow, dark peaty or mucky soils underlain by gray mineral soil, in humid regions, under swamp-forests.

BOG SOILS — Poorly drained dark peat or muck soils underlain by peat, mostly in humid regions, under swamp or marsh types of vegetation.

The areas of each great soil group shown on the map include areas of other groups too small to be shown separately. Especially are there small areas of the azonal and intrazonal groups included in the areas of zonal groups.

AZONAL

Soils without well-developed soil characteristics. (Many areas of these soils are included with other groups on the map.)

LITHOSOLS AND SHALLOW SOILS (ARID - SUBHUMID)
Shallow soils consisting largely of an imperfectly weathered mass of rock fragments, largely but not exclusively on steep slopes.
(HUMID)

SANDS (DRY) — Very sandy soils.

ALLUVIAL SOILS — Soils developing from recently deposited alluvium that have had little or no modification by processes of soil formation.

figure 2-2
Legend for map of great soil groups.

31

figure 2-3

Southwest Butte near Mesa Verde, Colo. Erosion here is geologic and not brought about or accelerated by the activities of mankind. (Photo by United States Soil Conservation Service.)

EROSION

Factors Which Influence Erosion. Normal or geologic erosion (Fig. 2-3) is a natural and age-old process of development on the earth's surface and is generally thought to proceed over the ages no faster than soil formation. It is not to be confused with accelerated erosion induced by the activities of men. It is with the latter that conservation practices are concerned, but many of the factors influencing erosion apply to both types. Climatic factors such as temperature variations, rainfall, and wind are powerful. Freezing and thawing loosen the surface of the soil and subject it to easy removal by washing. Rainfall, except of the gentler kind, has a beating and loosening effect on the surface which is almost explosive (Fig. 2-4), and when it cannot be absorbed rapidly it runs off in excess, carrying loosened soil particles with it. *Amount, frequency, and character of rainfall* are all, therefore, important factors. *Character of the soil itself* as to permeability, texture, and content of organic material may limit or multiply the erosive effect of rainfall both by failure to absorb water quickly or by the ease with which soil particles may be suspended in water. *Vegetative cover,* such as trees, grass, shrubs, and weeds, affects erosion by breaking the beating power of hard rains so that water drips rather than beats on the soil, by cushioning with leaf litter or sod the beat of raindrops, and by increasing the absorptive capacity of the soil through networks of roots and the building up of organic content (Fig. 2-5). *Slope,* because water runs downhill, is obviously important as a factor affecting erosion. The steeper the slope,

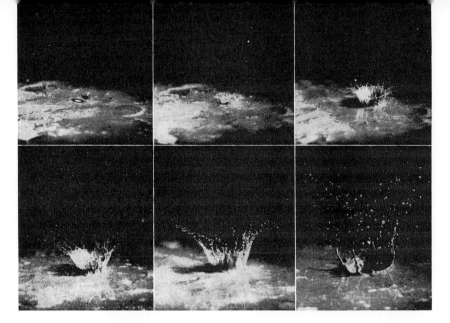

figure 2-4
The beating and soil-moving power of a raindrop. (Photo by United States Soil Conservation Service.)

the faster will be the flow of the stream of whatever size and the greater its carrying and grinding power. Since accelerated erosion is being considered, the action of men in connection with the above factors is assumed and, as their manipulators, men become the most powerful factor affecting erosion. This is particularly true with respect to wind erosion,

figure 2-5
Diagram of soil and water loss from 4 years' observation under differing conditions of cover at Bethany, Mo., on Shelby loam with an 8 per cent slope under a 40-inch average annual rainfall. (Photo by United States Soil Conservation Service.)

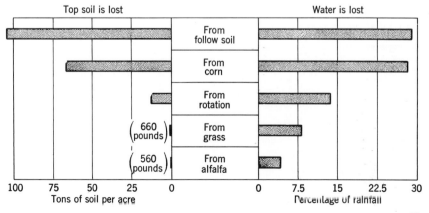

which is most severe when men have removed vegetative cover and paid too little attention to safe cultivation practices.

Kinds of Erosion. Wind and water individually or in combination are the erosional agents that wear away the land. Wind often does more spectacular work as a mover of soils than water does. Dust storms are more terrifying than muddy streams. However, wind must carry sand before it can cut, and even a strong wind cannot lift sand very high. Running water, therefore, is the more effective erosional agent. It is not just the water itself that erodes the land but suspended particles of rock and chemicals dissolved in the water. The abrasive particles help to disintegrate the rock, and the chemicals contribute to its decomposition. Running-water erosion leaves a striking set of scars on the landscape; it may be designated as sheet erosion, rill erosion, gully erosion, and riparian, or riverbank, erosion.

Sheet erosion is the removal of soil in small but uniform amounts as it becomes suspended in excess rainfall and is carried away over slight slopes from the entire area. The very fact that it goes on unnoticed puts the landowner off guard, and it therefore becomes important in amount with repeated storms. About the only evidence one can see is small accumulations of washed soil in some low, flat spots in the fields.

Rill erosion is more severe than sheet erosion and creates many individual small streams over the surface which start or follow some mark or depression and cut rapidly (Fig. 2-6). Total soil removal is heavy during even a single storm.

Gully erosion occurs when uncontrolled rills become wider V-shaped channels, broadening and deepening as they descend. Gullies may also start almost suddenly where heavy rainfall and runoff strike a depression or weak spot on the soil surface. Enormous amounts of soil are removed,

figure 2-6
Rill erosion on northern Rocky Mountain range land. (Photo by United States Forest Service.)

figure 2-7
*Gully in native pasture, South Dakota. (Photo by B. C. McLean,
United States Soil Conservation Service.)*

and great canyonlike gashes appear which make plowing impossible
(Fig. 2-7).

Riparian, or riverbank, erosion consists of the weakening and under-
cutting of banks by river currents and the caving of these banks into the
stream. It is really a variation of gully erosion where the gully becomes
or consists of a regularly flowing stream, but the cutting is more lateral
than vertical (Fig. 2-8).

Wind erosion will be considered as only one type, since it varies more
with intensity than with the pattern it leaves on the surface. The wind
may produce the general dust storm which fills the air to a great height
and carries the finest soil particles for many miles, or it may pick up and
carry for short distances soil particles which are too large or heavy to be
called "dust" (Fig. 2-11), or it may succeed only in rolling or causing
to hop certain particles too heavy to move otherwise. In the latter
instance, soil not only is removed from the place where it belongs but is
caught against some fence, building, or other obstruction and accumulates until it covers valuable improvements or forms a dune which
moves slowly but powerfully, burying at least temporarily anything in its
path, be it farm, forest, or village. While any one of these movements
may be a part of geological erosion, any one may also be accelerated by
removal of the vegetative cover such as the native sod in wind-swept
territory. This occurred in the so-called "dust bowl" section in northern

figure 2-8

Stream-bank erosion cutting into a commercial persimmon orchard, California. (Photo by Ken Croeni, United States Soil Conservation Service.)

Texas, western Oklahoma, and southwestern Kansas, and in other parts of the Great Plains, following the breaking of the native sod for wheat growing during World War I and its subsequent neglect up to the early 1930s. Soil particles from this region were identified in some Eastern states and even on ships out in the Atlantic Ocean. Great suffering followed the economic breakdown of wheat farming in this region, and many families were forced to move out.

The Effects of Erosion and the Threats of Damage. When it is remembered that men have it within their power to control soil erosion to a great extent, the need for prompt action becomes apparent from figures on soil loss and its accompanying human suffering.

A detailed summary of eroded area is given in Table 2-2 from estimates based largely on reconnaissance surveys.[6]

Hardly any major agricultural region is unaffected, and in some degree production of every staple commodity has felt the blow. Heavily farmed areas in rolling country where crops are planted in rows and where

[6] Although later data comparable with those in this table are not available, it is significant that soil conservation districts and other related conservation districts covered 1,565,209,153 acres as of January 1, 1957. This indicates that an attack on erosion is being made over a major portion of the affected area. (See pages 63–64 for explanation of a soil conservation district.)

TABLE 2-2. DISTRIBUTION OF EROSION DAMAGE IN THE
UNITED STATES (EXCLUSIVE OF ALASKA AND HAWAII)

	Acres
Total land area (exclusive of large urban territory)	1,903,000,000
Erosion conditions not defined (such as deserts, scablands, and large Western mountain areas)	144,000,000
Total land area (exclusive of mountains, mesas, and badlands) divided into:	
Ruined or severely damaged	282,000,000
Moderately damaged	775,000,000
Cropland (harvested, crop failure and lying fallow):	
Ruined for cultivation	50,000,000
Severely damaged	50,000,000
One-half to all topsoil gone	100,000,000
Erosion process beginning	100,000,000

cotton, corn, and tobacco dominate the market suffer most severely from water erosion. Wind erosion is most severe in the Great Plains and in high-level country farther west.

Estimates based on a large number of measurements on experimental plots at soil-erosion experiment stations throughout the country put the amount of soil removed annually by wind and water from the crop and pasture lands of the United States at 3 billion tons. This includes the top layer, which is the most productive part of the soil, and amounts to the removal of 7 inches of soil from an area of no less than 9 million acres. "Where does it go?" one may ask, and the answer is that it may blow halfway across the continent and be scattered so that at no point does it represent a usable accumulation; it may blow out to sea as it was observed to do in the 1935 dust storms; it may become a part of the 730 million tons per year that represent the silt discharge of the Mississippi River at its mouth; it may be deposited in a reservoir built to store water for power or irrigation (Fig. 2-9) where it not only is lost to cultivation but reduces the water-storage capacity behind the dam; it may cover cropland or improvements now in use to a ruinous depth; or, finally it may clog the channels of streams previously capable of carrying flood waters, interfere with navigation, or otherwise defeat the control and harnessing of runoff waters.

CONTROLLING EROSION

It is obvious that soil must be managed if it is not to be washed or blown away. In making it useful to mankind, every advantage must be taken of methods which will minimize these erosional forces.

Cover and Tillage. Vegetative cover may be forest, brush, sod, sparse herbaceous growth, orchard, hay, grain, or row crops such as corn, cotton,

figure 2-9

Erosion ruins reservoirs at times by filling them with silt. Mono Dam, Los Padres National Forest, California. Watershed is difficult to protect and has been subject to frequent fires. (Photo by United States Forest Service.)

tobacco, or potatoes. With any of these the use and pattern of cover is an important key to holding the soil in place (Fig. 2-10). The value of cover lies not only in actually covering and reinforcing the soil layer but in assuring that the portion of the rainfall which penetrates the soil shall reach it as relatively clear water. Otherwise it becomes laden with

figure 2-10
Aerial view of contoured strip cropping, Wisconsin. (Photo by E. W. Cole, United States Soil Conservation Service.)

surface particles of soil which clog the tiny "pores" and slow down or stop the *infiltration,* a term used to denote the passage of water into the soil.

Study of the rates of infiltration and of the results of rainfall on soils under varying treatments has yielded some of the most useful data now available for practical application. Duley and Miller[7] at the Missouri Agricultural Experiment Station found that over a period of 6 years, on plots of similar soil and slope, the one kept in sod lost less than one-eighth of the rainfall, eroded at what appeared to be 11/1,000 inch in 6 years, and at this rate would lose 7 inches of soil in about 3,500 years. The plot kept devoid of cover and spaded 4 inches deep, on the other hand, lost close to one-third of the rainfall, almost 1⅔ inches of soil in 6 years, and at this rate would lose 7 inches of soil in 24 years. Five other plots ranked in soil and water conservation from best to worst approximately as follows: rotation of corn, wheat, and clover; wheat annually; corn annually; not cultivated; spaded 8 inches deep. Lowdermilk found in laboratory tests that certain soils would lose 75 per cent of their absorptive power in a period of 8 hours when turbid water was used in place of clear water.[8]

Many claims for soil- and water-holding efficiency are made for so-called "trash agriculture," in which all plant residues are left on the soil. No turning of the soil as in ordinary plowing is done, but the trash is cut into the soil, and the entire soil layer is loosened before planting.

The rotation of crops in farming offers an opportunity to provide the particular crop with its tillage needs in alternate or occasional years whether it is planted in rows with the intervening soil exposed or sown as grain crops so that something resembling a temporary sod is produced. Thus there might in succeeding years be rotations of corn, oats, clover, alfalfa—or alfalfa, corn, oats—or cotton, cowpeas, corn, wheat.

Maintenance of permanent vegetative cover other than grass pasture or sod involves such practices as the use of soil for forest crops, stock raising on Western ranges (where sagebrush, intermittent grass, and herbaceous growth may take the place of continuous sod); and the use of the surface soil in banks or highway cuts and fills, parkways, parks, and lawns. So important is the prevention of erosion in these uses that vast sums of money are invested in such road-maintenance features as sodding, in retiring watershed lands entirely from use other than water catchment and storage, and even in forest planting of large areas.

Vegetative cover has its limitations in soil conservation practices, but

[7] F. L. Duley and M. T. Miller, Erosion and Surface Runoff under Different Soil Conditions, *Mo. Agr. Expt. Sta. Res. Bull.* 63, 1923, p. 44.

[8] Quoted by E. N. Munns, Forests and Floods, *South. Lumberman,* vol. 138, p. 60, 1930.

it is used to advantage in connection with good tillage practices and mechanically constructed devices to make the water "walk" (rather than run) off the land. Tillage is the preparation of the soil for putting in a crop and includes plowing and other mechanical methods of turning over and breaking up the surface layer. Whether such treatment is shallow or deep may affect the rate at which rainfall will be taken up by the soil and the resulting surplus that may bring about surface damage as it runs off. Whether the direction of plowing or "fitting," as the final process is sometimes called, follows an up-and-down-hill direction or follows the contour, it will affect the ability of the tilled soil to absorb water and the speed and power which the water attains. Whether the residues of former crops such as cornstalks, straw, and other unharvested materials are incorporated into the soil in tillage practices or are burned or removed for convenience will affect the power of the tilled soil to absorb water and to resist removal by wind. Whether the surface is finely divided or left in clods will certainly affect the removal by wind, and whether the surface is leveled or left in furrows will affect the settling or accumulating of soil particles as they blow over the surface (Fig. 2-11). Tillage, therefore, offers an opportunity to defend the soil from both water and wind erosion and, at the same time, to provide for the peculiar soil-preparation requirements of any important crop.

Making the water "walk" off the land, retarding its flow until it can be absorbed, diverting it from vulnerable spots (on the surface of the field), and protecting stream banks, roadsides, and shore residential and commercial sites from current and wave action are all part of any good

Wind erosion showing use of deep furrows to collect blowing soil, Oklahoma. (Photo by United States Soil Conservation Service.)

figure 2-11

figure 2-12

Contour plowing in Texas. A tillage method designed to prevent erosion. (Photo by United States Soil Conservation Service.)

soil-management program. Good tillage practices and some mechanically constructed devices are used to accomplish these goals. One of the simplest of the good tillage practices consists of plowing around the hills on the contour, instead of up and down the slopes (Fig. 2-12). Regardless of the crop to be planted, this direction of plowing and fitting prevents the kind of incipient channel which starts the surplus rainfall downhill on a destructive journey. Moreover, if strip cropping follows contour plowing, high water-retarding efficiency is obtained from any strips planted to close-grown crops, such as alfalfa and wheat. Even intertilled crops such as tobacco and potatoes, have a better chance to retard and absorb runoff. Contour plowing in dry country has also excellent possibilities for conserving rainfall which would otherwise run off and cause some erosion. Deep, wide furrows catch and hold excess rainfall, and by use of an implement known as a damming lister, or basin-forming lister, a furrow can be made which throws the soil to both sides and leaves a dam at intervals in the furrow. The effect is to dot the contour-following plowed area with hundreds of tiny ponds or basins, which assure good distribution of the saved rainfall.

In a crude set of demonstration plots in Livingston County, Michigan, the average annual loss of soil in a period of 8 years, from 1938 to 1946, was 36.24 tons per acre from plots of various crops planted in rows up and down the slope, and 5.82 tons from those planted on contour, more than six times as great a loss just from unwise direction of cultivation and planting. Soil loss per acre on the up-and-down-hill plots for the period of April 1, 1945, to April 1, 1947, for various crops amounted to corn,

figure 2-13

Green beans between rows of sunflowers planted as a wind-break. (Photo by Robert B. Branstead, United States Soil Conservation Service.)

6.05 tons; oats, 2.15 tons; and hay, 0.1 ton. On contoured plots the losses were corn, 1.35 tons; oats, 0.05 ton; and hay, 0.05 ton.[9]

The traditional practice of dividing up farms into rectangular fields to match and parallel property lines is slowly giving way to division on a

[9] *Annual Report,* 1946, Fenton Soil Conservation District, Fenton, Mich., p. 6.

Plowing terrace to maintain its shape and height. (Photo by United States Soil Conservation Service.)

figure 2-14

band or strip pattern. Here one crop alternates with another in a sort of ribbon pattern, with the *close-grown*, or sodlike, crops alternating with those planted in rows and sometimes spoken of as *intertilled*. Strips may be placed on contour, traverse the existing field parallel to a boundary line, be placed to protect some particular spot or strip where erosion is starting, or be placed at right angles to the direction of the prevailing wind (Fig. 2-13). They would then be designated, respectively, as contour strips (Fig. 2-12), field strips, buffer strips, and wind strips.

Terracing. In regions of heavy rainfall and soils particularly subject to erosion, terraces (Fig. 2-14) may be used at the foot of any one or more crop strips. These devices are wide, shallow channels approximately on contour, but designed with enough fall *along* the contour to lead any surplus runoff around the slope to an outlet into a grassed or paved waterway usually located along the edge of the field. The latter channel may end up in an open drainage ditch or a stream, but it disposes of the surplus runoff safely and, of course, must frequently be definitely constructed and always maintained in sod or pavement. Terraces as just discussed are of the sort illustrated in Figs. 2-14 and 2-15. There are also bench terraces constructed in various parts of the world on steep slopes, maintained with heavy sodding or with masonry retaining walls, and permitting agriculture on otherwise prohibitive sites.

Diversion Ditches. A terrace usually amounts to a diversion channel because it "walks" the water off the land instead of holding it for further

Terrace with diversion ditch in action almost too soon. Strips are to be planted both above and below the ditch, and the ditch and terrace will be seeded, fertilized, and limed. Livingston County, Mich. (Photo by United States Soil Conservation Service.)

figure 2-13

figure 2-16

Sodded waterway in corn strips, Muskingum County, Ohio. Excess rainwater drains from the lower edge of strips into grassed waterway and leaves the field undamaged. (Photo by United States Soil Conservation Service.)

absorption (Fig. 2-15), but a diversion ditch may be a more abrupt channel curving around the head of a set of rills or an incipient gully. In this form surplus runoff is diverted quickly onto safe sod or level areas where it can be absorbed (Fig. 2-16).

Contour Furrows. Differing from continuous contour plowing, terraces, or short diversion ditches, contour furrows are usually single deep furrows at wide intervals and as nearly as possible on exact contour (Fig. 2-17). They are designed not to divert surplus runoff but to catch and

Contour furrows on a seeded field, Okanogan County, Wash. Severe runoff has occurred without evidence of erosion. (Photo by United States Soil Conservation Service.)

figure 2-17

retain it until absorbed. They amount, therefore, to elongated ponds, intermittently wet and dry, depending on rainfall. They are of special value on drier sodded pastures for moisture retention.

Gully-reclamation Devices. Reinforcing the banks or surfaces of the gully side walls with brush or straw, and using such material particularly at the vulnerable heads of gullies, is perhaps the simplest "gully-choking" method. Brush, log, and masonry dams across the path of the gully vary in cost but are all expensive in labor and material. If well constructed, they bring about accumulations of silt, thus stabilizing the surface for revegetation and, of course, reducing the cutting power of runoff waters.

Any and all of these methods and devices again tie in well with the use of vegetative cover (Fig. 2-18), which is difficult to establish otherwise. Rebuilding of a real soil in a gully is a slow process, but forest crops of some value will sometimes take hold and eventually produce revenue in addition to their service in reinforcing and protecting the gully surface.

Riparian or stream-bank erosion requires heroic measures for control, and costs are high. Mankind frequently is competing with the stream for its natural "playground." The very old jetty device must be used where the current is swift and jetties or barriers of piling can be established. Still another method is somewhat like the surface treatment of gully walls. Here the stream bank is sloped to a degree where it can be more easily stabilized, and a network or blanket of brush, fence wire, rock, or a combination of the three, is anchored in place, and willow trees or cuttings are planted in and above the blanket. Stone riprap or sloping walls must occasionally be used near the low water line if the current is swift and the jetty type of structure impracticable.

Wave erosion on lake and ocean shores indicates even more expensive control works if valuable residence and commercial establishments and public works are to be sure of their space. Frequently, builders have stubbornly refused to realize that oceans and lakes are not through with their natural game of geological erosion and that man cannot hope to compete with nature in occupying the shores. Breakwaters, masonry walls, groins (Fig. 2-19), and tree planting have been resorted to. Although it is beyond the customary field of soil conservation, the problem is locally of vast importance and requires increasing study, planning, and action.

Windbreaks and Shelterbelts. A *windbreak* may mean anything from a fence to a forest, and the term is frequently used to designate one or more rows of trees planted in a direction which is at right angles to that of the prevailing winds and designed to prevent soil blowing and severe evaporation of soil moisture and to moderate the temperature locally.

(a)

figure 2-18
Gully control. Huge gully controlled by sloping and sodding coupled by diversion of excess runoff, Texas. (a) Before treatment: gully resulted from unprotected terrace outlets. (b) After treatment: banks have been sloped and sodded, terrace rerun, and excess terrace water diverted from old gullies by vegetative diversion channel. (Photo by United States Soil Conservation Service.)

(b)

figure 2-19

Checking wave erosion by means of rock-filled timber cribs which act as groins. They are placed at right angles to the shore line: the ones shown are already partly covered with sand and are building up good beach. (Photo by E. F. Brater, courtesy of Engineering Research Institute, University of Michigan.)

The term *shelterbelt* is more narrowly used to designate a belt consisting of several rows of trees and shrubs located as just described for a windbreak. The prevention of wind erosion on a local scale is practiced all the way from using bands or strips of grain or hay to reduce the blowing of muck-soil particles with their cutting effect on tender truck-crop plants (Fig. 2-20) to the use of 165-foot-wide shelterbelts consisting of as

A 66-year-old red-cedar windbreak or shelterbelt, Seward County, Nebr. Field and farm home protected. (Photo by United States Soil Conservation Service.)

figure 2-20

many as twenty or more rows of shrubs and trees. Sometimes in the Great Plains region such plantings must be fenced from livestock and watered systematically until they become established.

It is generally agreed that the effects of wind on soil removal, accelerated evaporation, and temperature change are felt to a leeward distance equivalent to twenty times the height of the shelterbelt. Thus, a large portion of a square field ¼ mile, or 1,320 feet, on each side and having an area of 40 acres might benefit from a 60-foot-tall shelterbelt. The planting would have three rows of cottonwood trees in the middle of it and would be placed at the windward edge of the field. (See Fig. 2-21 in which the cottonwoods have not yet reached that height.) It should be borne in mind that the effect of these shelterbelts is local and that it would take a vast program of checkerboard outlining the dust-bowl region with them before dust storms could be influenced appreciably. The work of the Prairie States Forestry Project in attacking wind erosion will be discussed later, as will other means by which action on soil conservation problems can be brought about.

NUTRIENT MATERIALS IN THE SOIL

If soil waste were completely halted and water made available to all soils, they could be reduced to very low productivity through cropping unless the elements essential to the plant growth could be maintained in adequate measure. This is the second great soil conservation problem. Plants require considerable quantities of nitrogen, phosphorus, potassium, carbon, calcium, oxygen, hydrogen, and sulfur, although not necessarily in the order named. Lesser amounts of iron and magnesium are required, and very small amounts of cobalt, zinc, copper, manganese, and boron have been shown to be necessary to certain plants. The first three of these, nitrogen, phosphorous, and potassium, have come to be called *fertilizer*

figure 2-21
Diagram showing the effect of a shelterbelt. (Kansas State Board of Agriculture.)

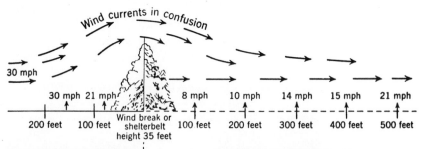

Wind currents in confusion

30 mph

30 mph   21 mph   8 mph   10 mph   14 mph   15 mph   21 mph

200 feet   100 feet   Wind break or shelterbelt height 35 feet   100 feet   200 feet   300 feet   400 feet   500 feet

Some influence extends to 175 feet on the windward side

Some protection will extend to 1500 feet on the leeward side *elements* in the commercial fertilizer industry. Thus, when a bag of fertilizer contains, for example, the label "3-12-12" or "0-10-4," the figures indicate the proportions, in the order given, of available nitrogen, phosphorus, and potassium compounds in the total fertilizing material. The last five elements mentioned above, cobalt, zinc, copper, manganese, and boron, are known as the *trace elements*. Even though required in very small quantities, their absence may profoundly reduce the rate of maturing, resistance to disease, or some other factor influencing successful production of a given crop.

The ordinary person not particularly interested in farming or gardening probably reads and hears more about calcium than any other element important in plant growth, but usually the term *lime*, or *liming the soil*, is what he hears, since lime is a material composed mostly of calcium. Soils are frequently deficient in calcium, nitrogen, phosphorus, and potassium; hence, these elements are most often included in commercial fertilizers.

Nitrogen, oxygen, hydrogen, and carbon come nearest to being inexhaustible in nature. They occur or circulate in air and water and enter into most of the minerals found in the soil. Making these elements available to plants, however, is another matter, tied in, as will be understood later, to the grower's knowledge and practices on the land.

Nitrogen varies in amount from one-twentieth to one-fifth of 1 per cent by weight in the better forest soils and as much as one-fourth to three-tenths of 1 per cent in the black prairie soils, and it occurs in even greater amounts in certain of the peats and muck soils. In actual weight per acre to a depth of 6 to 7 inches, known as the plow layer, this would mean an average of something like 4,000 pounds (out of the total 2 million pounds of soil)—hardly a load for a small dump truck.

Unfortunately, phosphorus is not too well distributed in the important farming soils. The average amount per acre in the plow layer for soils in general is 3,000 pounds. This somewhat scant supply, plus heavy removal in crops which leave the farm, and traditional neglect in maintaining the supply through fertilization and crop rotation make the phosphorus problem relatively serious.

Potassium, or potash (K_2O), is widely and generously distributed in the soils of this country. The average for the general run of soils is 2 per cent by weight in the top 6 or 7 inches of the plow layer. This amounts to 40,000 pounds of potash to the acre, whereas the amount of nitrogen does not exceed 10 per cent of such a figure and the phosphoric acid content is even lower.

Loss of Essential Nutrient Materials. Uneven occurrence of essential nutrient materials is not the only trouble met in the nutrient-maintenance phase of soil conservation. Progressive loss through cropping, leaching in drainage water, removal by erosion when the soil itself is lost, and modification by fire are examples of deficits caused by removal of nutrients. Examples of heavy removal of phosphorus include the large amounts which leave the farm in the grain, the livestock, the poultry, and the dairy products which are sold. Frequently the only return is that contained in the animal manures and plant wastes which the owner plows under. These in turn are drawn upon by the next crop. While complete exhaustion of a soil is rare, the abandoned farmhouse with idle acres about it is eloquent of thoughtless cropping practice as well as of erosion or of bad judgment in the original selection of the land.

Ground fires which follow or accompany forest fires, grass fires, and muck fires, such as those which occur in the Everglades and in drained marshlands in the Middle West, also seriously deplete nutrients. Sometimes in the latter instance the entire soil is reduced to ash or is so modified as to be unproductive.

HOW NUTRIENT MATERIALS MAY BE MAINTAINED IN SOILS

Crop residues such as cornstalks, straw, vegetable tops, and stubble; special crops such as soybeans, grasses, clover, and buckwheat which are plowed under while green (called green manures); animal manures made up of solid excreta, urine, and straw or other bedding material; guano; leafmold; compost; agricultural lime and marl; rock phosphate; potash salts; ammonium sulfate; compounds of peat and mineral salts; ground dry sludge from sewage systems; and a great many other materials comprise the fertilizers and modifiers of the soil which may be added or returned in cropping practice. In general too little of these materials is used to replace the nutrients lost to the soils when the crops are sold and removed.

Examples of sources and procedures in applying these materials (Fig. 2-22), starting with the simpler ones, follow:

Adding Organic Materials. Crop residues (Fig. 2-23), green manures, animal manures, guano, and peat compounds are used both to modify the physical condition of the soil to gain greater aeration, water absorption, and easier working qualities and to supply certain nutrient elements, particularly nitrogen, phosphorus, and potash. The living organisms in the soil also perform their function of making nutrient materials more readily available in soils which contain generous supplies of organic materials.

What goes on in a living soil is difficult to understand or even to believe until one thinks of the organic material as "fuel for bacterial fires in the soil, which operates as a factory producing plant nutrients." The organic

figure 2-22

Aerial application of fertilizers was demonstrated on farm test demonstrations in several states during 1963. This photo was taken in the Elk River Basin, Tennessee.

material in this "burning" process produces, among other things, carbon dioxide and ash. The former makes possible a supply of acidified soil water which acts as a solvent for many otherwise unavailable mineral nutrients. In the whole process, nitrogen and other nutrients in the organic material itself become available. The use of the term "burning" is appropriate when one realizes that he may be standing on an acre of ground warmed up to its job on a hot July day and burning carbon at the rate equivalent to 1.6 pounds of good-grade soft coal per hour and generating perhaps as much as 1 horsepower of energy. Organic matter then is the source of indispensable power to change nutrient elements into forms available to growing plants.

CROP RESIDUES Enormous quantities of the crop residues mentioned are produced, and whereas United States farmers formerly burned them

51

figure 2-23
Turning under Balboa rye in Tennessee. This is an example of using
a green manure for soil improvement. Near Murfreesburo, Tenn.
(Photo by United States Soil Conservation Service.)

in many instances in order to make plowing and fitting more convenient, they are now being returned to the soil in increasing volume. New types of machinery as well as better knowledge of the value of the materials have influenced this trend. Cornstalks can be quickly broken up and leveled, the straw and chaff from such crops as grain and soybeans can be returned at once to the surface by the combine harvester which threshes as it cuts, and devices for practicing "trash agriculture" include those which stir but do not turn over the soil and which "cut into" the soil the residues left on the surface. In harvesting oats, rye, barley, and wheat with the older "binder," the straw is removed, blown into a stack at a later threshing site, and infrequently returned to the field, except as it gets there as bedding in manure. The same is true when "fodder corn" or silage corn is removed and fed to stock at distant barns or feed lots.

GREEN MANURES Clover, cowpeas, soybeans, and other legumes used as green-manure crops have the power to fix nitrogen from the air and, when plowed under, add organic material to the soil. This will be discussed later. Winter wheat, rye, buckwheat, and certain of the vetches are also used and are particularly valuable when they can be seeded with regular season crops to grow slowly through the colder seasons. In this way they "salvage" certain nutrients which might otherwise be lost by leaching during the wetter parts of the year but are thus returned when the manure crop is plowed under. Commercial products using peat may or may not be "sweetened" with some mineral fertilizer; they are sold for use on specialized crops and have their principal values as soil modifiers. Middle Western cities with a problem of removing heavy street-tree and lawn-tree leaffall find an outlet for this material in nearby lands devoted to specialized crops. Similarly, organic wastes are "composted" for use by commercial gardeners and nurserymen. Composting is a process of accumulating leaves, straw, and other plant residues with soil, keeping the heap or pit moist and aerated, and allowing the material to heat and decompose before adding it to the soil. Addition of animal manures and commercial fertilizer materials in small amounts hasten the composting process.

ANIMAL MANURE   Animal manure accumulated on the farms contains nitrogen, phosphorus, potash, calcium, sulfur, and traces of other nutrient materials needed by plants. It also serves as organic materials needed by plants and in improving the working quality and water absorption of the soil. Whether or not it increases crop production depends upon the way it is stored and allowed to decompose before it is applied to the land. Manure should be considered at this point as organic material which introduces certain microorganisms into the soil and modifies the soil in addition to supplying it with nitrogen and other elements.

Leaching from storage piles exposed to heavy rainfall, improper fermentation, and drying out before being incorporated with the soil are common sources of loss of nutrient materials in manure. With 1 billion tons of manure available yearly on American farms, capable of producing 3 million dollars' worth of increase in crops and equivalent to $440 for each of the country's 6,800,000 farm operators, it is probable that not until recently has more than one-third of the potential value been realized.

Rotation of Crops. Advantages of alternating crops as against growing a single crop continuously or having no plan whatever include plant-disease and insect control and erosion control, as well as the maintenance of fertility, but rotation is discussed here as a means of maintaining organic matter and plant nutrients in the soil. It must be "a good" or "the right" rotation to accomplish this, and good rotations do not always agree with the farm operator's idea of what is due him in return for his effort. This conflict gives rise to the expressions "soil-building crops" and "soil-depleting crops," the planting of which was the basis for much of the subsidy payments to farmers under the old Agricultural Adjustment Administration's program (later, the Production and Marketing Administration). Including a legume and a sod crop along with such crops as corn, oats, wheat, sugar beets, tobacco, or cotton can accomplish two things: (1) the fixation of nitrogen by the legume crop and (2) the maintenance of the organic-matter content of the soil to some extent. Clover, peanuts, soybeans, cowpeas, alfalfa, and other legumes have the power to bring about a fixation of nitrogen from the air somewhat in the following manner: With certain bacteria present or introduced, and with favorable soil and moisture conditions, legumes form nodules on their roots in which the bacteria live and develop. These bacteria have the ability to convert atmospheric nitrogen into compounds usable by the plant. Some of the "fixed" nitrogen compounds remain in the roots and stubble or vines even if the entire crop is not plowed under.

The turning under of grass sods naturally adds organic matter, and it is in a form which is quite properly incorporated into the soil. If the entire crop is plowed under instead of being harvested for hay or seed, so much the better for soil fertility.

What happens to the crops in rotations, whether manures and other fertilizers are applied in the course of the rotation, what kind of tillage is practiced, and how irrigation water is used—all may affect a chosen rotation for better or for worse. Removal of the nitrogen-fixing crops may remove critical amounts of phosphorus and potassium.

Results from a rotation are more difficult to identify than those from fertilizing and other practices used at the same time, but crop rotation, skillfully practiced, can amount to very effective soil conservation.

Supplying Lime as a Nutrient and Soil Amendment. Sight should not be lost of the fact that lime supplies the calcium necessary as an actual nutrient material in plant growth, as well as acting to "sweeten" an acid soil. Although the latter effect is the better known of the two, both are essential in growing many legumes and certain other important crops. In growing legumes the high calcium requirement is very important. Perhaps the reason for thinking of lime primarily as a soil amendment is that as a nutrient material it is present in sufficient quantities. Yet under general farming conditions in the North Central states, lime leaves the farm to the extent of 100 to 500 pounds per acre per year over and above the amount returned in manure and crop residues. Just how it "amends" the soil concerns, for example, the prevention of an actual toxic or poisoning effect of acids on plant tissues and the rendering available of needed phosphorus to growing plants. Calcium as a nutrient, as well as iron, manganese, copper, zinc, and magnesium, is known to be less available in highly acidic soils.

The chief sources of lime are ground limestone and marl, a natural product underlying certain marshes. Both of these materials vary in purity and calcium content and are applied to the land without refinement. Prepared lime includes burnt or caustic lime and slaked or hydrated lime. The latter is prepared by adding water to burnt lime which in turn is a product of burning raw limestone. Limestone deposits are widely distributed, and agricultural lime in its natural forms is available at reasonable prices. Many such deposits are developed by groups of farmers on a cooperative plan. Lime has also been supplied on a subsidy basis under the Production and Marketing Administration program.

Maintaining Nitrogen in the Soil. In addition to the nitrogen returned to the soil in manures, plant residues, and green-manure crops when they are plowed under, all of which are most important, numerous commercial products are applied directly to the soil where the locally available materials are insufficient. These may include anhydrous ammonia, ammonium sulfate (well known as a by-product of the coke industry), cottonseed meal, dried blood, fish scrap, linseed meal, garbage and slaughterhouse tankage, urea, sewage sludge, and sodium nitrate (much of which is imported from Chile in the form of the relatively pure "Chile saltpeter"). Synthetic sodium nitrate is also manufactured in this country. Guano is imported from South America, and although rich in nitrogen, it is also valued for its content of phosphorus. Deposits from caves frequented by bats in the Southwestern United States are also being marketed.

Some of these materials are unstable under certain circumstances in agriculture, particularly in truck and greenhouse enterprises. The techniques of applying them are varied and require care and planning.

Maintaining Phosphorus in the Soil. Inherent deficiencies in certain soils, removal in soil erosion, and removal by crops—all emphasize the importance of maintaining an adequate supply of phosphorus in the soil. Phosphate rock which occurs in considerable quantities in the Southeast and in the Northern Rocky Mountain territory of the United States is the principal source of phosphates, as they are called by the fertilizer manufacturers. Where the phosphorus content is low in the rock, processes of concentrating the product into "superphosphate" bring about savings in shipping and application costs. The phosphorus content, expressed in terms of phosphoric acid, of these products may run as high as 48 per cent by weight. Animal bones furnished an early source of phosphorus for use on the land, and bone meal for fertilizer is now an important by-product of the meat-packing industry. Farm manures and recovered sewage materials are other important sources. Much convincing experimental work has been done on the use of phosphorus in growing and improving the quality of important crops, and it is comforting to know that such an important element occurs in such abundance in the United States, even though the supply is not inexhaustible. Skill in the use of phosphorous fertilizers is necessary in order to be sure that they are readily available to plants and do not form insoluble compounds with other minerals either present in or added to the soil.

Maintaining the Potash Supply. Potash, as it is commonly called in the fertilizer industry, although widely distributed, is deficient in certain leached sandy soils and in most muck soils and must be added to them in some form of cropping practice. Manure is a ready source of this element, particularly where used for fertilizing alfalfa and other heavily rooted plants with vigorous "feeding" habits. Commercial potash fertilizers were formerly imported into the United States in large quantities from the Stassfurt fields in Germany and the Alsatian fields nearby, which are vast in extent. Deposits in New Mexico and Texas now yield considerable quantities, and by-product sources include the cement, sugar, and blast-furnace industries. A large number of the mixed commercial fertilizers contain potash, and while not so nearly the limiting plant nutrient in many soils as phosphorus is said to be, it is still important and presents a real maintenance problem.

Maintaining the Trace Elements. Although knowledge of the necessity of copper, cobalt, zinc, boron, lead, iodine, fluorine, and nickel in the soil is comparatively recent, the addition of these elements has paid good dividends in crop increases and to some extent has prevented failures from disease or other nutritional causes. These elements are usually purchased as mixed fertilizers or are blended before application to the soil. The mixtures are somewhat expensive and must be used in connection with soil analyses and thorough knowledge of the needs of the particular crop.

Increasing Productive Power through Maintaining Nutrient Materials in the Soil. It is well to remember here that conservation involves not only use without unnecessary waste but improving the productivity of any given resource where possible and desirable. Certainly the use of all the soil-amending and nutrient-returning materials mentioned in the foregoing pages offers examples of this part of the conservation process as far as the soil is concerned. If dumping and distributing mineral salts on a field, year after year, and removing them in large part the same season in the form of a crop sounds like a tiresome and futile business, these considerations should be emphasized: (1) the results per unit of human effort are increased; (2) human life is thus made more abundant in terms of food, clothing, and health; and (3) the soil resource is passed on to the next generation in a sustained productive condition.

BIBLIOGRAPHY

BENNETT, HUGH H.: Soil Conservation, McGraw-Hill Book Company, New York, 1939.
Conservation News, National Wildlife Federation, Washington, D.C., April, 1962.
DANA, SAMUEL T.: Forest and Range Policy, McGraw-Hill Book Company, New York, 1959.
DULEY, F. L., AND M. F. MILLER: Erosion and Surface Run-off under Different Soil Conditions, *Mo. Agr. Expt. Sta. Res. Bull.* 23, 1923.

The Exchange, New York Stock Exchange, New York, October, 1964.

GUSTAFSON, A. F., AND ASSOCIATES: Conservation in the United States, Comstock Publishing Associates, a division of Cornell University Press, Ithaca, N.Y., 1949.

Holes in the Ground, *Cornell Rural School Leaflet,* vol. 35, November, 1941.

KELLOGG, CHARLES E.: The Soils That Support Us, The Macmillan Company, New York, 1941.

Land, Yearbook of U.S. Dept. Agr., 1958.

LYON, T. LYTTLETON, AND HARRY O. BUCKMAN: The Nature and Property of Soils, 3d ed., The Macmillan Company, New York, 1937.

MARBUT, C. F.: Soils, Their Genesis, Classification and Development, Lectures before the Graduate School of the U.S. Department of Agriculture, February to May, 1928. (Unpublished.)

Our Public Lands, quarterly magazine of Bureau of Land Management, U.S. Department of the Interior, April and July, 1951.

PARKINS, A. E. AND J. R. WHITAKER: Our Natural Resources and Their Conservation, John Wiley & Sons, Inc., New York, 1939.

PIEMEISEL, ROBERT L., FRANCIS R. LAWSON, AND EUBANKS CARSNER: Weeds, Insects, Plant Diseases, and Dust Storms, *Sci. Monthly,* vol. 73, pp. 124–128, August, 1951.

Soil Conservation, monthly magazine of U.S. Soil Conservation Service.

Soils and Men, Yearbook of U.S. Dept. Agr., 1937.

Soil, Yearbook of U.S. Dept. Agr., 1957.

VAN HISE, CHARLES R., AND LOOMIS HAVEMEYER: Conservation of Our Natural Resources, The Macmillan Company, New York, 1930.

WOOTEN, HUGH H., AND JAMES R. ANDERSON: Major Uses of Land in the United States, Summary for 1954, U.S. Department of Agriculture, 1957.

3 SOIL: HUMAN PROBLEMS

AFTER A DISCUSSION of the physical problems of keeping the soil from washing away and of maintaining the nutrient materials in the soil, the question arises, "How shall the farmers, the bankers, the statesmen, the absentee landowners, and the people—all of whom have a stake in soil conservation—bring it about?"

In the United States, public opinion and its formalized expression in government have always favored private use and ownership of productive land. Economic necessity forces such private users and owners to aim at goals which can be realized within a lifetime—a period within which the entrepreneur can reasonably expect to improve his own material status. For this reason long-term soil conservation policies which might appear to be most effective from the standpoints of technology and of broad, national interest are likely to be recognized at the local level as unrealistic and hence to be greatly modified or largely ignored.

Self-interest, even when highly enlightened, does not automatically bring about the action called for by such enlightenment. In a democracy, therefore, where it is not customary to punish men for inadequate stewardship of natural resources, people seek ways to employ mild restraints and rewards as incentives to good stewardship of land. Examples of these are found in the practices of certain banks which base credit in the form of crop loans on agreements to use certain erosion-control measures; in the premium prices sometimes offered in the purchase of high-grade farm products; in the advice and demonstration supplied by state and Federal agencies to landowners and farm operators; in the actual subsidies of cash or fertilizer offered for the growing of soil-building crops; in encouragement through loans and technical assistance of cooperative farm-operator groups who may help themselves to practice soil conservation through the common use of specialized machinery, group buying, and the pooling of operations on adjoining properties; in publicly guided resettlement programs to help failing farm operators to better chances of success; and in the laws which make the operation of these devices easier and which authorize research and educational measures.

Such incentives may be grouped into three broad programs: (1) research and education, (2) promotion, and (3) technical and financial assistance. The last, especially, is more characteristic of the attack on soil conservation problems than on those of conserving other natural resources, but because soil conservation programs must reach so many individual owners and operators, the success or failure of all these measures is a good indication of how conservation is practiced in a democracy.

Research and Education. The tremendous mass of research data on the two great problems of keeping the soil in place and maintaining its content of nutrient materials has resulted mainly from the work of the state agricultural experiment stations and the forest and range experiment stations of the United States Forest Service. Scientists and other scholars of considerable number located with other agencies too numerous to mention have also made their contributions. Such research must go on constantly even though there is bound to be a lag between what is known to be good practice and what is actually practiced. The available methods and devices discussed so far are the results of such research.

Education, strictly considered, would perhaps be confined to preparing certain men as scientists, leaders, and actual farm operators. Technically educated people are indispensable in a soil conservation program. More broadly considered, education involves interpretation of what is known, to farm operators particularly, but also to bankers and investment companies, to lawmakers, and to the ordinary citizen who in a democracy may never know, or may forget, that his life depends upon the soil and the way it is managed. Demonstrating economic benefits is important. This kind of education must be more systematic and less evangelical in character than the thing we know as *promotion*, which will be discussed later. It goes forward through the itinerant teacher's efforts as an "extension" worker from a state college of agriculture; through factual and carefully prepared scientific publications, both technical and popular; through field demonstrations to groups of farm operators; through youth groups such as the 4-H Clubs and the Future Farmers of America, particularly in "club" projects where actual projects are carried out; through lectures, particularly to nonfarm people; through better understanding of fundamental accounting principles; and through press, radio, and TV in their more serious and factual articles, news reports, and forums. (Remember that this is not yet promotion and that an attempt is being made to describe *education* in the sense of interpreting known facts and accepted principles.) Increasingly, a bank, implement company, fertilizer concern, railroad, or colonization company may employ staff men technically equipped to educate both employer and customer. They can often accomplish wonders.

Promotion. Creating in people the desire to conserve the soil is certainly not to be accomplished through research and education alone. Citizens of a democracy are inclined to value liberty and happiness more than life based on good management of natural resources. Evangelism in the sense of clever advertising (Fig. 3-1) and other selling techniques is not only necessary but is generally acceptable to citizens of a democracy. Appeals are made to self-interest, patriotism, desire for recognition, pride in offspring, religious convictions, and any other human desire or emotion that can be identified. Everything from a photograph of an ill-nourished

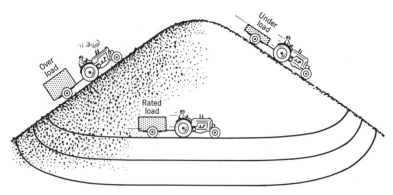

figure 3-1
Contour farming saves power. Cartoon from the bulletin "Level Farming on Sloping Fields," a promotion device used by J. I. Case Company. (Kansas State Board of Agriculture.)

child in front of a bleak home on eroded land to an illustrated lecture to selected businessmen in a great city may be called into play. If such *promotion* can precede, accompany, or follow what we have called education, so much the better. Announcing of rewards such as easier bank credit, subsidy in cash or kind, available technical advice and help, opportunity to join in a cooperative movement—in so far as they amount only to publicizing such incentives—also come properly under the heading of promotion.

After the technical talent and leadership have been recruited and the mind of the farm operator has been prepared, there remains the action phase in which technical assistance and convenient financing and procedure are indicated.

Technical and Financial Assistance. How a farm operator or landowner is to conserve soil and make a living at the same time, with assurance of increased long-range values, are frequently questions the public must help to answer. The public through its government at various levels supplies this answer with the service of its technicians; with incentive payments for the use of good practices; with credit; and with supplies of seed, fertilizer, trees, shrubs, and other materials. All these things, when furnished to a landowner, amount to subsidy, a thing which various *industrial* concerns in this democracy have enjoyed in one way or another for many years. In the discussion of the many laws and procedures involved in such a program, subsidies will be mentioned in connection with the retirement of submarginal land, agricultural stabilization and conservation, soil conservation districts, and small-watershed programs.

RETIREMENT OF SUBMARGINAL LANDS AND RESETTLEMENT   In conserving the human powers of families who had selected and settled on land which had inadequate power to support them, the Federal government in the 1930s, through its Resettlement Administration, purchased and retired considerable acreage, allocating it to other uses and helping the families by resettling them on better and sometimes larger farms, or otherwise furnishing opportunity for self-help. All land purchases were made with the consent of the owner and under the authority of the Jones-Bankhead Farm Tenant Act.

The task of continuing this improvement of economic opportunity has been assumed by a succession of governmental organizations. Among these are the Office of Rural Areas Development, which helps local farm groups in the promotion of economic growth and new opportunities, and the Farmers Home Administration, which extends credit and technical assistance to farmers. Such loans have established an encouraging record of repayment. A result of these and other incentives has been the conservation of both human powers and soil.

AGRICULTURAL STABILIZATION AND CONSERVATION SERVICE   This agency through its Agricultural Conservation Program in 3,065 counties provides cost-sharing assistance for soil, water, wildlife, and woodland conservation practices involving both individual farms and community activities. It also aids the development and encouragement of efficient and profitable farm operations through commodity loans, price supports, storage-facility loans, and production adjustments. Through grants of financial assistance and cost-sharing of needed conservation measures, it helps farmers and ranchers convert cropland to pasture, woodland, wildlife habitat, and income-producing recreational facilities.[1]

Soil Conservation Districts. Prior to 1935 several agencies in the Federal government were involved in activities pertaining to soil erosion. In 1935 these activities were coordinated by the establishment of the Soil Erosion Service in the Department of Agriculture. In April of the same year congressional action directed the Secretary of Agriculture to establish within his department an agency to be known as the Soil Conservation Service and to be assigned tasks of research, survey of soil erosion and possibilities of water conservation, demonstration, dissemination of information, and cooperation with other public agencies on national, state, and local levels. Subsequently the Service received other assignments including a national program of flood control, snow surveys, and research on the relationship between weather and soil erosion. Later reorganiza-

[1] Rural Areas Development Handbook, U.S. Dept. of Agr., Agr. Handbook 245, June, 1963.

tions of the Department of Agriculture have transferred most of these research functions to the Agricultural Research Service.

In February of 1937, President Franklin D. Roosevelt addressed a letter to the governors of all the states urging the adoption of model legislation which would authorize the establishment of a soil-conservation-districts program. It is through this program that soil conservation in farming districts throughout the country has gone forward most rapidly. Any state legislature may enact a law authorizing the setting up of soil conservation districts where landowners may vote themselves into co-operative soil conservation programs in a manner similar to that used in establishing drainage districts or school districts. Such groups can then accomplish things which as individuals they would not be equipped to do. Since 1937, when the first districts were organized, all the states have authorized them by law, and by the end of 1962 their number had reached a total of 2,936. These districts cover 1.7 billion acres of land, which comprise 93 per cent of the farm land and 96 per cent of the farms and ranches in the United States; they sponsor, or share in the sponsor-ship of, 98 per cent of all the nation's small-watershed programs; and their grass-roots character is clear from the fact that more than 14,500 persons serve without pay on their governing bodies.[2]

When a district is organized it may request technical assistance and the loan of heavy machinery, purchase trees and shrubs collectively and distribute them to its members for planting, and carry forward a program of soil conservation practices in accordance with farm plans which are worked out by the farm-operator in cooperation with the technical staff assigned by the Soil Conservation Service. The form of these cooperative agreements varies among states and districts, but in general (1) the land-owner or operator agrees to prepare and follow a conservation plan for using his land within its capability and treating it according to its needs; and (2) the district agrees to provide a soil and land-capability map, information, technical assistance, and other services and materials as are available and are needed to help the cooperator carry out the plan (Fig. 3-2).[3]

The land-use-capability classifications were made during a survey taken by the Conservation Needs Inventory Committee under the leadership of the Soil Conservation Service. The agricultural land resources of the United States were surveyed to determine their capabilities, their uses, and their soil- and water-conservation needs. This county-by-county survey, begun in 1958 and completed in 1961, covered all rural land area

[2] Robert L. Geiger and Georgie A. Keller, *Organization and Development of the Soil Conservation Service*, U.S. Dept. Agr., SCS-CI-13, June, 1964.

[3] *Soil Conservation Districts*, Soil Conservation Service, U.S. Dept. of Agr., PA 417, January, 1965.

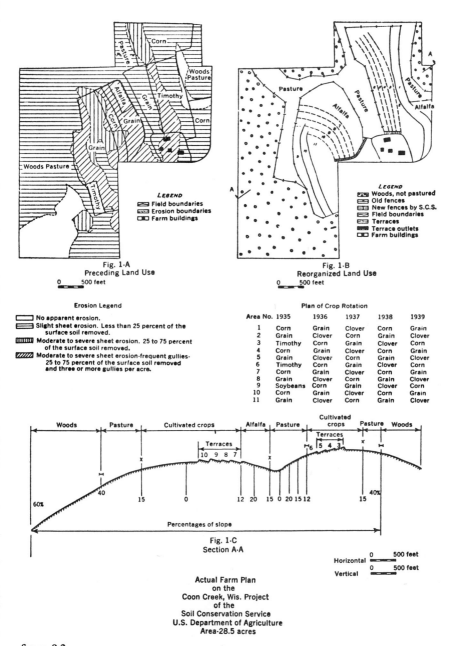

LEGEND
- Field boundaries
- Erosion boundaries
- Farm buildings

Fig. 1-A
Preceding Land Use
0 500 feet

LEGEND
- Woods, not pastured
- Old fences
- New fences by S.C.S.
- Field boundaries
- Terraces
- Terrace outlets
- Farm buildings

Fig. 1-B
Reorganized Land Use
0 500 feet

Erosion Legend

- No apparent erosion.
- Slight sheet erosion. Less than 25 percent of the surface soil removed.
- Moderate to severe sheet erosion. 25 to 75 percent of the surface soil removed.
- Moderate to severe sheet erosion-frequent gullies- 25 to 75 percent of the surface soil removed and three or more gullies per acre.

Plan of Crop Rotation

Area No.	1935	1936	1937	1938	1939
1	Corn	Grain	Clover	Corn	Grain
2	Grain	Clover	Corn	Grain	Clover
3	Timothy	Corn	Grain	Clover	Corn
4	Corn	Grain	Clover	Corn	Grain
5	Grain	Clover	Corn	Grain	Clover
6	Timothy	Corn	Grain	Clover	Corn
7	Corn	Grain	Clover	Corn	Grain
8	Grain	Clover	Corn	Grain	Clover
9	Soybeans	Corn	Grain	Clover	Corn
10	Corn	Grain	Clover	Corn	Grain
11	Grain	Clover	Corn	Grain	Clover

Percentages of slope

Fig. 1-C
Section A-A

Horizontal 0 500 feet
Vertical 0 500 feet

Actual Farm Plan
on the
Coon Creek, Wis. Project
of the
Soil Conservation Service
U.S. Department of Agriculture
Area-28.5 acres

figure 3-2
Farm plan prepared by a Wisconsin Soil Conservation District technical advisor and the farm owner. Narrative portion will contain directions concerning rotation, etc. (United States Soil Conservation Service.)

in private ownership or owned by states or other local governments. It involved participation of more than 30,000 people in 3,000 counties. The resulting land-use-capability maps help the landowner to determine the use of each acre of agricultural land within its capabilities and the treatment of each acre in accordance with its needs for protection and improvement. This nation-wide inventory of the physical needs of agricultural land pointed to four major conservation problems. The most widespread of these is a susceptibility to erosion; it is the dominant problem on 53 per cent of the area included in the inventory. Of the total area, 25 per cent showed unfavorable soil conditions in the root zone, 17 per cent had excess water either in the soil or on its surface (Fig. 3-3), and 5 per cent was located in an area with adverse climate conditions. There are eight classes of land-use capability (Fig. 3-4), as follows:

Class I. Lands which can be cultivated safely following good local practices with the assurance of fair yields of adaptable crops but requiring no special soil conservation practices.

Class II. Lands which, if cultivated with expectation of fair yields, require simple soil conservation practices, such as, for example, contour cultivation and simple rotations.

Field of corn on inadequately drained land, Illinois. (Photo by G. F. Loyd, United States Soil Conservation Service.)

figure 3-3

figure 3-4
Division of California ranch into land-capability classes. (Photo by United States Soil Conservation Service.)

Class III. Lands which can be safely cultivated only with use of intensive practices such as terracing, strip cropping in very narrow bands, heavy fertilization, or tile drainage.

Class IV. Lands which can be cultivated only in a limited way and should be kept as nearly as possible in pasture and hay only.

Classes V to VIII. Lands which are not suitable for ordinary cultivation and which generally should be kept in permanent vegetation. About 44 per cent of the non-Federal agricultural land, or 642 million acres, is in these classes.[4]

THE SMALL-WATERSHEDS PROGRAM   Because many of the smaller watersheds of the country, which contribute to rapid runoff and floods, include land that comes under neither the Soil Conservation Districts nor the larger downstream works for flood control, irrigation, and other purposes, a Watershed and Flood Control Act (Public Law 566) was passed by the Congress in 1954. It not only provides for these neglected lands but seeks, through cooperation of residents and communities of the entire watershed area, to work out a complete system of land and water management. Such a plan may cover the prevention of erosion (Fig. 3-5), the building of works to alleviate flood damage, reforestation, fire control, pollution control, and the development of hunting, fishing, and other outdoor-recreation facilities and opportunities. The initiative must be taken by the local citizens, although limited help and money may be contributed by the Federal government when an application is approved by the state government concerned and it is shown that help is needed but is not available under any other Federal program.

The Soil Conservation Service is authorized to furnish technical and

[4] Agricultural Land Resources, U.S. Dept. Agr., Agr. Inform. Bull. 263, May, 1962.

67

figure 3-5   (b)
Erosion and flood control in small watershed, Iowa. (a) Rapidly advancing gully head destroyed bridge 3 years earlier; (b) road structure which replaced bridge shown in (a) above. (Photos by R. Proctor and Eldon Weber, United States Soil Conservation Service.)

some financial aid to local organizations both when they are planning and, later, carrying out works of improvement for flood prevention and for the conservation, development, utilization, and disposal of water in small watersheds totaling not more than 250,000 acres each. Certain costs may be borne entirely by the Federal government, and provision is made for long-time loans to the local organization on generous terms. This law brought some order to earlier programs in which appropriations had been made under a Flood Control Act of 1936 for eleven watersheds covering about 30 million acres and for sixty new projects authorized by the Congress in 1953. The distinctive feature of this program is its local initiation and management, with *limited* Federal leadership and financing.

It is discussed here rather than in the treatment of floods because of its erosion-control objectives.

How Soil Conservation Can Be Assured on Nonfarm Lands. While the most fertile lands of the country are in private ownership and in relatively small parcels, they do not comprise the whole soil conservation problem or require the only exercise of the tools of research and education, promotion, or technical aid and financing. Lands that nobody loves but that need care if they are not to wash or blow away or become totally unproductive include the following: public pasture or range lands in the Western states, Indian lands (public in the sense that each Indian tribe is literally a "nation" and that the Federal government as guardian has certain land-management obligations), cutover forest lands in large or scattered blocks, and strip-mined coal and other mineral lands which may be private today and public tomorrow through tax reversion, exchange, or sale to public agencies. Here the physical problems have to do with such things as grass, logging waste, and brush fires; with overgrazing, moisture conservation, and cloudburst floods; and with the use of more extensive soil conservation practices where the owner or custodian does not live on the land. The relatively low value of these lands, in spite of their indispensability to the livestock and recreation industries and their watershed values, operates against an intelligent interest in them on the part of the public. The Congress, for example, has taken the position that any administration of the public range under the Taylor Grazing Act of 1934 must pay its way on the basis of grazing revenue alone. Presumably, as representing the people, the Congress speaks for the people. In so speaking, the Congress used some of the "education" it received from a former cabinet officer who testified that it would be only moderately costly to administer these lands and implied that revenue was not important. The results of the failure of *education* in this instance are evident in the failure of the Federal government to assume adequately its role of proprietor and to provide adequately, through skillful and thorough control of livestock grazing and management of the range, for conserving the soil. Tremendous possibilities for rehabilitating and improving the public ranges exist in the language of the Taylor Grazing Act, and increasing good is being accomplished in spite of meager appropriations. More technical assistance, dictated by better-educated congressmen, range users, and the people as a whole, is the crying need. Grazing lands, consisting of the brush areas, open meadows, and other scattered areas within the national forests and managed under a different system and much more intensively by another Federal department, are generally in better condition. Their soils are being conserved.

The story in the preceding paragraph is one of somewhat unsatisfactory conservation effort in a democracy. One of the reasons it *can* happen is that education in its broad sense can fail even under a type of government which believes profoundly *in* education.

Indian lands in New Mexico, Wyoming, and other Western states totaling close to 35 million acres, suffering from overgrazing, and located on watersheds contributing to great irrigation projects, require widespread public efforts at erosion control. Here the attack, while similar to the district and demonstration procedure used in humid regions, must emphasize low costs and far-flung efforts to reestablish vegetative cover and reduce grazing injury. This means interference with an established, if unsound, local economy and way of life. The answer is not to be found in resettlement or in meager appropriations. The Soil Conservation Service cooperates here with the Indian Service, the states, the private owners, and the water users.

Tree planting and pasture development on strip-mined coal lands, stream-bank control in some of the cutover areas, reforestation of cutover lands, sodding and shrub planting on highway cuts and fills, reinforcing of ocean and lake shores and influencing thoughtless citizens to realize that the oceans and the Great Lakes are still in the process of geological erosion and that some shores are not to be invaded by cottages and hotels, and the acquisition and management of reservoir lands by cities and by such agencies as the Tennessee Valley Authority—all these are examples of miscellaneous efforts at soil-erosion control. Such undertakings are variously financed and administered, and technical skill and advice are being increasingly employed.

Research, education, promotion, and the furnishing of technical and financial aid on these nonfarm projects are more difficult than in the close-knit groups of farm cooperators. Nonresident owners and custodians of land are not apt pupils, nor do promotion tactics affect them so successfully. These lower-value lands will enter the soil conservation picture more and more with the development of the great river-valley projects to be discussed later.

BIBLIOGRAPHY

Agricultural Land Resources, *U.S. Dept. Agr., Agr. Inform. Bull.* 263, May, 1962.
Farmer's World, Yearbook of U.S. Dept. Agr., 1964.
GEIGER, ROBERT L., JR., AND GEORGIE A. KELLER: Organization and Development of the Soil Conservation Service, a reference for employees, U.S. Department of Agriculture, SCS-CI-13, June, 1964.
KELLOGG, CHARLES E.: Soil-use Planning for Individuals and Public Goals, *Bull. of the Atomic Scientists,* November, 1964, pp. 15–18.
KELLOGG, CHARLES E.: Why a New System of Soil Classification? *Soil Sci.* vol. 96, no. 1, pp. 1–5, July, 1963.

Land, Yearbook of U.S. Dept. Agr., 1958.

Rural Areas Development Handbook, *U.S. Dept. Agr., Agr. Handbook* 245, June, 1963.

Soil and Water Conservation Needs, *U.S. Dept. Agr. Misc. Publ.* 971, 1965.

Soil Conservation at Home, Soil Conservation Service, *U.S. Dept. of Agr., Agr. Inform. Bull.* 244, February, 1963.

Soil Conservation Districts, Soil Conservation Service, *U.S. Dept. Agr.,* PA 417, January, 1965.

The Measure of Our Land, *U.S. Dept. Agr.,* PA 128, February, 1951.

4 WATER: 1

THE WATER WHICH we take today with little thought for a thousand uses may last year have been part of a cloud, a tumbling mountain stream, a falling rain, or may have been at rest in a quiet lake or deep in the earth as a liquid or as frost. Water moves in a "hydrologic cycle," described admirably 2,000 years ago in the Scriptures: "All the rivers run into the sea; yet the sea is not full; unto the place from whence the rivers come, thither they return again." Less poetically explained, starting at the surface of ocean, lake, or stream, the essential features of the cycle are the following: evaporation which is supplemented by the moisture transpired from plants; storage in the atmosphere as vapor; condensation; precipitation in the form of rain, hail, or snow; infiltration into the surface soil of the earth, addition to ground water, or collection into streams, rivers, lakes, and oceans, where it is again subject to evaporation.

Evaporation is sometimes spoken of as *flyoff;* the movement downhill, whether over a flat surface, in tiny rills, or as great rivers, as *runoff;* the movement into the ground as soil moisture or finding its way to the underground reservoirs, as *cutoff.* But there can be no "off" without an "on." Perhaps, with apology to some of the people who use these terms, we should speak of precipitation as "fall on."

In the hydrologic cycle which is represented in the diagram (Fig. 4-1), any control or manipulation of the inexhaustible supply of water which men can exert must occur principally at the stages of runoff and

figure 4-1
The hydrologic cycle. (United States Soil Conservation Service.)

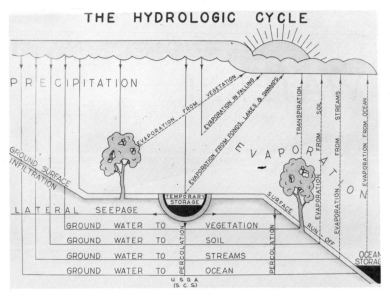

cutoff, and men have much to learn at both stages. The supply and availability at any given point are variable and may easily become uncertain. They can cause suffering by their absence or by their overabundance. Along with atmosphere, sunshine, and soil, they are essential to human life. The conservation of water, therefore, is of compelling importance, even down to keeping the household faucets in repair.

Men speak of "harnessing" rivers, of "controlling" and "alleviating" floods, of "delivering" water for irrigation, of "improving" lakes and streams to maintain good fishing, of "softening" and "metering" water for domestic and industrial use, of "impounding" water for power, recreation, and stock raising, and of "charting" waters of proper depth and freedom from obstruction for navigation. All these activities are the efforts of men to conserve water as a natural resource, and it is not strange that various uses conflict at times and that conservation in one direction may become waste in another.

How Water is Measured. In order to understand and appreciate the problems of water supply, some notion of the quantities needed and of the terms in which they are expressed must be held in mind. Water is measured by volume and by rate of flow. The simplest unit to remember, and the basic one, is the cubic foot. Reduced to gallons, 7½ of them would make a cubic foot, or if you can only think in "fifths" it would figure out to 37½. The unit known as an acre-foot of water means the equivalent of water 1 foot deep covering an entire acre (about the size of a football field), or 43,560 cubic feet which would be 325,872 gallons. If the term acre-inch is used, one-twelfth this volume is indicated.

The cubic foot per second is the basic unit indicating rate of flow. Here, water moving at the velocity of 1 foot every second will fill a flume 1 foot wide and 1 foot deep. Gallons per minute (abbreviated gpm) may be visualized as a flow unit by remembering that 450 gallons per minute is equivalent to 1 cubic foot per second. Such a flow would produce about 1 acre-inch per hour or 2 acre-feet per 24-hour day.

The "miner's inch" is also a flow unit, but it is not uniform in the various Western states where it is used. The number of miner's inches to the cubic foot per second varies, for example, from 38.4 in Colorado to 40 in Oregon and 50 in Southern California.[1]

Annual Rainfall on the United States. If it is assumed that 30 inches is the mean annual rainfall over the United States, 5 billion acre-feet of water comes down on the country every year. That amounts to almost 35 acre-feet for every inhabitant, or to the entire annual flow of the Mississippi River ten times over. What happens to it? Well, it is estimated that one-half of it evaporates, giving no opportunity for capture; one-sixth

[1] M. R. Lewis, Practical Irrigation, *U.S. Dept. Agr. Farmers' Bull.* 1922, 1943, p. 16.

gets away in the runoff, some of it having been temporarily captured and used along its journey to the sea; one-sixth is used and transpired into the atmosphere by plants; another sixth joins the "reservoirs" of underground water from which it may be captured to some extent for use.[2]

Uses of the Runoff and the Cutoff. There is some virtue in an attempt to classify the uses of water at those stages of the cycle where men can exercise some control and management of the resource.

No one has successfully challenged the statement Frederick H. Newell[3] made in 1930 on the uses of the runoff, ranked in order of importance to the comfort, health, and prosperity of mankind as follows:

1. Water supply for domestic and municipal purposes
2. Transportation and dilution of waste, or sanitation
3. Food production: irrigation, drainage
4. Water power: hydroelectric development
5. Recreation: fishing, boating, swimming, skating
6. Navigation: lakes, rivers, canals

Because Newell, however, was confining his classification to the runoff and because of startling changes since 1930 in the demand for and uses of water supply from whatever stages of the cycle, the following classification and ranking of uses for water which is subject to a measure of capture is suggested:

1. Water supply for domestic and municipal purposes
2. Transportation and dilution of waste
3. Manufacture and processing of natural-resource materials
4. Food production, including the growing but not the processing of plant and animal crops
5. Water power, both hydroelectric and steam
6. Recreation: fishing, hunting waterfowl, boating, swimming, winter sports, enjoying scenery
7. Navigation, for whatever purpose save recreation and on any water

In any such grouping as the above, the uses overlap, supplement, and sometimes interfere with each other. For example, municipal use includes, along with the supply of drinking water, the transportation of certain wastes; food production may be the dominating purpose of impounding water in arid regions, and yet a reservoir may offer recreation all the way from furnishing a restful scene to attracting waterfowl for

[2] W. J. McGee, Water as a Resource, *An. Amer. Acad.*, vol. 33, pp. 521–534, 1898.
[3] Frederick H. Newell, Water, in Conservation of Our Natural Resources, Charles R. Van Hise and Loomis Havemeyer eds., The Macmillan Company, New York, 1930, p. 134.

the hunter; and a navigable, power-producing, waste-transporting stream may surrender, because of these services, any recreation values otherwise inherent.

It should also be remembered that, unless water can be in a measure captured, controlled, and outguessed in its variability of supply, any one use may be sharply and sometimes suddenly curtailed. Just how well men succeed in managing this natural resource will be discussed later, and a special section on alleviating floods is included in the following chapter.

WATER FOR DOMESTIC AND MUNICIPAL PURPOSES

Relatively few people in the United States have suffered long from thirst or from lack of water for personal cleanliness, for cooking, or for other comforts and conveniences. Nor have many lived in communities where water supply was critically short for fire control, watering of lawns and gardens, operation of laundries, and other small, essential service businesses. These are "domestic and municipal purposes," and they require on the average more than 100 gallons of water per day per person. Such uses are recognized as of first importance, and the supplying of communities with adequate amounts of water is not infrequently the limiting factor in their growth and development. Problems of supply run all the way from finding new sources to augment inadequate systems to treating water for safe human consumption and for "hardness," regulating amounts used, and developing separate mains through which untreated supplies may be obtained for fire control. These are problems of conserving water as a natural resource.

Communities obtain their water supplies from streams and lakes and from wells and springs which tap underground accumulations. Settlements along any range of mountains are likely to enjoy supplies diverted from mountain streams or pumped from gravel cones at the mouths of canyons. Large cities along the Great Lakes take their supplies from these cold and never-failing bodies of water. In the South and Middle West the village or city water tower or standpipe is frequently the most prominent skyline feature and may indicate that the water supply is pumped from wells. Here also some renovated water from polluted streams may be used. In the arid West and Southwest domestic and municipal supplies often come from the same sources as water for the irrigation of agricultural crops. These include reservoirs with both their canal systems and their pumping stations drawing on underground water. Increasing industrial use of water from village and city systems and its requirement for air conditioning have raised the old figure of 100 gallons per person per day considerably in systems once considered adequate.

Importance of Ground Water. A vast amount of water in the *aquifer,* or ground-water reservoir, moves about or rests as ground water. It is a part of the hydrologic cycle, and it yields about one-fifth of the water used by this nation. It is widely distributed where three conditions are met: (1) Water falling directly on the land or flowing over the surface in streams penetrates beneath the surface in quantities sufficient to exceed the field capacity of the soil; that is, it moves downward through the zone of aeration under the influence of gravity; (2) the rocks beneath the soil are permeable enough to transmit this water; and (3) the rate of infiltration is sufficient that the zone of saturation formed in the lower part of the permeable rocks will be built up to a perceptible thickness by the time the lateral flow increases to a rate equal to the rate of infiltration from the surface.

Ground water exists at least intermittently under these conditions in a large part of the world. For this water to become a usable resource, however, three further conditions must be met: (1) The "rocks," including such unconsolidated material as sand, gravel, clay and soil, are permeable enough to yield supplies of water to wells, springs, or streams; (2) the zone of saturation is perennial, or at least persists long enough each season to allow practical exploitation; and (3) the mineral substances dissolved by the water as it travels through the soil and rocks do not reach such concentrations as to make the water unfit for the desired use at the place where the water is needed.[4]

Effective development and management of ground-water supplies are handicapped by lack of knowledge concerning ground-water hydrology. The states appear to be aware of the importance of ground water, and a number of management programs are being considered on this level.

Reduction of Water Losses to Phreatophytes. It takes considerable imagination to realize that appreciable amounts of water are lost to the worthless vegetation which grows in desert situations. But these phreatophytes, as they are called, may account for as much as an estimated 25 million acre-feet annually of ground water in the seventeen Western states.[5] This water is used by the plants, transpired, and evaporated from the leaves. Attempts to deal with this loss include destroying the plants mechanically and draining or pumping off the water they need. The worst of these plants, salt cedar, is spreading. Others are willows, greasewood, and rabbitbrush. The Senate Select Committee on National

[4] C. L. McGuinness, The Role of Ground Water in the National Water Situation, *U.S. Geol. Surv. Water Supply Paper* 1800, 1963, p. 22.

[5] T. W. Robinson, Phreatophytes, *U.S. Geol. Surv. Water Supply Paper* 1423, 1958. (Quoted by C. L. McGuinness, The Role of Ground Water in the National Water Situation, *U.S. Geol. Surv. Water Supply Paper* 1800, 1963, p. 94.)

Water Resources estimates that possible savings of from 1 million to 6 million acre-feet of water per year might be obtained at a cost of $40 to $100 per acre for the initial clearing and $7 per acre per year thereafter for maintenance. The lower figure appears economically worth while, but only if 3 to 4 acre-feet of water might be salvaged from each acre of land.[6] Use of the saved water would require either pumping or some means of making it available to some useful crop, such as alfalfa, on the area treated. Intensive study and experimentation is under way in the Rio Grande Valley in New Mexico, the Humboldt River Valley near Winnemucca, Nevada, and the Gila River Valley in Arizona.[7] State water laws will need attention to determine legal uses of this salvaged water if the practice becomes widespread.

Salvage of Waste Water. The losses of needed water incurred in the one-time use of water for cooling and sanitary purposes by industry and for municipal sewage are astronomical. Attempts to recover waste water are becoming more numerous throughout the country. Some ten million gallons of treated sewage effluent from the Baltimore, Maryland, system is now sold to a steel mill. Water used for cooling in industrial plants may be very little contaminated and can be used for the recharging of aquifers and for irrigation if proper health precautions are observed. Treated water from sewage is being used near San Bernardino, California, for watering shrubbery along a freeway, and the city of Ontario, California, uses such water on a municipal golf course. Although state health departments are still cautious about approving various uses of treated water from sewage, the possibilities of more than one-time use of water for the transportation of waste are very great. The prospect of using reclaimed water for injection wells is mentioned on page 80.

Depletion of Underground Water Supplies. Still another problem in conserving ground water for community use involves both amount and quality and has to do with too great depletion of underground supplies. Here, through lowering of water levels or unregulated drilling for oil or brines, the water supply becomes at the same time inadequate and unfit for human consumption. Two examples will make this clearer.

Drilling for oil, gas, brines, and water itself and mining coal and other minerals in many parts of the United States frequently tap the wrong deposit or, for example, encounter brine when oil is sought. Sometimes this occurs at great depths. Then when an oil well, a gas well, or a test drilling for any purpose is left "unplugged" or inadequately closed with concrete, salt or mineral waters migrate upward into beds containing

[6] Senate Select Committee on National Water Resources, Report, 1961a, p. 53.
[7] *Annual Report of the Secretary of the Interior,* 1962, p. 350.

fresh water. The heavier the use from such beds, the faster the brackish condition of the fresh water will develop, but in any event the supply for community use is ruined. The only remedy for such a situation is a law, rigidly enforced, regulating the drilling and leaving safe of such wells. Michigan has such a law.

The second example involves an area of several hundred square miles in a Pacific coast state where the use of water by a score or more of communities exceeds the return to the underground sources by approximately one-half each year. This has brought about a critical lowering of the water level until it is now estimated to be 25 feet lower than sea level. The underground basin is close to the Pacific Ocean, and the invasion of salt water from the ocean is estimated at the rate of more than a mile a year. Here overuse threatens the entire supply and may make it necessary to "import" water for the area from a great distance and at all but prohibitive cost.

Failure to foresee a situation of this kind seems now to be indefensible, but it is part of the sort of public indifference which is likely to occur anywhere in a democracy, through ignorance and through a tendency to neglect the responsibilities of citizenship. On the other hand, no other type of government shows the stubborn refusal to give up, once a problem is understood. This spirit is evident in the action taken in the Pacific coast state discussed above. A series of "injection wells" have been established in a line roughly parallel to the coast, into which fresh water will be pumped to form a water "wall." This arrangement, it is believed, will act as a sort of fresh-water dam to prevent further invasion of salt water from the ocean. The actual drilling of these wells was under way in 1963 and completion of the system was planned for 1966. The fresh water for this "wall" is excess Colorado River water, and when this is no longer available, reclaimed waste water which is proved to be usable will furnish the supply.

Waste Due to Evaporation and Seepage. Getting back to the surface, another bold venture is evident in the use of devices to prevent water losses from evaporation and seepage and in the search for new ones. Roofs and floating covers are employed over small reservoirs in the West. Considerable interest, moreover, has been shown in the use of cetyl alcohol, also called hexadecanol, to spread a thin film over water bodies suffering from excessive evaporation. The latter procedure has been successfully tested in Australia. The chemical does not affect the taste of the water. Costs in the Australian venture were 2 to 3 cents per 1,000 gallons of water saved, and there was a 50 per cent reduction in evaporation loss. Similar experiments in Illinois ponds cost an estimated 8 cents per 1,000 gallons saved, with a 22 to 43 per cent reduction in evapora-

figure 4-2
*Irrigating canal in California, lined with plastic material to prevent
loss from seepage. (California Farmer.)*

tion loss. Other locations where this film method has been tried are
Southern California, Arizona, Texas, and Oklahoma.[8]

Even more daring is experimentation to prevent loss from seepage by
lining ponds and ditches with continuous sheets of plastic material similar
to that used in shower curtains (Fig. 4-2).

Farm Water Supplies. It should be remembered that not everyone lives
in a town or city and that domestic water systems on thousands of farms
which are not served by a publicly operated irrigation project represent
problems of supply and quality second only to those of densely populated
communities. Again wells and springs are drawn upon, and problems
of surface pollution must be guarded against. Because it is difficult,
however, to separate human use of water on farms from use in producing
plant and animal crops, farm water problems will be further discussed
under Water for Food Production.

Requirements for Household Water. Satisfactory household water,
besides being adequate in amount, must be clear; free from harmful
bacteria; odorless; free from disagreeable taste, including "flatness";
and "soft," i.e., free from excess calcium and magnesium salts.

Clearness adds to the attractive appearance of water, and although
it is not a dependable indication of purity, it does dispel the idea that
turbid water conveys, namely, unfitness for use. Freedom from harmful
bacteria is fundamental, and while the cynic may say, as a Western
water consumer did, that he'd just as soon drink an aquarium as a
graveyard, treatment with chlorine gas or other chemicals which kills
bacteria, coagulation which entangles and removes them, and boiling

[8] V. K. La Mer, *Natl. Acad. Sci. U.S. Publ.* 942, 1963, p. 438. (Quoted by V. K.
La Mer and Thomas W. Healy in *Science*, vol. 148, p. 40, Table 1, 1965.)

which destroys them are methods of assuring "purity" in the sense of making any pathogenic organisms harmless. Disagreeable odors in drinking water may come from sulfur compounds, algae, gases from the accumulation of organic matter in a reservoir, or the presence of traces of industrial wastes which have found their way into underground water supplies. Sometimes chlorine and other reagents used to make water safe also make it disagreeable in taste. Other tastes are closely allied to the odors and their causes mentioned above. Water should not be "tasteless" to the degree of "flatness." So-called hard water contains more than 60 parts per million by volume of calcium or magnesium salts which are deposited on pipes and utensils and which interfere with the cleansing function of soaps. The amount of these salts can be reduced by precipitating them at central or household plants, both of which methods are common in inland Lake-state communities. One such city supplying water to 50,000 people and a few small industries, removes 10 tons of salts, including some treating materials, each day from its water and is paying for its plant by a small monthly charge accompanying the citizens' water bills (Fig. 4-3).

In addition to assuring a supply which measures up to the above specifications, a problem of carelessness and waste must be met in conserving the water of any community and avoiding the cost of delivering, if indeed it can be done, more water than necessary. With all the good intentions and propaganda imaginable, it is still found to be good practice with water users to measure the amounts used and charge on the basis of meter readings.

The plan for paying off the cost of the water-softener plant mentioned above and the device of metering the use of water are two methods of assuring equitable distribution of a natural resource. Fairness in distribution, in other words, is assured, and this is a part of good conservation.

Obtaining Fresh Water from the Sea and from Brackish Sources. A look into the future and its need for water can hardly neglect the oceans as sources of fresh water through desalting. As a start on working out such possibilities, the Congress in 1952 authorized a program of research and development of improved processes for converting saline water to fresh water. In 1955 the program was extended, and a number of educational institutions and other research organizations have made valuable contributions to the known processes.

The program looks not only to the oceans but to widely distributed areas which produce brackish water (Fig. 4-4). In fact, the first community in the country to furnish fresh water to its citizens through desalinization was Coalinga, California, a community in Fresno County,

figure 4-3

Water-softening plant of the city of Ann Arbor, Mich.; settling and coagulating basins in middle foreground. Water from various sources runs from 180 to 400 parts per million of calcium and magnesium salts. This content is reduced to 80 parts per million. (Ann Arbor City Water Department.)

where water from inland wells is brackish. Here a small municipally operated plant reduces the 2,200 parts per million of mineral salts in well water to 300 to 350 parts and has separate pipe to deliver the treated water to households. Formerly, water was hauled 45 miles at a cost,

figure 4-4
Brackish water areas in the United States. From a preliminary survey by the Office of Saline Water. (U.S. Department of the Interior.)

mostly for transportation, of $7.05 per thousand gallons. Cost was reduced to $1.43 per 1,000 gallons for production and appropriate separate rates established for limited amounts of desalted water pumped through a special municipal distibution system. Brackish water, transported through another set of pipes and adequate for purposes other than drinking and cooking, costs a flat rate of $3.50 a month. Persons who live outside the village may purchase the fresh water in bulk at 5 gallons for 10 cents or 500 gallons for $7.50. The plant cost less than $100,000 and turns out 28,000 gallons of fresh water a day. The desalinization process used is known as electrodialysis (Fig. 4-5). Although such an arrangement is practicable for a small community, it could hardly be used for a metropolitan area.[9]

The Federal program mentioned above planned five regional experimental plants, two of them to work on brackish water and three on sea water. The first one completed is at Freeport, Texas, and uses a distillation process known as long-tube multiple effect. It produces 1 million gallons of fresh water daily from Gulf water and supplies the city of Freeport. Cost of production runs from $1.00 to $1.25 per 1,000 gallons, but because the plant is experimental, the water is sold to customers for about one-fifth of that figure.

The second plant, at Webster, South Dakota, was placed in operation in October, 1961, with a capacity of 250,000 gallons per day. Electrodialysis is used, and a content of 1,800 dissolved parts of salt per million is reduced to less than 275 parts per million.

[9] Ray Hebert, State Water Planning Embraces Sea Studies, *Los Angeles Times,* Oct. 19, 1961.

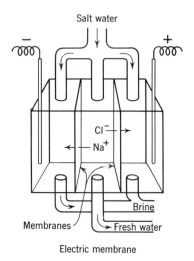

Salt water

Cl⁻

Na⁺

Brine

Membranes

Fresh water

Electric membrane

figure 4-5
Electrodialysis, a process for removing salt from sea or brackish water. Chlorine, one element of salt, is attracted through a film into a positive brine chamber where it can be disposed of, and sodium, the other element, is attracted to a negative brine chamber. This makes the salt water fresh. (U.S. Department of the Interior.)

figure 4-6
Experimental plant at Point Loma, Calif., for removing salt from sea water. This plant operated for 2 years at a capacity of 1 million gallons a day. It was dismantled in 1963 and shipped to Cuba to furnish water to the Guantanamo Naval Base. The process used in this plant was known as multistage flash distillation. (Photo by Roy Jarvis, courtesy of San Diego Evening Tribune.)

The third of the experimental plants was built at Point Loma, a part of the city of San Diego, California, and was financed by the Federal government, the state, and the city. (Fig. 4-6). It was operated for more than 2 years at a capacity of 1 million gallons a day, and its product cost approximately $1.00 per 1,000 gallons. It furnished about 1⅓ per cent of the San Diego city supply at 20 cents per 1,000 gallons until it was dismantled and shipped to Cuba in the spring of 1964 to serve the Guantanamo Naval Base. This plant used an evaporation process known as multistage flash evaporation. Contracts for replacing the plant at Point Loma were let in 1964.

In Roswell, New Mexico, a fourth plant was completed in 1963 and put into operation in July of that year. It has a capacity of 1 million gallons per day and provides the city of Roswell with a portion of its supply. A forced-vapor-circulation process is used, and the plant obtains fresh water from brackish water.

A fifth experimental plant of 250 million gallons capacity per day will use two freezing processes and will profit from the successful operation of two smaller experimental plants. It is located at Wrightsville Beach, North Carolina, and will work on sea water.

Operation experience and cost reduction should result from the establishment of these five plants, and, meanwhile, additional research involving these and numerous other processes promises eventual reductions to 50 cents per 1,000 gallons. This appears likely to come about by increasing the capacity of existing experimental plants and by developing water desalting combined with thermo-electric power production. The 1963 report of the Secretary of the Interior contains this statement: "Progress made it increasingly clear that the gap between the cost of water production from saline plants and the conventional methods for municipal and industrial uses was closing rapidly."[10]

WATER FOR WASTE DILUTION AND TRANSPORTATION

On page 76, waste transportation and dilution is ranked as the second most important use of runoff and, indeed, of all water. Human and industrial waste must be disposed of, and water is essential, in most cases, for transporting it to treatment points, for diluting and oxidizing it, and for carrying it away after treatment. This is true of sewered communities and most industries, particularly those dealing with food, mineral products, chemicals, and minerals. The problem is to use water for these purposes without ruining it for other uses, in other words, to prevent pollution. There is no simple or easy way to accomplish this, and in a democracy everyone must take a hand, if only by paying taxes, regardless of cost. The use of salvaged water is one way of reducing costs, as mentioned on page 79, and use and sale of by-products of waste treatment is another.

Treatment of Sewage. Although many sewage-disposal plants have beautiful buildings and are pleasantly landscaped, they do not attract many visitors. Few people are sufficiently interested in understanding how sewage is treated. The steps involved cost money, and citizens should understand why. First of all, the raw sewage must be collected and transported to a point for treatment. This requires water all along the line. Next comes the quick removal by settling of the inorganic solids, such as sand, gravel, glass, and bits of metal, and the screening out of these materials. This is followed by one of several primary treatment processes which remove the organic solids by skimming and settling. Now, if the remaining liquid or sewage effluent is still too high in "organic loading" or too great in amount to be safely merged with receiving waters, secondary treatment follows. This is accomplished by one of several so-called purification or oxidation processes. Before this, a treatment intermediate between primary and secondary may have been used as sufficient. Expense increases usually with the amount of organic matter removed, and sanitary disposal of accumulated grit, screenings,

[10] *Annual Report of the Secretary of the Interior, 1963, p. 268, 1964.*

skimmings, and sewage solids must be provided for. The sewage solids constitute what is called *sludge* and have some fertilizing value when reduced to a form easily applied to the land.

The effluent discharged to receiving waters at best contains a considerable loading of harmful bacteria, unless it has been completely disinfected at the point of treatment. Waters of the receiving stream or lake are not considered safe for water supply or for swimming unless chlorinated. This much, however, should be said: the oxidation which occurs through merging the effluent with natural water does reduce the bacteria count proportionately, in general, to the percentage of removal of organic matter. The actual process of oxidation is discussed later under industrial wastes.

The Problem of Detergents. In the decade after World War II, products developed as soap substitutes for use in hard water, known as detergents, came onto the domestic market. Soon they constituted about 75 per cent of all household cleaning preparations. Discarded in sewage, detergents foam excessively and interfere with treatment; they also pollute streams and underground waters (Fig. 4-7). They can be manufactured with a decomposable quality which reduces the content of the alkyl benzene sulfonate (ABS), the foam-producing pollutant. Control laws are being sought in a number of states, Wisconsin being the first one to ban the use of "nondegradable" detergents, under a law passed late in 1963. Similar legislation is being considered by the Congress. Meanwhile, manufacturers and suppliers of raw materials are reported to be cooperating by changing over to the use of linear alkylate sulfonate, usually spoken of as LAS, instead of alkyl benzene sulfonate, as the principal ingredient of cleaning preparations. The former (LAS) has a

figure 4-7
Pile-up of foam caused by detergents immediately above inlet to a Pennsylvania fish hatchery. The new degradable detergents will prevent this. (Pennsylvania Fish Commission.)

figure 4-8
An industrial-waste-disposal installation. At the Dow Chemical Company, Midland, Mich., strong phenolic wastes are pumped from storage equalization ponds to the clarifying tank in the left foreground. From here they are piped to the trickling filter beds in the center and background, where they are sprayed over blast-furnace slag. A bacterial slime, which covers the entire surface of this slag, oxidizes the carbon of the phenolic matter. Each filter bed requires 1½ acres. (Photo by Dow Chemical Company.)

simpler structure and can be more easily broken down biologically after use; this sharply reduces its capacity to foam.[11] National legislation is also under congressional consideration with regard to pollution of water supplies by pesticides.

Treatment of Industrial Wastes. In addition to sewage discussed above, organic wastes from slaughterhouses, canneries, creameries, paper mills, chemical plants (Fig. 4-8), and tanneries constitute the principal industrial wastes which require oxidation. These wastes, whether or not they are diluted before reaching the receiving waters for transportation, contain large proportions of putrescible liquid which is oxygen-demanding in the presence of natural water. If the receiving stream is not overloaded, it can assimilate these liquids without injury, but the key to this result is the small amount of dissolved oxygen in natural water. This totals 9 to 13 parts per million, depending upon the time of year and the temperature. The warmer the water, the less the amount of dissolved oxygen available. This is why the odor of polluted waters is more offensive in summer and early autumn. From these facts it may be reasoned that, unless the stream can take these wastes during the warmest months of the year, the so-called "oxygen-balance control" will not be satisfactory. In other words, the stream has broken down as a safe transporter of waste.

[11] *Conservation News*, National Wildlife Federation, June 1, 1964, p. 5.

Oil refineries and certain chemical industries discharge phenolic wastes which are to some extent oxygen-demanding but which certainly do not yield to oxidation so far as the taste and odor which they impart to water are concerned. Similar trouble accompanies the discharge of creosol wastes from wood-distillation plants and the "black liquor" from pulp and paper mills using the sulfate process. One of the ironies of conservation effort is that chlorination of waters so polluted accentuates the taint, one part of chlorinated phenol in 500 million parts of water sometimes proving objectionable in a domestic water supply.

Salt brines, though frequent pollutants, are neither oxygen-demanding nor of bacterial significance; yet when they are discharged into waters needed for other purposes, they produce a condition frequently almost seven times saltier than sea water, which contains 30,000 parts per million of chlorides. Salt brines from oil fields and chemical plants are made up of chlorides of sodium, calcium, and magnesium dissolved, of course, in water. In concentrations after dilution of 4,000 parts per million or greater, they produce an artificial hardness, make the water unfit to drink, and injure fresh-water fish. Here the problem is neither one of bacteria nor of poisoning but can be solved only by tremendous dilution, usually prohibitive in cost, or by storing and finding some by-product use for the chlorides.

The cyanide, acid, and alkali industries also discharge pollutants which must be dealt with, and dilution here again is inadequate, since very low concentrations of cyanide salts are lethal to animal life.

Inert industrial wastes, including sands from stamp mills for treating gold and copper ores, coal- and gravel-washing wastes, stone-crusher-plant waste, and actual eroded soil, limit sharply the use of the receiving and transporting waters for *any* other purpose. All but the least valuable fishes are likely to be suffocated. Streams themselves are turbid and unattractive for sport. Then, in addition to this peculiar kind of "pollution," channels are clogged in all but the swiftest of streams and much of this waste ends up eventually in reservoirs constructed for irrigation, power, flood control, and the improvement of navigation. Expensive settling and return of these wastes to worked-out mines, gravel pits, and quarries sounds fantastic but may not be beyond the range of human need. "Polluting the landscape" has been turned to by certain enterprises of this character and may constitute the lesser of two evils, slag-, culm-, and chemical-waste piles not being unknown at present, particularly in mining regions. Control of water on the land, discussed under soil conservation, holds some hope for keeping streams clearer.

A final peculiar kind of water pollution comes from petroleum transportation and automobile servicing rather than from the refinery and oil-field wastes mentioned earlier. This is actually waste oil; it has to go somewhere, and, not infrequently, it may be seen on the surface of streams and harbors. Not only does it pollute the water, but it has been known to catch fire and to threaten shore structures. Greater salvage of such refuse offers one chance to limit it as a nuisance.

By-products from Water-borne Waste. The cost of transporting both municipal and industrial wastes will no doubt increase with time, and any application of scientific knowledge and ingenuity to this problem is bound to help. Development of by-products from waste is perhaps the most fruitful of these efforts.

One city of the Great Lakes has developed a nitrogen fertilizer from its sewer sludge and a sales program which returns a good revenue to the city treasury.

Sugar-beet companies struggling with four or five concentrations of pollutants which must be disposed of have found a market for dried pulp and certain by-products of lesser volume. One such company reported in 1943 a gross return on a single by-product equivalent to 10 per cent of the payment for beets and a return on another product which equaled the cost of its safe disposal.

The reclamation of pulp from the so-called "white water" of paper-pulp mills, as well as the reclamation of water used as a vehicle in the plant itself, has shown favorable results.

Hair and fleshings from tanneries have some value, and when reclaimed, they relieve transporting waters of a considerable load of putrescible materials.

Administering Safe Waste Transportation. At present the responsibility for safe transportation of waste by water is a state responsibility. The Federal government has had little power, even over interstate waters, in this particular. Highly organized boards, commissions, or committees cooperating with other appropriate state and national agencies are in operation in Connecticut, Illinois, Indiana, Louisiana, Michigan, Oregon, Pennsylvania, Washington, and Wisconsin. Generally, the cooperation of the offending municipalities, institutions, and industries is sought, and the laws, weak in many instances, are enforced with varying vigor. Stubborn resistance to a moderate Federal law has developed on the part of state authorities and industries in the name of "states' rights" without adequate assumption of *states' responsibility*. After more than a decade of waste-transportation problems occasioned by war industries and growing industrial populations, the Federal Water Pollution Control Law of 1948 (Taft-Barkley Act) was enacted by the Congress. It was to run for 3 years and was extended in 1951 and again in 1953. It was somewhat strengthened by amendment in 1956 which authorized more generous grants-in-aid for the construction of community sewage-treatment plants, Federal financial assistance in the working out of local pollution-control programs, research and advice to communities, and enforcement after investigation and hearings in interstate pollution cases upon request of either state concerned. The only mention of uniform state regulations was a mild mandate to encourage them through interstate compacts. Appropriations not to exceed 50 million dollars a year were authorized for a period of 5 years. In 1961, when attention was again required in the Congress, there was evident an unmistakable lag in local enforcement effort. The law was therefore changed to transfer the responsibility for initiating action from the Public Health Service to the Secretary of Health, Education, and Welfare, but the Public Health Service retained its operating functions. Appropriations were somewhat increased, and administration of the grants-in-aid to municipalities for construction of sewage-disposal works went forth in orderly fashion. But enforcement records were not improved. In 1965, legislative action separated pollution control activities from the Public Health Service, and in February, 1966, President Johnson directed their transfer to the Department of the Interior.

Safe Waste Transportation Is the Problem. Because so much is said and written from the viewpoint of the sportsman and nature lover, the real issue is frequently lost sight of in plans concerning the use of water for safe transportation of waste. Whatever can be done to reduce the amount of treated waste which is delivered to streams, lakes, and harbors is desirable. In spite of a reduction in the percentage of the total load of untreated waste dumped into streams by municipalities between 1930 and 1955, the total amount of municipal waste *increased* by 10 per cent. During this period the amount of untreated waste dumped by industry doubled, even though the percentage of the total load was reduced. This trend was persisting as late as 1964.

WATER FOR MANUFACTURE AND PROCESSING

It is not easy to identify or segregate uses of water for the manufacture and processing of ores, foods, textiles, chemicals, pulps, and beverages and for refrigeration, for such uses overlap domestic and municipal and waste-transportation groupings. A few examples, however, will indicate that this consumption of water is large.

The steel industry is, perhaps, the greatest user of water in manufacture, for 65,000 gallons is required to make 1 ton of iron ingots into steel and 18,000 gallons is used to make the ingots in the first place.

In the production of 1 ton of aluminum 120,000 gallons of water is required.

In the area of aviation fuel, 25 gallons of water is needed to produce 1 gallon of aviation gasoline and 2,500,000 gallons is required to produce

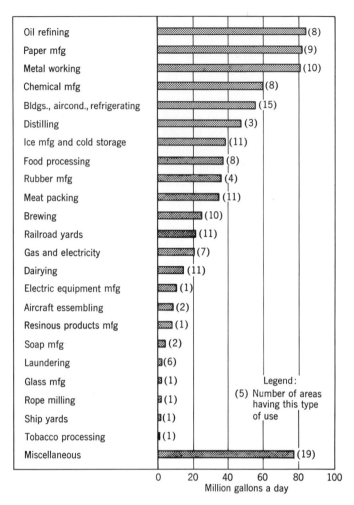

figure 4-9
Use of ground water by industries in twenty selected metropolitan areas (not including water from municipal systems). (Data from U.S. Geol. Survey Cir. 114, 1951.)

enough fuel for 1 hour's flight of 1,000 now obsolete World War II fighter planes. When it is borne in mind that an acre-foot is the equivalent of more than 325,000 gallons, these quantities of water begin to take on real significance (Fig. 4-9).

In the pulp and paper industry, water is used not only in reducing wood to pulp and pulp to paper but as a vehicle for moving material in various stages, from the actual wood right through to paper. A large mill may use as much as 50,000 gallons in the total processing of a ton of finished paper.

Chemical manufacturing is a heavy industrial user of water, any immediate salvage of which is impracticable. Creameries, sugar factories, packing houses, and canneries are among the food-processing plants utilizing large quantities of water and facing heavy problems of pollution abatement.

Condensation water use for individual steam plants in thousands of manufacturing enterprises overlaps the "power" group of uses and perhaps "domestic and municipal" uses, but it is really a firsthand industrial use. The same is true for the increasing use of water for the artificial production of ice and for the air conditioning of buildings, although many wells have been drilled by individual building proprietors as a less expensive means of obtaining a supply for this purpose. Department stores, theatres, and office buildings, while hardly considered industrial, present an unusual demand for water, and in their efforts to conserve it, they sometimes return cooling water to the underground reservoir. In some cities this is mandatory. Unless this return is accomplished so that it reaches a different formation than that producing the water originally, the entire underground supply is raised in temperature so that it is unfit for drinking without further cooling. Research on the application of less wasteful adaptations of refrigeration methods to the cooling of buildings is needed.

Conservation problems in all the uses of water for manufacture and processing are numerous and difficult. Supply, quality, safe disposal of used water, and treatment for hardness and high sulfur and iron content follow pretty closely the necessity of providing safe domestic and municipal supplies, and certainly when water is used as a vehicle for processing and a transporter of waste, the difficulties met in its conservation are greater.

WATER FOR FOOD PRODUCTION

Milk is 87 per cent water, vegetables run from 80 to 97 per cent, eggs contain 65 per cent, meat contains 60 per cent, and fish somewhat more. A fat steer needs about 80 pounds of water a day, and that amounts to about 10 gallons. It takes one-half that amount, or 5 gallons, to water forty chickens for a day.[12] Of the familiar farm crops, a pound dry weight requires 300 to 500 pounds of water for its production. Somewhere along the line, this much water has been taken up, transpired, or stored by the plants. Counting the water necessary to produce the crops consumed and

[12] Water for the Modern Farmstead, Rural Electrification Administration, U.S. Department of Agriculture, 1946, p. 1.

the amount taken directly by the animal, 1 pound of beef has required 15 to 30 *tons* of water in its production. Food cannot be produced without water and lots of it.

In discussing the use of water for food production, the term *production* will be used in the strict sense of growing rather than processing food crops, whether plant or animal. (If the term *crop* seems strange when used in connection with livestock, the reader should know that the expression "calf crop" is common on the Western range.) Food production, then, involves the use of water for producing food fishes, livestock, and waterfowl and for irrigation in arid portions of the country. To a lesser extent, and with different methods, water is also increasingly used for irrigation in the humid regions.

Animal Crops. FISHES Almost any stream or permanent body of water which is reasonably free from sewage and industrial wastes contains, or may be planted with, food fishes. Oyster culture is frequently spoken of as "farming," and the definite growing of warm-water fishes for food in farm ponds has become a popular practice in recent years. Yields up to 250 pounds per acre of water are possible with intensive management, and the farm food supply can thus be varied and increased (Fig. 4-10). These uses of water will be further discussed under Fisheries.

LIVESTOCK On any farm supporting animals for supplying beef, pork, mutton, or fowl, the work and meat animals will consume much more than one-half of all the water used. A glance back at the figures in the opening paragraph of this chapter will give the reason. The considerable quantities of water used in the production of eggs and dairy products, aside from watering the animals, add to the amounts of water necessary in this branch of food production.

On the Western range the availability of water is frequently the limiting factor in the use of natural forage by the vast numbers of cattle and sheep grazed there by the livestock industry. The stories of the range wars between sheep and cattle outfits had often to do with the control of meager supplies of water, and much of the expenditures of public and private funds today in improving the range goes for developing and protecting water supplies.

WATERFOWL Although waterfowl are taken almost entirely for sport, their size and number represent considerable food value, and they can be grown and a crop assured only if waters are provided for resting, breeding, and feeding while in the latitudes of the United States. Commercial raising of waterfowl requiring generous and unfailing water supply is handled as a poultry business and really is a type of farming. Other aspects of this food crop will be discussed under Wild-animal Life later in the text.

figure 4-10

Farm pond near Troy, Idaho, constructed in 1944 with capacity of 4.47 acre-feet. Planted with fish in 1946. (Photo by R. B. Branstead, United States Soil Conservation Service.)

Water for Irrigating Food Crops. While the foregoing uses of water for the production of food are taken for granted by the well-informed but not widely traveled citizen, he will be impressed and perhaps startled to see for the first time a green orchard or alfalfa field in an arid part of the West. And regardless of anything he has read about them, the great dams, reservoirs, "hillside rivers," and other intricate systems of canals, flumes, small ditches, and movable pipe which are commonplace in a region of irrigation agriculture will drive home the idea that no food is grown without water.

Of all the definitions of irrigation, the most succinct is the one settled on by Etcheverry[13] "the artificial application of water to lands whenever the rainfall is insufficient to meet the full requirements of crops." This puts even the "watering" or "sprinkling" practices, as they are

[13] By permission from Irrigation: Practice and Engineering by B. A. Etcheverry and S. T. Harding, 2d ed., vol. I, p. 1. Copyright 1933 by McGraw-Hill Book Company, New York.

commonly spoken of in the humid regions, into the group of practices correctly known as irrigation. (Whether with hose or gadget, one "irrigates" a lawn in the West, rather than "waters" or "sprinkles" it.)

Irrigation has been practiced for centuries. It has been known on the North American continent, if traces of irrigation systems are correctly interpreted, since the Mayan culture in Central America, and later it was known, as a matter of definite historical record, in connection with the early Spanish mission enterprises and in trading and mining settlements. The first extensive use of water in a strictly agricultural economy occurred when the Mormons settled in the Salt Lake Valley in Utah in 1847, just more than 100 years ago. All users of water for this purpose have had to learn how to apply it, how to make its distribution equitable, how to overcome concentrations of alkali and siltation of reservoirs and ditches, and dozens of other things which make irrigation agriculture complex and exacting.

From practically nothing in 1847, the irrigated acreage increased in this country to more than 3½ million acres in 1889, to 7½ million in 1902, and to about 33,163,000 in 1959.[14] The period of greatest increase in acreage, amounting to more than 12 million, stretched from 1899 to 1919, at which time the United States census reports arrive at the figure 19,191,716 acres. This interval closely coincides with the period from 1901 to 1921, when population seemed to many national leaders to be heading for a growth that would outrun potential food supplies.

Early efforts at irrigation were made individually or by neighborhood partnerships and informal cooperative agreements. Law and custom developed in arid and semiarid regions dictated the "location" of water rights in terms of "miner's inches" or other units. The water was guided by ditch from some point along a stream above the land to be irrigated and distributed as needed by gravity (Fig. 4-11). Little pumping was known. In more recent years vast systems of dams, reservoirs, and canals have been constructed both publicly and privately, and pumping of irrigation water has become highly developed. Examples of some of the public projects will be discussed further on in this chapter.

The thoughtful reader, having heard much of the difficulty of farming in general to achieve "parity" with industry in the prices of products, will begin to inquire how the expense of bringing water artificially to land can be anything but prohibitive. The answer lies in the accumulated and unleached mineral salts which make newly irrigated land much more productive, the greater periods of sunshine and growing weather prevalent in arid and semiarid regions making possible more than one crop a year, the specialized character of the appropriate crops and their

---

[14] *Statistical Abstract of the United States,* 1963, Bureau of the Census, p. 637.

figure 4-11
Scene from hill overlooking lush peach lands along the government canal near Palisade, Colo. Grand Valley Project. (Photo by Stan Rasmussen, U.S. Bureau of Reclamation.)

high market values, and the control which it is possible to exercise in the application of water (Fig. 4-12). This last feature has more recently brought about increasing, though still hardly extensive, use of water in humid regions, where it is usually applied by sprinkling systems. Thus, some control over crop failure in dry years can be exerted. Sooner or later, water laws will have to be changed in the humid regions to cover increasing consumptive use. Demands here by recreation and industry make the application of arid-region appropriation procedure inequitable.

Although the proportion of irrigated croplands to all croplands, about 5 to 6 per cent, coincides somewhat closely with the same figure for tonnage, the value of both land and crops is much higher and the importance to local Western economy, usually dominated by livestock, mineral, and lumber enterprises, is tremendous. On the U.S. Reclamation Bureau projects alone, which amount to less than one-fifth the entire area, the alfalfa and forage crops were sufficient during the period covered by World War II to have produced 150 pounds of meat per man for an army of 4 million men for 4 years.[15] Grass-crop values alone per acre on 4,195,832 acres in cultivation in 1945 were $103.72.[16]

HOW IRRIGATION WATER IS PROVIDED Individual, cooperative, and publicly financed irrigation projects have been mentioned briefly, but it is

[15] Natural Resource Problems, *Annual Report of the Secretary of the Interior,* 1946, pp. 23–24.
[16] *Ibid.,* p. 60.

figure 4-12

A well-planned irrigation system using siphons from ditch enables this Montana farmer to water his 25-acre beet field with 5 hours of actual labor. Crow Creek unit, Missouri River Basin Project. (Photo by C. A. Knell, U.S. Bureau of Reclamation.)

well here to set down all the procedures thus far employed and to discuss their relative significance as a democracy's way of handling one natural resource for one specific purpose.

Individual and cooperative projects were the result of a struggle to live a bit more abundantly in pioneer days. Miners who held placer claims on river bars and gravel deposits at the mouths of canyons raised vegetables and alfalfa in small areas in summer and used the water from the same source for hydraulic mining in winter. Stockmen needing water for cattle and sheep at ranch headquarters developed all the water they could and irrigated meadows and pastures. Fruit growing came early into the picture and demanded more ambitious irrigation works. Observation of neighbors' crops and joining up with successful growers finally became unwieldly and probably led to the next method.

Collective action to obtain and distribute water took on the same course as the need for schools, drains, fire control, sanitation, and, more recently, soil conservation, namely, the establishment of a district follow-ing the majority vote of the landowners within a given territory. The district becomes a sort of governmental unit to accomplish a specific purpose—in this instance to gain control of water and bring it to the land. On the theory that each property owner benefits from the district's activities, costs are assessed in much the same manner as taxes. (A full discussion of soil conservation districts may be referred to on page 63.)

In perfect good faith, twelve of the Western states were put into the arid-land-reclamation business in the 1890s with the passage of the Carey Act in 1894. Federal lands in any of the public-land states could be selected up to a million acres per state, acquired without cost by the state, and developed for colonization and sale under the supervision of state officers who necessarily took this duty on as a side line. Private enterprise could come into the picture with somewhat dangerous financ-ing arrangements and with no guarantee that the development would be sound or that water would be sufficient for permanent agriculture. The total area selected, developed under this arrangement, and passed into private ownership was relatively small—less than a million acres. Forgivable ignorance probably defeated the objective.

No phase of conservation effort in a democracy is more likely to intrigue the public or to enlist its support than the sort of thing which steps up productive power and extends opportunity for a greater number of citizens to make a living. It is not strange, therefore, that after long agitation to get around financial and other obstacles the Reclamation Act was passed in 1902. This law put the Federal government squarely into the irrigation-water development business and charged it with iron-ing out large-scale questions of water rights, property relations, con-struction, water distribution, and settlement of irrigated land. Money was to come from a revolving fund to be replenished from the sale of developed lands, from settlement fees, and from earmarked revenue from the sale of public lands of whatever nature. Coming on the heels of the exhaustion of the better homestead lands in the Middle West, the authorized program was prosecuted with vigor both for the develop-ment and serving of Federal lands to be homesteaded and for delivering water to existing and badly served farms and communities.

In the original law as amended, there is an acreage limitation on the delivery of irrigating water from federally constructed projects: a single person is entitled to water for 160 acres; a married couple, to water for 320 acres. This limitation has bothered the large operator on the "factory-type" farm of greater extent, and although one of the objectives of the law is fair distribution and the widening of economic opportunity, the limitation has been set aside in a number of projects either by congressional action or by administrative decision. The most sweeping instance of the latter is now being questioned in the Imperial Valley of California where Colorado River water is furnished by the Federal government to "farms" as large as 9,000 acres. This practice is based on a 1932 decision which rests on prior water rights of lands developed by private capital.[17]

The story of the operation of the Reclamation Act and its various amendments is long and complicated, but it has proved that a democracy can work out devices for developing its latent productive powers and achieve some success in spreading equitably the economic opportunities which its citizens demand. One may risk the opinion that its original purpose, which was *not* the production of power, might have avoided much trouble in its application if the Department of the Interior in the past 4 decades had not used it so enthusiastically as a power-production instrument. This action resulted both from local needs for power and from the increasing difficulty met by water users in paying off the cost of irrigation projects. (Power revenues, of course, cut down the costs of the latter.) But the act in letter and in spirit is now a far cry from the ideas held in 1902.

Little has been published on the development of irrigated land for commercial sale, and yet some very successful projects, taking particular care to select rich and easily watered lands, were carried out. The 1919 United States census reported more than 1,900,000 acres of this type under irrigation, with an investment of more than 85 million dollars.

The United States as guardian, and to some extent manager, of properties held in trust for the Indian tribes has developed irrigation on a number of reservations, slightly more than a quarter of a million acres total having been reported in 1919. This had grown to 837,000 acres in 1962. Crops produced were valued at 67.3 million dollars.

A few thousand acres of state and institutional lands and properties in miscellaneous ownerships have their own water locations and irrigation systems. These will never bulk large in the total area of irrigated lands.

HOW THE RECLAMATION BUREAU PROJECTS ARE ADMINISTERED Lands in newly developed irrigation projects under the management of the Bureau of Reclamation of the Department of the Interior are subject to entry under the homestead laws (Fig. 4-13), but costs for the developed irrigation water, since assurance of the supply goes with title to the land, must be paid for in annual installments spread over 50 to 60 years including a 10-year development period. Sale of power developed at

[17] *Western Water News*, vol. 17, pp. 1 and 4, March, 1965; and *Los Angeles Times*, editorial, March 11, 1965.

figure 4-13
Temporary building on wheat farm (above) in Washington in 1952.
Same location after irrigation (below) in 1961. Columbia Basin Project.
(Photos by F. B. Pomeroy (above) and E. Hertzog (below), U.S.
Bureau of Reclamation.)

the dams lightens this load on the settler, but he must still be a good
farmer and businessman to make his payments (Fig. 4-13). The local
project office of the Bureau operates the water-distribution and power
features of the areas, promotes sound irrigation and farming practices,
and otherwise seeks the productive use of the water and land resources.
The Bureau operates in the seventeen arid and semiarid Western states,
and its many projects vary in area to be served from a few thousand acres
to more than a million. Since its establishment in 1902 and until June 30,
1963, it had out-Bunyaned Paul of the lumber woods by constructing or
rehabilitating 171 storage reservoirs with a total storage capacity of

approximately 93 million acre-feet; 26,000 miles of main canals and laterals; 9,000 miles of main drains; 44 power plants with a total installed capacity of 5,466,550 kilowatts and with a total output in 1963 of 29 billion kilowatthours, including that from some Federal plants not built by the Bureau of Reclamation, but for which the Bureau acts as marketing agent; and 461 pumping plants with a total of 917,000 horsepower.

Today's diet-conscious Americans will be interested to learn that an important and growing share of the nation's fresh and processed fruits and vegetables comes from the family farms on reclamation projects. In 1963, for example, the reclamation production of 1.2 billion pounds of fresh lettuce was equivalent to providing a full year's supply for 59 million people. Reclamation-grown cantaloupes in 1963 were sufficient to meet the equivalent yearly consumption of 55 million Americans.

NEW IRRIGATION PROJECTS Owing to the rapidly multiplying demands on the limited water resources of the fast growing West, new projects envision, to a much greater extent than those established early in the century, multiple-purpose use of water. The uses would include not only irrigation but power production, improved navigation, flood alleviation, recreational and fish and wildlife development, and municipal water supply—all rivaling the *food-production* purpose which is the basis of this immediate discussion, and which was, indeed, one of the aims of the original Reclamation Act of 1902. All these new projects have extremely interesting features, from the tunnel under the continental divide (and, incidentally, under a national park) of the Colorado–Big Thompson Project to the giant, concrete-arch Glen Canyon Dam on the Arizona-Utah border, designed to store 27 million acre-feet of Colorado River water for the rapidly growing, water-short, Southwestern states.

Three of the larger projects or systems will now be considered:

The people of a democracy have built one of their largest dams following somewhat the example of the icecap of former ages, which plugged up a canyon of the Columbia River and diverted its flow so that it cut a great trough, or coulee, along which the river went its own way for a while. In Fig. 4-14 it may be seen that the river, through the coulee and other diversions, deposited a vast delta before the ice plug gave way and allowed it to resume its path in the great bend. Eventually the coulee and the deposit were left high and dry, and the former, with a dike at each end, now serves as a "balancing" reservoir into which waters from the backed-up river are pumped for use in irrigating the delta lands. Power generated at the dam is used for this purpose. Ultimately, project water will be available for more than a million acres. The first excava-

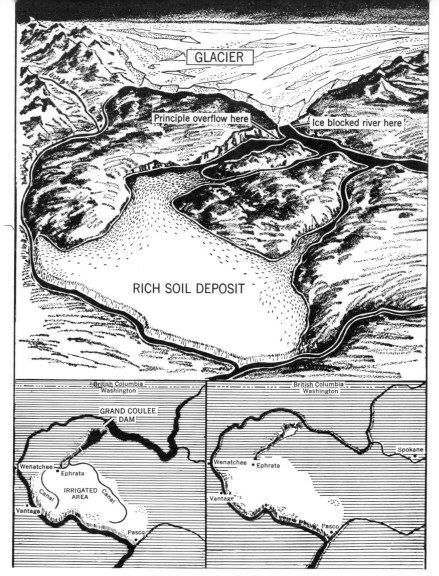

How the Grand Coulee happened geologically. The coulee is now the equalizing reservoir into which the Columbia River water is pumped by power generated at the dam and from which water flows to irrigate the ancient delta. (Industrial News, published by Gates Rubber Company.)

tion on the main canal was well under way by July 1, 1946, and the six giant pumps on the river, each with a capacity nearly sufficient to supply the domestic needs of New York City, were in action for the eventual delivery of water to 66,000 acres during the 1952 irrigation season. Meanwhile, for each of the 176 full- and part-time farming units of Federal land opened to settlement on the project that year, there were 110 applications. Additional acreage has been available each year since.

103

figure 4-15
Aerial view of ancient delta lands (above) to be irrigated, 1952.
Same view (below), 1960. (Photos by F. B. Pomeroy (above) and E.
Hertzog (below), U.S. Bureau of Reclamation.)

By 1963, 2,425 farm units were operated by family farmers on the
Columbia Basin Project, and irrigation water was available to 459,070
irrigable acres, nearly one-half the acreage envisioned for ultimate development. (Fig. 4-15). This whole Grand Coulee development, which is
a part of the Great Columbia Basin plan, will be mentioned again later
under Power Production.

At the head of the list of Western states in irrigation agriculture,
California has moved a step closer to achieving the unified management
of the Sacramento and San Joaquin Rivers, the two great valleys which
together form the 500-mile-long Central Valley. Water from winter rains
and spring snowmelt in the northern mountain ranges is conserved and
stored by the Central Valley Project's great Federal Shasta Dam and the
recently completed Trinity Dam, to be distributed throughout the year
through a series of other dams, canals, and pumps to thirsty lands stretching nearly 500 miles to the southern tip of the San Joaquin Valley. The
Federal San Luis unit, most recent addition to the Central Valley
Project now in the construction stage, will bring full and supplemental

water supplies to more than 500,000 acres of fertile farm lands in the San Joaquin Valley and will serve as an important link in the state's plan to transport surplus water from the north to the population centers south of the Tehachapi Mountains. The San Luis unit marks a giant stride forward in Federal-state cooperation in resource development. A recently executed agreement by which the Federal government and the state government will finance 45 per cent and 55 per cent, respectively, of the construction costs of the jointly used facilities will result in substantial savings to the cooperating agencies and, thus, to the taxpayer. Upon completion of all presently authorized developments, the Bureau of Reclamation through its Central Valley Project will provide irrigation-water supplies to approximately 1.75 million acres of highly productive farm lands extending from Redding in the north to Bakersfield in the south. In addition, more than 350,000 acre-feet of water will be made available to help satisfy the growing needs of domestic, municipal, and industrial water users. This project is vast in cost and significance and, like the Grand Coulee and other Columbia Basin enterprises, is for multiple purposes, including all those mentioned in connection with the one to the north and perhaps being even more significant in supplying water for municipalities.

The heat and high local blood pressure generated in the last few years by discussions of a Missouri Valley Authority have, for the present, subsided somewhat. But there are still piecemeal attacks on the problem of improving the economy of about one-sixth of the area of the United States and about one-twentieth of its population—for that is what the Missouri River, touching ten states, represents. The so-called "unified" Pick-Sloan plan battled out by General Lewis Pick of the Corps of Engineers, United States Army, and W. G. Sloan of the Bureau of Reclamation is now in operation. The plan will involve the expenditure of 400 million dollars by 1966; the construction of more than 100 dams, eight of them high and large; an attempt to hold the river to its channel from Sioux City, Iowa, to St. Louis by bigger and better levees; production of power; improvement of navigation; and, finally, production of food, almost as an incidental. The distressing feature of this somewhat hastily drawn plan, authorized by the Omnibus Flood Control Bill of 1944, is its assignment of the job to two bureaus of the Federal government authorized to give little attention to practices on the land but to start work at various points on the river. The only hope that the river will not continue to carry its 600-odd parts per million of soil materials, destroy many of the world's greatest waterfowl refuge grounds, and really fail to achieve a permanent agriculture for the valley is the existence of a Missouri Valley Inter-Agency Committee upon which

Federal and state soil-conservation, forestry, and wild-animal-life interests are represented along with the two *construction* agencies. The voice of this committee is heard, but its power to coordinate so great an undertaking has not proven significant. Its possibilities as a democratic way of doing things are great.

Among the facilities contributing somewhat to food production in the Missouri Basin are the Fort Peck Dam in Montana, the Fort Randall Reservoir in South Dakota, and the Garrison Dam in North Dakota— all on the Missouri River and all built by the Corps of Engineers of the United States Army. The Yellowtail Dam on the Bighorn River in Montana, now under construction, is a Bureau of Reclamation project. Numerous canals in Nebraska and Kansas were completed in 1962 and 1963 by this Bureau. Water for the production of food is essential whether in humid or arid regions.

Cotton is about the only nonfood crop grown on irrigated land, and its acreage on reclamation projects is decreasing; but the production of nonsurplus crops is increasing.

Drainage and Food Production. While ridding land of too much water in order to increase its capacity to produce food is hardly using water for food production, it should be mentioned here. On the positive side something needs to be said to offset the frequent statements that land drainage is all bad because it destroys wild-animal habitats, fails to pay out in crop production, aggravates flood damage, and dries out the marshes so they can be destroyed easily by fire.

First of all drainage is necessary on other than marsh lands (1) because an excess of water frequently results from prolonged storms in humid regions; and (2) because irrigation practice often results in a concentration of mineral salts carried in received water if too much is allowed to accumulate on crop lands. Most of the important crop plants will tolerate little alkali, and from their use the soil may be easily "sickened."

Drainage as a help to extensive growing of specified crops such as truck, mint, and bulbs usually involves major works, including great trunk drains as well as the tiling and ditching of fields and the clearing and straightening of natural waterways. Here the drainage district, similar to the irrigation district discussed earlier on page 99, is used, and where well planned on tested soils and in appropriate terrain, it may bring into production new lands of great fertility. In addition to lands important because rich though arid, vast areas of potentially productive wet lands now in use for the more extensive production of wild animals and timber and for the stabilization of water levels may be looked to for new farm lands in the event of great need.

Mint, sugar beets, potatoes, onions, and celery now occupy thousands of acres in Indiana and Michigan where the early explorers and trappers had concluded that the country was one vast, dismal, worthless swamp. In fact the commander of the garrison at Saginaw in 1822 is reported to have written the War Department that nothing but Indians, muskrats, and bullfrogs could live there. (What a wildlife sanctuary!) Starting about 60 years later, however, 8 million acres had been drained by 1940 with an investment of 40 million dollars.[18] Many other areas available for drainage lie in the Southeastern part of the United States.

It was estimated in 1927 that enough land was then drained to meet the demand for cultivation for 35 years.[19] That would bring it up to the year 1962, and the Soil Conservation Service of the Department of Agriculture since about 1946 has had a definite policy of promoting the drainage of new lands within farms. The Bureau of Reclamation of the Department of the Interior also looks toward extending its activities to this field as the need increases for providing homes for displaced cotton farmers in the South.

By 1920 close to 65,500,000 acres had been drained with an investment of $372,274,000. By 1940 this had grown to 87 million acres in drainage projects representing an investment of $691,725,000. Figures for the same year show more than 70 million acres occupied and 49,614,000 planted.[20] By 1950 the total acreage drained had increased to almost 103 million acres. By 1959 the total investment exceeded 8 hundred million dollars.

It is not easy to prophesy how much of the remaining 75 million-odd acres of wet lands, many of which need clearing as well as draining, will eventually be brought under cultivation. (Some undrained lands, in fact, bring in money to the owner as they are. For instance, one tract of marsh-land on a Pennsylvania farm contains about sixty muskrat "houses"; by selling the muskrat pelts, the owner continues to clear about $15 per acre per year from this otherwise idle land.) Better planning to assure that land drained will be productive, that it will justify development costs, and that it will not disorganize programs of conserving other valuable natural resources point the only road to sound over-all wet-land conservation. Some of the conflicts of use met in draining land will be touched upon under Flood Control and under Wild-animal Resources.

[18] C. V. Ballard, Water in Its Relation to Agriculture, *Michigan's Water Problems,* Michigan Department of Conservation, Lansing, Mich., 1944, pp. 28–29.
[19] R. P. Teele, Economics of Land Reclamation, A. W. Shaw Company, Chicago, 1927, p. 201. Also, Land Reclamation Policies in the United States, *U.S. Dept. Agr. Bull.* 1257, 1924, p. 28.
[20] *Statistical Abstract of the United States,* 1951, p. 553.

BIBLIOGRAPHY

Annual Reports of the Secretary of the Interior, 1962–1963.

BALLARD, C. V.: Water in Its Relation to Agriculture, Michigan's Water Problems, Michigan Department of Conservation, 1944.

BROWN, HARRISON, JAMES BONNER, AND JOHN WIER: The Next Hundred Years, The Viking Press, Inc., New York, 1957.

Conservation News, National Wildlife Federation, Washington, D.C., June 1, 1964.

DEWHURST, J. FREDERIC, AND ASSOCIATES: America's Needs and Resources, The Twentieth Century Fund, New York, 1947.

ELY, RICHARD T., AND GEORGE S. WEHRWEIN: Land Economics, The Macmillan Company, New York, 1940.

ETCHEVERRY, B. A., AND S. T. HARDING: Irrigation: Practice and Engineering, 2d ed., vol. I, McGraw-Hill Book Company, Inc., New York, 1933.

HEDRICK, EDWARD: Making Water Plentiful, *Sci. News Letter,* vol. 72, Aug. 31, 1957.

LA MER, V. K., AND THOMAS W. HEALY: Evaporation of Water: Its Retardation by Monolayers, *Science,* vol. 148, Apr. 2, 1965.

LANDSBERG, HANS H., LEONARD L. FISCHMAN, AND JOSEPH L. FISHER: Resources in America's Future, The Johns Hopkins Press, Baltimore, 1962.

MCGUINNESS, C. L.: The Role of Ground Water in the National Water Situation, *U.S. Geol. Surv. Water Supply Paper* 1800, 1963.

MCGEE, W. J.: Water as a Resource, *An. Amer. Acad.,* vol. 33, 1898.

SENATE SELECT COMMITTEE ON NATIONAL WATER RESOURCES: Report, 1961a.

Statistical Abstract of the United States, 1963, U.S. Bureau of the Census.

TAYLOR, DON: Seal Ditches, Reservoirs: Save Irrigation Dollars, *Calif. Farmer,* San Francisco, July 7, 1962.

TEELE, R. P.: Economics of Land Reclamation, A. W. Shaw Company, Chicago, 1927.

Valley of Light, Annual Report of Tennessee Valley Authority, Knoxville, Tenn., 1963.

VAN HISE, CHARLES R., AND LOOMIS HAVEMEYER: Conservation of Our Natural Resources, The Macmillan Company, New York, 1930.

Water, Yearbook of U.S. Dept. Agr., 1955.

Water for the Modern Farmstead, Rural Electrification Administration, U.S. Department of Agriculture, 1946.

World Almanac, New York World-Telegram and The Sun, New York, 1964.

5 WATER: II

THE UNITED STATES is well supplied with sources of power, from its mineral fuels and the muscles of its people and animals to the vast volume of water flowing downhill and finding itself increasingly harnessed. This natural wealth is reflected in the power consumption of the nation, which was estimated even before World War II to exceed that of Great Britain by 50 per cent, to be twice that of Germany, ten times that of Japan, and 150 times that of China. It is a far cry from the crude grist mills and sawmills built along the streams by the colonists even to the small municipal steam plant owned and operated by any one of numerous communities, and farther to the vast installments of the public utilities or a TVA. And yet water has always been in the picture and will continue to be important in filling the demand for power. Condensation-water problems even in the most efficient steam plant, are not easy. One company serving southeastern Michigan uses in just one of its four plants 300 million gallons of water every 24 hours—almost 900 acre-feet—and the water must be reasonably soft and free of algae.[1] Another plant in Georgia uses similar amounts (Fig. 5-1).

Power from flowing water has had an interesting development. The first mills had to be located near the streams, and any work to be performed by them was delivered and collected at the site. The development of the steam engine made it possible to locate the power plant more conveniently. Then came the use of electric current for power and its transmission by wire for considerable distances to locations where it was required. Following this, unusual developments in high-pressure boilers for steam plants put steam back into competition with water power for producing electrical current. At present, the production of hydroelectric power is one of several multiple purposes of river-valley development coupled with new industrial and farm demands, and it has given added significance to the use of water for producing power. In fact, some of the great Federal river-valley projects almost exhibit the picture of the power "tail" wagging the multiple-purpose "dog."

How Hydroelectric Power Is Measured. Before the status of hydroelectric power is discussed quantitatively, the units in which it is expressed should be understood. One horsepower, it has been agreed since the days of James Watt, represents the power required to raise a weight of 33,000 pounds 1 foot in 1 minute's time. A watt in measuring electrical power is equivalent to $\frac{1}{746}$ horsepower, and a kilowatt is 1,000 times that much, or approximately $1\frac{1}{3}$ horsepower. The kilowatthour then, which one eyes with varying degrees of weariness on his light bill, is equivalent to the service of $1\frac{1}{3}$ horses working for him for 1 hour. If the horses had to live on what this service costs, they would not do so well.

[1] Lynes D. Boomers, Water in Its Relation to Industry and Commerce, Michigan's Water Problems. Michigan Department of Conservation, Lansing, Mich., 1944, p. 49.

Yates steam power plant of Georgia Power Company. For each 24-hour period it uses 373,680,000 gallons of water for cooling (this is borrowed from and returned to a nearby river), 420,000 gallons (equal to more than 11/3 acre-feet) for replacement due to loss in the boiler-feedwater cycle, and 9,000 gallons of sanitary water. (Georgia Power Company and McGraw-Hill, Inc., by whom picture is copyrighted. Used by permission.)

How can one visualize more clearly what 1 horsepower means in terms of falling water? Well, at 60 or 70 miles an hour, a 100-horsepower engine in an automobile will be doing just 100 times 1 horsepower's work. Now, to get that ride from water power, a column of water falling a distance of 67½ feet at the rate of 9 cubic feet per second would have to be employed. So that is water power and horsepower in terms of an automobile ride.

Still another term used in computing the possible power output of a stream is *firm power*, sometimes also called *minimum* or *primary power*. This term is used in connection with horsepower and means the amount of water power constantly available at the rate of flow during the lowest 2 weeks of the year. When the flow of a stream is augmented by turning water from another source into it, the verb form "to firm the flow" or "firming up the stream" is sometimes used.

Recent Consumption of Power and Energy in the United States. The total amount of energy used for all purposes in this country each year increased sixfold in the 40 years from 1889 to 1929, then slumped until about 1937 when it went back to the 1929 figure. In this period water power produced less than 4 percent of the *total energy*,[2] and this and similar figures are sometimes quoted to indicate that water power is unimportant. On the other hand, the percentage for power alone was much higher, and in 1920 the nation had a hydroelectric power production of 15.95 billion kilowatthours. After some ups and downs, this amounted to 18.2 billion kilowatthours in 1961. This was 17.2 per cent of total power production.[3] A convenient rounding off of the figure today can be remembered as slightly more than one-sixth of the total power production.

The figure for *installed capacity* is similar to this, since in 1961 about 36.2 million kilowatts of installed water-power capacity in a total installed capacity of 198.4 million kilowatts was reported. This amounts to 18.2 per cent.[4]

The Federal Power Commission, about which more will be said later, ascribes the healthy demand for electric power from all sources to four circumstances:

1. Growing demand in the country for the products of the relatively modern electrometallurgical and electrochemical industries
2. Increasing application of electricity to modernized processes in the older industries
3. Steadily increasing use of electricity in the home
4. Rapid development of rural electricity[5]

Extent of Water-power Resources. According to a national power survey, the results of which are given in Table 5-1, the undeveloped water power in the United States amounted to 112,700,000 kilowatts as of January, 1962. This figure for estimated undeveloped water power, however, cannot be added to the developed water-wheel capacity of installed water power to get a round figure for the total developed and undeveloped water-power resources. Table 5-1 is therefore, principally valuable for showing the geographical distribution of these resources and the increase in their development from 1939 to 1962.

To get a comparison between total water-power resources and those now developed in terms of horsepower, both of which are based on installed water-wheel and turbine capacity, the rounded-off estimate of 36.2 million kilowatts as the 1961 total is used in Table 5-1. This figure indicates that only one-third of known potential capacity was developed as of 1962.

[2] Our Energy Resources, 1939, Natural Resources Committee, Government Printing Office, p. 3.
[3] *Statistical Abstract of the United States*, 1963, U.S. Bureau of the Census, p. 534.
[4] *Ibid.*, p. 535.
[5] *Ibid.*

TABLE 5-1. DEVELOPED AND UNDEVELOPED WATER POWER
IN THE UNITED STATES

Region	Rated kilowatt capacity of actual installations of all water wheels and turbines		Estimated undeveloped water power (not directly comparable to other two columns)
	December, 1939	December, 1961	January, 1962
United States	12,075,000	36,193,000	112,700,000
New England: Maine, N.H., Vt., Mass., Conn., R.I.	1,115,000	1,518,000	2,800,000
Middle Atlantic: N.Y., N.J., Pa.	1,633,000	3,852,000	5,700,000
East North Central: Ohio, Ind., Ill., Mich., Wis.	790,000	924,000	3,000,000
West North Central: Minn., Iowa, Mo., N. Dak., S. Dak., Nebr., Kans.	537,000	1,694,000	6,200,000
South Atlantic: Del., Md., D.C., Va., W. Va. N.C., S.C., Ga., Fla.	2,224,000	3,795,000	8,900,000
East South Central: Ky., Tenn., Ala., Miss.	1,270,000	3,953,000	4,300,000
West South Central: Ark., La., Okla., Tex.	140,000	948,000	3,800,000
Mountain: Mont., Idaho, Wyo., Colo., N. Mex., Ariz., Utah, Nev.	1,583,000	4,821,000	24,100,000
Pacific: Wash., Oreg., Calif., Alaska, Hawaii	2,783,000	14,694,000	54,100,000

SOURCE: *Statistical Abstract of the United States*, 1963, U.S. Bureau of the Census, p. 535.

Further study of Table 5-1 will reveal something of a natural dislocation of water-power resources with respect to concentrations of population and industry as they are usually visualized. By far the greatest proportion of undeveloped power, some 70 per cent, is in the two Western regions, while slightly less than 15 per cent is available to the three Atlantic seaboard regions. Installed water-wheel and turbine capacity is also somewhat greater in the Western regions. The East and West North

Central regions, with heavy concentrations of population and industry, are low both in water-power resources and installed capacity.

These relationships are significant in two particulars: (1) Water power, if unavailable, cannot be used as a substitute for coal in the over-simplified long-time argument for using replaceable for irreplaceable natural resources; (2) potential water power offers, in regions where it is plentiful and adapted to development, a hope for new locations for industry and population as economic opportunity widens, in accordance with the objectives of democracy.

Power from Multiple-purpose River-valley Development. None of the great river valleys of the United States is without a history of floods. Many of the rivers are used for water transportation, most of them are used for power, all the Western ones for irrigation, all for recreation to a greater or lesser extent, and river fishing for commercial reasons as well as for recreation is still of some importance. Rivers have a way of ignoring the state boundaries set by men, and get their water from the runoff of rainfall from vast watersheds. The production of power is one beneficial use of water, but one which may or may not be thoughtfully and skillfully reconciled with control of a great river for other purposes. This situation sets the stage for multiple-purpose river-valley development under unified leadership, with the total welfare of people as the major objective.

Irrigation farmers and the Bureau of Reclamation look to the power developed on the Colorado, the Columbia, the Missouri, and in the Central Valley of California to reduce the costs of irrigation farming, both through a supply of power to lighten their work and increase their efficiency and through earning revenue from power sales, which will mean that a lesser amount must be paid for irrigation benefits. The people who live in the valley of the Tennessee enjoyed the early benefits of an increase in power from 8.3 billion kilowatthours in 1930 to 15.8 billion in 1940 and, from 1936 to 1944, of a 630 per cent gain in electric service to farms. There were also healthy increases in salaries and wages and in manufacturing.[6] Because the Tennessee is the only river-valley project enjoying unit leadership in its development, the nation-wide interest in its production of power makes this river appropriate for discussion here.

THE TENNESSEE VALLEY AUTHORITY AND ITS WORK TVA are the letters which denote the type of administrative organization set up by the act of 1933 for the purpose of increasing the security, well-being, and productive power of the people through developing the basic resources of the

[6] An M.V.A. or Stagnation, National Farmers Union, Denver, Colo., undated pamphlet of about 1945, pp. 4–5.

Tennessee Valley and its river. In an authority, a commission (in this instance three trained and capable men) is granted broad governmental powers to accomplish a tough job usually requiring a large organization, generous funds, and imperative cooperation with related agencies. But TVA is also the nickname for this vast undertaking on a regional scale as well as for the outfit in charge.

The heaviest rainfall in the Eastern United States comes down in the Tennessee Valley. If it lands on a thick patch of forest or a well-established hayfield, its beating power does little harm and much of it sinks into the leaf mold, sod, and soil. But with heavy settlement, forest clearing, and mountainside farming, the destructive power of rainfall has been at work for nearly a hundred years, and by 1930 the valley was not supporting its millions of people adequately.

The task assigned to the TVA in 1933 was first to stop this destruction of productive powers and second to make the water on the land and in the river more useful and productive than ever before. Soil, water, land and river, people and their resources contribute what the TVA calls a unity, and each of the various parts of its water-control tasks—navigation improvement, flood alleviation, power production, development and experimental manufacture of new mineral fertilizers, encouragement of modern forestry practice, and the management of private forest lands—is inseparably related to all the others.

The 68.5 billion kilowatthours of electric power which the Authority produced and distributed in 1963 demonstrates the interlocking character of all conservation undertakings. In 22 years of actual operation, TVA has built twenty-one dams and integrated their operation with eleven which had been constructed previously (Fig. 5-2). The integration brings about these desirable "chain reactions:" It produces electricity with which it develops and demonstrates new mineral fertilizers (Fig. 5-3); these are then available to farmers on the land and enable them to shift to less destructive crops and forms of cultivation. The products of livestock farming and diversified soil-management and forest-management systems use the electricity in their processing, both for power and refrigeration, and people find employment in the new plants. Shipment of products to market and of needed materials from outside uses the deepened and controlled waterway at reasonable rates. Meanwhile fisheries, both sport and commercial, are improved in the nine long, lakelike reservoirs at whose dams the electricity is produced (Fig. 5-4). The sale of power to distributing companies and cooperatives puts more people to work, and revenue goes not only to the retiring of publicly advanced costs for construction but to supplement local taxes in lieu of revenues lost from land occupied by conservation works.

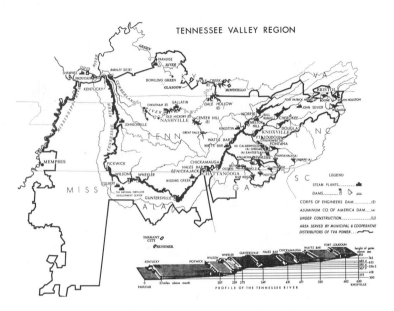

figure 5-2
Area served by TVA. (Map by Tennessee Valley Authority.)

Thus, hydroelectric power from the Tennessee River, important as it is in the role which rates the greater part of TVA's publicity, affects the management of every other natural resource in the valley, including its people. And the Authority can see to it that power is equitably distributed and that its development complements, rather than conflicts with, other beneficial uses of the river. Demand for power is so great that some steam plants have been necessary (Fig. 5-5).

Aerial view of experimental fertilizer plant of the TVA at Muscle Shoals, Ala., with Wilson Dam in background. (Photo by Tennessee Valley Authority.)

figure 5-3

figure 5-4

The mainstream TVA lakes, in addition to offering good sport fishing, support a million-dollar commercial fishery. The annual take is around 5 million pounds. Catfish are the most popular commercial species and constitute the bulk of the catch. These fishermen have done well. (Photo by Tennessee Valley Authority.)

TVA's power market cannot be supplied from its various water-power installations. Additional steam plants have been necessary. This one at Kingston on Watts Bar Lake in Tennessee, built from 1951 to 1955, with a combined capacity of 1,600,000 kilowatts, is the largest steam plant in the United States. At 80 per cent load factor it will consume 4,300,000 tons of coal in a year. (Photo by Tennessee Valley Authority.)

figure 5-5

117

The TVA will be referred to further in the later sections of this chapter for it has made significant contributions in the fields of mineral developments, recreation, navigation, fishery management and flood control.

THE MISSOURI RIVER BASIN   The reader is here referred to the discussion of the Missouri Valley Authority on pages 105–106. After 44 years of construction work the Bureau of Reclamation found itself lined up under the 1944 Flood Control Act with the Corps of Engineers of the United States Army, whose legal water business is largely defined in terms of flood control and the improvement of navigation. The Corps of Engineers, however, operates the power plant at the great Fort Randall Dam in Montana (Fig. 5-6), which generates more than 400 million kilowatthours of electric energy. This output is marketed by the Bureau of Reclamation. The Office of Indian Affairs, the various state agencies, the Fish and Wildlife Service, the Soil Conservation Service, mineral interests and livestock interests—all have a tremendous stake in the outcome of any plan for the Missouri River Basin. The device used to assure the "unity," which to a great extent is achieved elsewhere by the TVA, is the interagency committee previously mentioned. This may or may not be able to assure adequate consideration for power production at the 100 dams and to relate it to the total conservation objective.

THE CENTRAL VALLEY PROJECT   Production of hydroelectric power looms large in the Central Valley of California even before agreement has been reached as to just how the development project as a whole shall be managed. The great Shasta Dam with its power plant operating 13.5 per cent overload during the entire year from July 1, 1945, to June 30,

Fort Randall Dam, built by Army Engineers near Pickstown, S. Dak., on the Missouri River, backs up 6,100,000 acre-feet of water at full capacity and serves multiple purposes of which power production is one. The power generated is marketed by the Bureau of Reclamation. (Photo by Corps of Engineers, United States Army.)

figure 5-6

1946, generated 1,486,578,600 kilowatthours, the major portion of which was sold to a large utility company under a war-duration contract. Subsequent and similar contracts, terminating in 1961, had been entered into since 1948. Additional power from the Trinity River Project having become available early in 1963, new contracts with the above-mentioned utility company and preferential customers were being worked out. While the Bureau of Reclamation operates the Central Valley Project, it cooperates with the state of California in the slow development of a state water plan in which the proposed construction of the San Luis unit in the southern San Joaquin Valley figures importantly. As mentioned on page 104, construction work on the San Luis Dam was started in 1963. The water comes from the Feather River in northern California. An interesting feature of the Central Valley Project, which illustrates the complexity of river-valley problems and which must be integrated with desirable power production, is the need for a flow of stored water to prevent ocean-water encroachment on 450,000 acres of rich delta land at the mouths of the Sacramento and the San Joaquin Rivers.[7]

Other river-valley projects which develop vast volumes of power are the Columbia Basin, with its Grand Coulee and Bonneville power installations, and the Colorado, with its Hoover (Boulder) Dam.

PUBLIC VERSUS PRIVATE CONTROL   The Flood Control Act of 1944 provides that preference in the disposal of power from projects built with Federal funds be granted to public and cooperative agencies such as municipalities and rural-electrification cooperatives. By whatever plans these river resources are controlled and brought into service, hydroelectric power, not only in its production but in its equitable distribution, offers the tough kind of problem that a democracy must face. Total-river-basin thinking and planning are indispensable (Fig. 5-7).

A radical change in policy with change in administration in 1953 tossed this problem into the laps of local agencies and public utilities, particularly with reference to the sale and distribution of power produced by publicly financed works. More significantly, however, the new policy frowns on construction at Federal expense, to say nothing of Federal operation of new projects which private capital may be able to undertake more or less on its own terms. As an example, a decision to abandon plans for Federal construction of the Hell's Canyon dam on the Snake River between Idaho and Oregon in favor of a number of smaller ventures financed by private capital may be cited. Proponents of the single high dam insist that it would produce considerably more power and would not interfere with the management of important wild-animal re-

[7] Natural Resources Problems, *Annual Report of the Secretary of the Interior,* 1946, p. 89.

sources in the area flooded. Decision in favor of the three smaller dams appears to be based on savings in cost. Another example appeared in the famous Dixon-Yates affair in 1954. The Tennessee Valley Authority was furnishing so much power to the Atomic Energy Commission that shortage for some of its other customers, including Memphis and vicinity, appeared to be developing. TVA proposed to build a steam plant to make up the shortage. But the Administration favored the application of the Mississippi Valley Generating Company (Dixon-Yates) to build a plant with private capital at West Memphis in Arkansas to replace the power furnished by TVA to the Atomic Energy Commission. There was considerable argument over comparative costs, the awkwardness of the arrangement, the consideration of only one bid, elements of subsidy, and other questions brought up by two congressional committees, but upon order of President Eisenhower and the approval of his Bureau of the Budget, the Atomic Energy Commission signed a contract with the applicant. Then the city of Memphis decided to build its own power plant and the above contract was canceled. Friends of TVA interpreted this entire affair as a bold stroke by the administration in favor of private power over public power and a definite blow to the life of TVA. The Memphis steam plant of 750,000-kilowatt capacity was built and will be leased to TVA in 1965 instead of being operated locally. Its output will be added to the low-cost energy supply for the western end of the TVA system. Meanwhile TVA is supplying Memphis with power for its summer peak loads when the city produces no surplus.

How Water-power Enterprises Are Regulated. Because any control of large power resources can lead to monopoly, it is appropriate that development and distribution be subject to a measure of public regulation just as trade, transportation, and the practice of the professions are regulated. On the side of equitable distribution, which is essential to conservation of natural resources, most of the states have long had a measure of rate regulation on the distribution of power under their "public-service commissions," "railroad commissions," and similar bodies. Federal regulation for conservation purposes was authorized in 1920 with the passage of the Federal Power Act, 12 years after the White House conference of 1908 had included such a recommendation in its "Declaration of Principles." Meanwhile, however, withdrawal of water-power sites on Federal land had gone forward with other land withdrawals for study and possible reservation, and public interest had grown steadily in the nation's water-power resources.

The Federal Power Act signed by President Woodrow Wilson on June 10, 1920, assumed rightly that ownership of land at a power site and the duty of looking after the interests of the people of the United States as the owners justified licensing and regulation of water-power enterprises. Since the navigability of any stream might also be affected by power development, the commerce clause of the Constitution was put squarely behind the Commission's powers. The Congress, however, assumed that any work which an ex-officio Federal Power Commission, created by this act, might have to do could be taken care of neatly by borrowing help from other Federal departments. Only a chief engineer and a small office force were provided to handle a mass of applications and inquiries. Lack of funds and personnel persisted for more than a decade, until, finally in 1935, the law was amended to provide for five full-time, skilled commissioners and for greatly expanding the technical force. The work of the Commission was also defined more carefully to cover (1) passing upon applications for developing power on waters of the public lands and navigable waters elsewhere, (2) supervising interstate wholesale power rates, (3) devising and promoting the use of uniform accounting systems by licensed companies, (4) passing upon mergers and issuance of securities, (5) studying power resources and rates, and (6) cooperating with state regulatory commissions.

Since 1935, the duties of the Federal Power Commission have increased, and they now extend to certain power problems other than those wholly connected with water power. In 1938 Congress conferred upon the Commission the jurisdiction over interstate natural-gas rates in addition to other duties in regulating the natural-gas industry. Efforts to have this action repealed were unsuccessful. The Federal Inter-Agency River Basin Committee established in 1943, from which the various local river-basin committees have developed, includes a representative of the Federal Power Commission to assist in obtaining more complete cooperation of all interests in river-basin development. The Commission has also made numerous studies of power resources, typical of which is the one requested by the Senate Committee on Foreign Affairs on the marketability of the potential power output of the St. Lawrence River (12 billion kilowatthours annually). This study concluded that this output could be put to full use a short time after the completion of the proposed project. It showed also that the cost of producing and delivering the energy to load centers would be cheaper than the production costs alone (principally fuel and labor) of a like amount of energy at any existing steam electric plant in the area, if fixed charges on the steam plant were excluded.

Still another and very interesting study by the Commission under its mandate in the Federal Power Act to "conduct investigations regarding the generation of electric energy, however produced," has to do with wind-power units. In this study it is estimated that power from efficiently designed wind-power generators scattered widely over the territory served could furnish 20 per cent of the energy of a large network.

In a 1955 study of electricity rates in cities of 50,000 or more population throughout the United States, the Commission reported that in the Pacific division, which takes in Washington, Oregon, and California, the lowest monthly bills for residential electric service (for 250 kilowatthours) ranged from $3.20 to $4.65 and the highest, from $4.61 to $6.78. This compared with $6.75 to $8.51 for the lowest and $8.32 to $9.53 for the highest in the New England states division.[8] These two geographical divisions proved to be the least expensive and the most expensive, respectively. The lowest figures from the Pacific division are from communities served by public power projects, while all other figures, except the $6.75 for New England, come from communities served by private enterprises. These figures are more interesting, however, than significant, since no account is taken of differences in cost of power production. On the other hand, rate regulation by the Commission, now well established as to constitutionality, resulted in effecting reductions of almost 40 million dollars in interstate wholesale rates as far back as 1946. This begins to bring equitable distribution of the benefits of conserving a natural resource right down to the ultimate consumer.

According to the Federal Power Commission, the total electric-energy requirement for the nation in 1955 was about 553 billion kilowatthours, and the projected requirement for 1980 is 2,159 billion kilowatthours. Industrial use accounted for almost one-half this consumption in 1955 and nonfarm residential use for about one-fifth.[9] The total figure for kilowatthour consumption of these and other classes represents an increase of 365 billion kilowatthours over the 188 billion total of 1940—almost 200 per cent. Back in 1929, the average production worker in manufacturing or mining used about 3 kilowatthours for every hour he worked. In 1955 he used four times as much, or approximately 12 kilowatthours. Steel, aluminum, and atomic-energy plants are the heaviest industrial consumers of electric energy. Estimates are vague concerning the proportions of the above increases, but water power will have to hold up its end. Table 5-1 on page 113 may be referred to for figures on potential water-power resources from which some of the future needs must be met.

Recent Water-power Proposals. Before this discussion of the use of water to produce power is ended, a number of recent proposals should be mentioned. First, an "inter-tie" arrangement financed by private and public funds for transmitting surplus power produced in the Northwest Pacific area to the Southwest was being worked out in 1964. Involved

---

[8] Typical Residential Electric Bills, 1956, Federal Power Commission, 1956, pp. 4 and 9.

[9] Estimated Future Power Requirements of the United States by Regions, 1955–1980, Federal Power Commission, 1956, pp. 12, 13, and 17. Also Electric Power in Relation to the Nation's Water Resources, U.S. Senate Select Committee on National Water Resources, Committee Print 10, 1960, pp. 1–8.

are the Bureau of Reclamation, the Bonneville Power Administration in the Northwest, the city of Los Angeles, three private companies in the Southwest. The project is considered to be self-liquidating, and construction of the first transmission lines was authorized late in 1964.

New interest has been shown in a proposed International Passamaquoddy Tidal Power Project on a 100-square-mile bay of this name off the Bay of Fundy. Tides on the latter have the greatest rise and fall in the world, and in Passamaquoddy Bay they rise to a maximum of 29 feet and a minimum of 12.7 feet. Holding back these tides in the St. John River for release at low tide to produce power requires vast engineering works. The most recent study by a Department of the Interior committee declares that the project is practicable and recommends its approval by the United States and Canada.[10]

Following a decision by the United States Supreme Court which set the basic division of Colorado River water among California, Arizona, and Nevada and made the Department of the Interior umpire when water supplies were insufficient to apply the division formula, the Department's Pacific Southwest Water Plan was proposed. Power production appeared as an objective in a part of this plan. Two dams would be built on the river, one at Bridge Canyon below Grand Canyon National Park and the other above the park at Marble Canyon. These dams would not add to the supply of water but would produce power, the revenue from which would go into a Pacific Southwest Development Fund to help finance the entire plan including the purchase of water imported from other regions. This Pacific Southwest Water Plan was being considered by the Eighty-ninth Congress in 1965.[11]

A daring project is the North American Water and Power Alliance (NAWAPA). This is proposed by the Ralph M. Parsons Company of Los Angeles, an engineering firm which has made all of the studies up to 1965. Much of the water would be drawn from the Yukon and Peace Rivers; stored in the Rocky Mountain Trench extending from the region of Libby, Montana, northwest, well into Canada; and distributed throughout Canada, the United States as far east as the Great Lakes, and Mexico. This is a vast continental concept estimated to cost 100 billion dollars and requiring 20 years to complete. A full-scale feasibility study by the United States and Canadian governments is proposed by the company.[12]

To produce power in Alaska on the Yukon River, studies of the Rampart Dam site and the basin above it by the Army Corps of Engineers and the Department of the Interior were undertaken in 1963 and 1964.

[10] Interior Study Group Recommends Passamaquoddy Power Project, *Conservation News*, Sept. 1, 1964, pp. 10 and 11.
[11] *Izaak Walton Magazine*, August-September, 1964, p. 17.
[12] Water for North America, *Science*, vol. 147, p. 113, Jan. 8, 1965.

As a result an area of 9 million acres of public lands has been classified by the Department of the Interior as a power site for the proposed project. A lake somewhat larger than Lake Erie would be formed. It would be 280 miles long and have a maximum width of 80 miles. It would inundate 400 miles of the main stream of the Yukon and an additional 12,600 miles of tributary streams. It is estimated to cost 1.3 billion dollars and would require 20 years just to fill the reservoir. A report was to be made to the Congress in 1965. The project is opposed by the Fish and Wildlife Service and by many sportsmen and scientists because of its inevitable destruction of wildlife habitat.[13]

Another enormous project will be undertaken in nine Rocky Mountain states in 1965 or 1966 by a group of ten private companies known as the Western Energy Supply and Transmission Associates. It is estimated to cost more than 10 billion dollars, will use nuclear energy, coal *and* water power, and hopes to be delivering electrical power by 1989.[14]

Power is a productive use of falling water, and wherever the productivity of water can be increased, *with due consideration for other natural resources and values involved,* it is being conserved. Frequently also the same water that turns a wheel or turbine may irrigate a crop, water a deer, float a barge, wash away a treated industrial waste, put out a city fire, and go on its way without tearing up soil or destroying buildings and even human life. In the course of these adventures it has saved irreplaceable mineral fuel at the power and transportation stages. This is conservation.

The Competitive Position of Thermonuclear Power. In view of the tremendous progress being made in atomic research and the increasing knowledge of ways to apply nuclear energy to peacetime uses, the question, of course, arises concerning the prospect of substituting nuclear energy for water and fossil fuels in the production of power. While this is more fully discussed under Mineral Fuels (page 339), it may be noted here that the economic and scientific problems are far from being solved; so nuclear energy has not yet begun seriously to affect our economy. It is predicted that the use of fossil fuels will be available at lesser cost than nuclear fuels for many years in terms of the size and expense of the plants necessary to use the latter.[15]

WATER FOR RECREATION

It is difficult to imagine satisfactory outdoor recreation, with its importance to the health and power—both spiritual and mental—of people,

[13] *Conservation News,* Feb. 15, 1965, pp. 12–13.
[14] Release by the National Manufacturers Association in Escondido (Calif.), *Times-Advocate,* Oct. 23, 1964.
[15] Sam H. Schurr, Some Observations on the Economics of Atomic Power, *Reprint* 41, Resources for the Future, Inc. Washington, D.C., 1963, p. 16.

without water in the picture. A parched, waterless outdoor scene may exhibit gorgeous sunsets, and a dry pine forest may furnish fragrance and beauty, but men must have water to drink, to use in the simple necessities of outdoor camp and picnic activities, to look at, to swim in, and for recreational bathing, boating, and water skiing. The sound of running water is also pleasant in an outdoor setting, and in winter water in the forms of ice and snow offers opportunity for skating, skiing, tobogganing, and decorating oneself with clothing that would rival Solomon's in all his glory. Sport fishing and the hunting of waterfowl as the favored recreations of millions put increasing pressure on streams, lakes, ponds, and reservoirs which must serve other purposes as well.

It is not too much to say that water is indispensable to outdoor recreation nor that almost all the bodies of water of whatever size in this country are used for recreation.

Water as a Part of the Natural Scene. A great many people get their only outdoor recreation through their eyes (Fig. 5-7). A landscape with a stream or waterfall or lake near or far away proclaims its value in terms of dollars and even in terms of international agreement over use of the water. It is an actual fact that much of the price of lake lots or riverside residence property is represented in the unearned control of a

View on Hiwassee Lake, TVA. Recreation is a major use of TVA waters. This quiet scene hardly suggests the 52,000 pleasure boats kept on TVA lakes or the investment of 156 million dollars in recreation by states, counties, cities, private individuals, and companies. (Photo by Tennessee Valley Authority.)

figure 5-7

water scene. Ridiculously small proportions of beaches, lake shore, and river shore throughout the country are in public ownership for exclusive recreational and scenic use. Isle Royale in Lake Superior, one of our more recently dedicated national parks, is a lovely land mass which would be just another stretch of northern country but for the great, cold, clear lake around it and its own inland waters. Cumberland Falls in Kentucky, now a state park, is valuable principally for the water scene. It was purchased and presented to the state by a family of wealth and just escaped being developed for power purposes. The decision of a Kentucky judge that the use of water to look at constitutes "no use at all" is no longer valid.

Niagara Falls with its 165-foot drop represents one of the world's greatest opportunities for the development of power, having a remarkably uniform flow of about 220,000 cubic feet per second, capable of generating 5 million horsepower, which is something like 6 per cent of the total installed water-wheel capacity of the United States at present. Moreover, the falls themselves were once fenced off from view on the American side, and a fee was charged by private interests for a chance to view the scene. Public sentiment through the years has asserted itself, with the result that public interests now control the view from both sides. A treaty has been entered into between the United States and Great Britain in behalf of Canada recognizing the equitable share of both countries in the flow of the stream but calling a permanent halt to further power and industrial encroachment on the scene. Actually the treaty reserves three-quarters of the water of the falls for scenery alone.

Further evidence of the public appreciation of water for its aesthetic values has been evident over the years in the spirited opposition to industrial invasion of Western national parks for the use of park waters for power and irrigation projects.

Water for Camping, Picnicking, and Sport. The little water the users of a pleasant spot may need for drinking and simple outdoor cooking has often been the limiting factor in the development of day-use or camping areas in public forests, parks, and other lands. Nor is such a problem confined always to arid regions, for too many streams and springs in humid localities are likely to be unsafe for drinking simply because of heavy concentrations of industry, agriculture, and population. Ironically enough, too, one of the great difficulties met in administering outdoor areas for picnic and camp use is maintaining the safety of the water supply against human carelessness in use.

Water sports include canoeing, sailing, swimming, water skiing, surfing, rowing, motorboat racing, and organized games, such as water polo, the latter being more commonly played in indoor pools. For these sports, clean, accessible, safe, and attractive waters are essential. Surveys of recreation preferences show a vast discrepancy in most localities between preferences for water sports on the one hand and opportunity to participate in them on the other. And frequently these sports themselves interfere with each other so that special waters are needed. Certainly the owner of a noisy motorboat has his rights, but they should not extend to all waters where they interfere with swimmers, canoeists, and seekers of wilderness solitude. Nor should airplanes for sport be allowed to invade wilderness waters. A considerable part of the reason for these conflicts and frustrations is unavailability of water facilities. State and Federal authorities are aware of this situation and have attempted to meet it in the following ways: (1) by lease or purchase of additional water-front sites for public use, (2) by construction of dams for impounding artificial lakes exclusively devoted to recreational use, (3) by organizing the recreational facilities on the growing number of multiple-purpose reservoirs,[16] (4) by promoting the cleanup and treatment of waters heretofore unsafe for recreational use, and (5) by developing with camping facilities and making accessible public water all the way from ocean beaches to canoe landings and portage trails in state forests. On the municipal and county front, water for outdoor swimming pools becomes important, frequently making heavy demands on underground supplies.

Fishing and hunting, also important exclusively as sports, should be mentioned here as well as later on under Wild-animal Life, because fishing and hunting of waterfowl are impossible without clean, accessible waters in vast stretches of stream and marsh and in well-managed lakes, ponds, and artificially impounded bodies. It is also important to know that the strongest leadership in behalf of preventing water pollution comes from organizations of sportsmen of the more constructive type. The Izaak Walton League of America deserves special commendation on this score. State leasing for public use of stream banks from the riparian owners and purchase and development of access sites for fishermen out of license receipts have become necessary in some states. It is not strange that one hears more and more the terms "rod pressure" and "gun pressure" in the discussions of conserving water for fishermen and hunters to use.

The conservation problems met in using water for recreation are those of (1) assuring availability and accessibility, (2) assuring freedom from pollution, and (3) establishing recreation in its broadest sense as a major

[16] This, since 1953, has been a halfhearted policy. Both the Bureau of Reclamation and the Army Engineers in acquiring reservoir sites have restricted purchase of flowage areas, refusing to acquire bordering lands important for wild-animal welfare and for other recreational values. The Bureau of Budget reported adversely on a Senate bill to correct this in the Eighty-fifth Congress, declaring that unless recreational values are of national significance, any land acquired for such purchases should be "resold to local interests within a reasonable period of time."

beneficial use of water and seeing to it that such use is granted its share of priority.

WATER FOR NAVIGATION AND TRANSPORTATION

One of the oldest uses of water is the one in which men have made it their highways for travel and burden carrying by boat, floating of logs and pulpwood, and carrying away of waste. Waste transportation has already been discussed, log and pulpwood driving will be covered in the chapter on forests, and there is left here the use of oceans, lakes, coastal inlets, rivers, and canals for shipping.

This subject involves a kind of conservation which, so far as inland waters are concerned, frequently appears as a sort of premium and non-conflicting result when waters are controlled and developed for other major uses. Yet the average American citizen through the years has been conditioned to think of rivers and harbor appropriations as pork-barrel legislation. Why? The answers to this question perhaps lie in the facts that much of this water is actually little used for this purpose as against other uses; that freight movements by water are slow and that they move from wharf to wharf and port to port rather than from warehouse, farm, or mine to plant, store, or home; that the vast scale of improvement and maintenance required has not attracted private investment; that in colder climates inland waterways are not open year long; and possibly that in a "free competitive economy" much more than just "the economics of the thing" have been used to oppose waterway development.

It should be pointed out here that, historically, navigation was the only use of water specifically mentioned in the Constitution of the United States and that the "commerce clause" is the basis for much important conservation legislation, notably in the fields of water power and forest resources.

To their credit it may be said that ocean waters are indispensable to commerce and to much of the communication and most of the travel between continents; that inlets and larger rivers are convenient extenders of ocean transportation; that because of navigable bodies of water, other transportation facilities, particularly in times of war and of great prosperity, are relieved of much tonnage and are free to concentrate on more urgent hauling; that many of the great natural waterways in this country are so located that they are the best means of handling cargoes of great bulk and weight with assured return hauls, where speed of delivery is not important (Fig. 5-8); and, finally, that improvement of rivers for navigation fits in well with a measure of control of floods, with their long record of damage to life and property. One other long-time advantage touching the needs of future generations is that water transportation requires less

figure 5-8

Mississippi River traffic at Saint Louis. Increase in the number of cargo commodities and of terminals for interchange to railroad and truck traffic is believed to have had a marked effect on the 4 million tons increase between 1961 and 1962 to a new high of 35 million tons. (Photo by Corps of Engineers, United States Army.)

use of irreplaceable metals and fuels than do other means of transportation.

Importance of Water Transportation. In 1961, the total tonnage moved by railroads in this country amounted to 2,315,539,908 short tons (2,000 pounds) as against 732,825,364 short tons[17] of all domestic water-borne commerce, more than one-half of which was river, canal, connecting-channel, and harbor transportation. The figure would be more unfavorable to water transportation if truck haul and pipeline transportation were added to rail-haul figures, but the business of the country cannot lightly brush off so great an inland and harbor shipping capacity (Fig. 5-9).

In order to present a country-wide picture of the growth of water-borne commerce, excluding certain duplications and harbor commerce from the figures quoted above, attention is called to Table 5-2, which is expressed in ton-miles.

OCEAN TRANSPORTATION The several million men who constituted the military and naval forces of the United States in World War II learned some things about oceans which should be a part of the education of every well-informed citizen. Perhaps the most important lesson is that ocean routes form life lines throughout the world and that nations, as well as armies, look to these routes for supply and for profitable outlet

---

[17] Corps of Engineers, U.S. Dept. of the Army.

figure 5-9

Typical inland-waterway tow of barges en route from Cairo, Ill., to Saint Paul, Minn.: eight barges of coal — 10,800 tons, six barges of petroleum products — 8,100 tons, and two barges of miscellaneous freight — 1,400 tons. Total tonnage, 20,300 tons. Total length, 1,178 feet. (Photo by Corps of Engineers, United States Army.)

of their products. Another one is that "freedom of the seas" is conservation of first importance in assuring any kind of world-wide, equitable distribution of natural resources. The depth and safety of harbors, constituting one of the limitations on the use of ocean waters for transportation, very properly become objectives in improvement and maintenance work, and meeting these objectives is a kind of conservation.

With more than 3,000 vessels in the country's merchant marine today, the conservation of ocean-harbor facilities assumes new importance.

TABLE 5-2. FREIGHT CARRIED ON INLAND WATERWAYS, 1961

System	Ton-miles
Atlantic coast waterways	27,251,444,000
Gulf coast waterways	17,765,885,000
Pacific coast waterways	5,523,384,000
Mississippi River system, including Ohio River and tributaries	72,325,599,000
Great Lakes system (excludes traffic between foreign ports, includes Alaskan waterways)	86,819,421,000
Other waterways	20,593,000
Total	209,706,326,000

Source: Corps of Engineers, U.S. Department of the Army.

THE ST. LAWRENCE SEAWAY The St. Lawrence River and the five Great Lakes—Michigan, Superior, Huron, Erie, and Ontario—with their improved connecting channels form the world's greatest inland waterway. Those who have worked to see the St. Lawrence Seaway completed envision Buffalo, Cleveland, Detroit, Milwaukee, and Chicago as great ocean ports. At present a healthy mild-weather commerce carries grain, limestone, and ore eastward and coal westward (Fig. 5-10). There are also imports to the United States of Canadian and European pulp and pulpwood. Shorter hauls of sand, gravel, automobiles, and miscellaneous cargo are common. Such traffic is possible only because of the dredging, improvement, and maintenance of connecting channels, important among which are the Saint Marys River between Lakes Superior and Huron, the Saint Clair and Detroit Rivers between Huron and Erie, and the Welland Ship Canal between Erie and Ontario, above Niagara Falls (Fig. 5-11). These improvements, on the other hand, and certain waterway hookups such as the Illinois Ship Canal, which drains Lake Michigan water into the Illinois River and thence to the Mississippi, have introduced some lake-level problems which require constant attention.

The lake levels of Erie, Huron, and Michigan are believed by some authorities to have been lowered during a 30-year period some 5 to 6 inches by diversions at Chicago and elsewhere. This seems insignificant, but it was important enough to carrier companies using large ships to have brought about litigation to reduce the amount of diverted water from 10,000 cubic feet per second to 1,500. As if this were not enough trouble, cyclical variations in lake levels, identified by studies of 125 years' records, must be dealt with in forecasting and maintaining navigability of this waterway.[18]

[18] Helen M. Martin, and others, They Need Not Vanish, Michigan Department of Conservation, Lansing, Mich., 1942, p. 201.

Lake boats passing in Saint Clair River—a part of St. Lawrence Seaway—between Lakes Saint Clair and Huron. Speed is regulated to prevent wave damage to shore property. (The Bulletin, Lake Carriers Association.)

figure 5-10

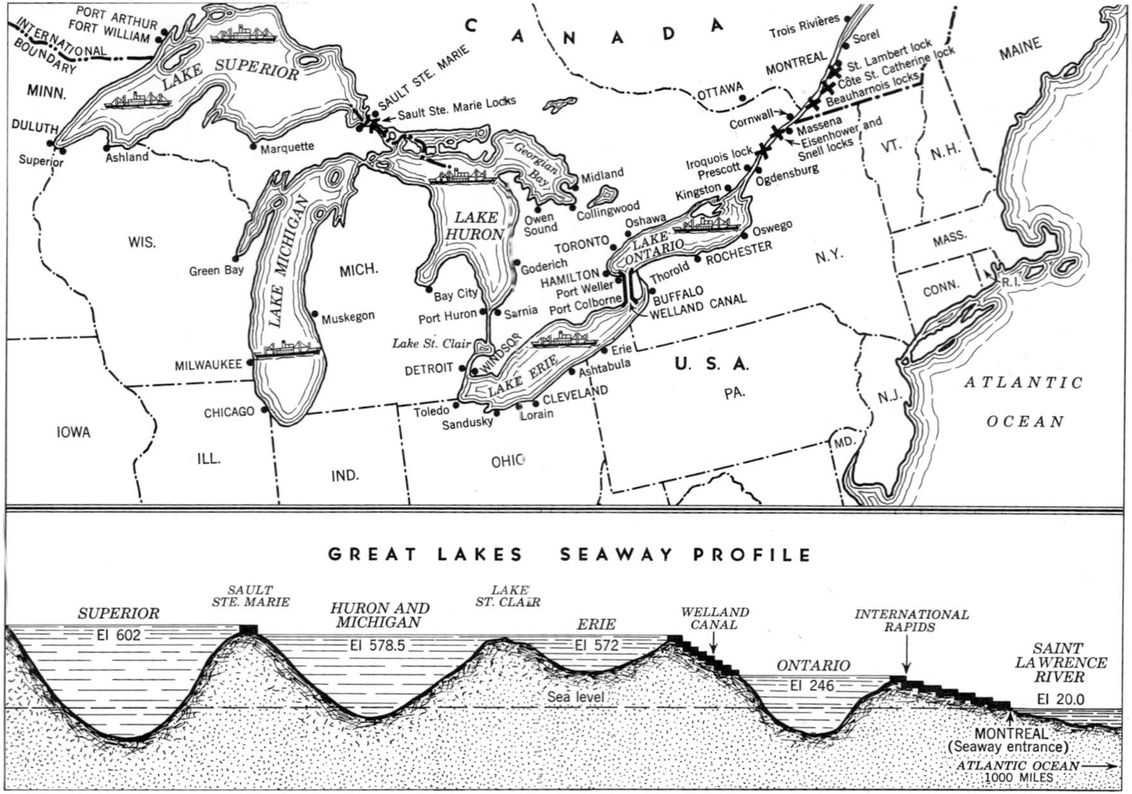

GREAT LAKES SEAWAY PROFILE

MAINE

ATLANTIC OCEAN

N.H.

MASS.

CONN.

VT.

N.Y.

N.J.

MD.

PA.

U.S.A.

C A N A D A

OTTAWA

MONTREAL

Trois Rivières
Sorel
St. Lambert lock
Côte St. Catherine lock
Beauharnois locks
Massena and
Eisenhower and
Snell locks
Cornwall
Iroquois lock
Prescott
Ogdensburg
Kingston
Oswego
LAKE ONTARIO
ROCHESTER
TORONTO
Oshawa
Port Weller
Thorold
Port Colborne
WELLAND CANAL
BUFFALO
Erie
LAKE ERIE
Ashtabula
CLEVELAND
Lorain
Sandusky
OHIO
Toledo
DETROIT
Lake St. Clair
LAKE ST. CLAIR
Windsor
Port Huron
Sarnia
Bay City
LAKE HURON
Goderich
HAMILTON
Owen Sound
Collingwood
Midland
Georgian Bay
MICH.
Muskegon
MILWAUKEE
Green Bay
WIS.
IND.
ILL.
CHICAGO
IOWA
LAKE MICHIGAN
Marquette
LAKE SUPERIOR
SAULT STE. MARIE
Sault Ste. Marie Locks
PORT ARTHUR
FORT WILLIAM
INTERNATIONAL BOUNDARY
MINN.
DULUTH
Superior
Ashland

SUPERIOR
El 602

SAULT
STE. MARIE

HURON AND
MICHIGAN
El 578.5

LAKE
ST. CLAIR

ERIE
El 572

WELLAND
CANAL

ONTARIO
El 246

INTERNATIONAL
RAPIDS

SAINT
LAWRENCE
RIVER
El 20.0

MONTREAL
(Seaway entrance)
ATLANTIC OCEAN →
1000 MILES

Sea level

figure 5-11

Profile of St. Lawrence Seaway—the world's greatest inland waterway. (Saint Lawrence Seaway Development Corporation.)

The importance of the Great Lakes to the steel industry will be understood in terms of transportation when it is considered that coal, iron ore, and limestone are the natural-resource materials needed and that in no one place in the country do they occur in the identical quantity and quality required except in northern Alabama. Great Lakes transportation, however, is instrumental in bringing together these separate materials from different localities so that the coke from the coal fields of Illinois and Pennsylvania meets the lake-borne limestone and iron ore at Chicago, Detroit, and Cleveland. The mills at these centers thus rival those at Pittsburgh and Youngstown, which have short hauls for coal but long hauls from the lake shore for other materials.

Improvement of the St. Lawrence River from the harbor at Montreal through Lake Ontario and the Welland Canal to Lake Erie—which involved deepening canals around rapids, enlarging the locks, and otherwise providing for large ocean-going ships—was completed in 1959. The participation of the United States in this joint venture with Canada was authorized in 1954 by the Congress. The work was part of a larger plan for a 27-foot-deep waterway which extends as far west as Duluth and Chicago. Upon completion of this part of the waterway, work was undertaken in 1957 to improve the connecting channels farther west—the Detroit and St. Clair Rivers between Lakes Erie and Huron and the Saint Marys River between Lakes Huron and Superior. This work was nearing completion in 1962, but the equipping of ports and deepening of harbors has lagged considerably.[19] Legislation for this improvement plan had been introduced in Congress in some form every session for 2 decades and had been roundly opposed by power interests, by citizens who saw in it ruination for the Port of New York, and by others who felt that Canada would profit more than the United States. The estimated cost was 260 million dollars for all the navigation improvements, of which the United States was to pay 165 million. The cost has exceeded this figure considerably. Bonds were issued to be retired in about 50 years from shipping tolls. (This pay-as-you-use plan assumes increasing importance when it is considered that two other proposals made about 1947, one for the Intercoastal Waterway and one for the expansion of the Mississippi River system, would cost a total of 745 million dollars. Smaller projects have brought total proposed Western expenditures up to 1,160 million dollars.[20])

The administration of this waterway is assigned to the Saint Lawrence Seaway Development Corporation in behalf of the United States and to the St. Lawrence Seaway Authority in behalf of Canada. Traffic started

[19] Release of Dec. 16, 1963 by Saint Lawrence Seaway Development Corporation.
[20] J. Frederic Dewhurst and Associates, *America's Needs and Resources*, The Twentieth Century Fund, New York, 1947, p. 8.

in 1962 on April 23 and closed on December 8, showing a 10 per cent cargo increase over 1961. The entire length of the "St. Lawrence–Great Lakes Seaway," which is the usual designation, is 2,342 miles, and it extends into the heart of the North American continent, touching four maritime provinces of Canada and eight states of the United States. It is the greatest inland water system in the world.[21]

After 5 full years of operation manufacturers are learning of possible savings on export shipment by the Seaway, as the following examples demonstrate: an automobile manufacturer found that he saved $30 a vehicle in shipping overseas; an exporter of bottling equipment saved close to $4,000 on one shipment from Wisconsin to France; and another company saved a half a million dollars on a shipment of 100 locomotives. Such savings prophesy greatly increased use of the facility for miscellaneous cargo, as well as ore, grain, pulpwood, newsprint, and coal.

COASTAL NAVIGATION   For safe domestic and light international trade along the Atlantic and Gulf coasts, increasing attention is being given to improvement of natural waterways paralleling the coasts but back of headlands, where water is relatively calm most of the time. Depths of 9 to 12 feet would be maintained in the natural waters and connecting canals from Massachusetts Bay intermittently southward to the mouth of the Mississippi. It was in connection with, but as an addition to, this program a few years ago that the Florida Ship Canal was proposed. This would have been a deep-water channel from the Saint Johns River across the narrow part of the peninsula to the Gulf of Mexico. Cost and threat to the quality of Florida's underground water supply appear to have discredited this plan. Meanwhile, work progresses on various segments of this great intracoastal waterway for steady use by craft of light draft.

RIVER AND CANAL NAVIGATION   A considerable number of the canals built in this country have connected rivers with each other or with larger bodies of water or have followed existing river channels as a part of their improvement of navigation. Rivers and canals are therefore discussed together. The best known of the latter are the New York State Barge Canal, formerly called the Erie Canal; the "Soo" Canal at Sault Sainte Marie between Lakes Superior and Huron, which carries tonnage exceeding that of the Panama and Suez Canals combined; the Illinois Ship Canal, carrying away Chicago's wastes; and the Cape Cod Canal, connecting Cape Cod Bay and Buzzards Bay, constructed privately and sold some years ago to the Federal government. Each one of these has its own peculiar distinction, and all persist against repeated charges of having

[21] Saint Lawrence Seaway Development Corporation, Report, Washington, D.C., 1962.

proved uneconomic or of dealing out subsidy to shippers alone. Great expense for building and operating locks, slowness of traffic, uselessness during freezing weather, inability to compete with the railroad, interference with water-level maintenance, and continual necessity of dredging because of siltation are stock arguments against canals in general as supplements of inland transportation in this day and age. Their use, however, is inevitable if rivers, lakes, and other inland bodies of water are to be employed for navigation.

Short, heavily used, and indispensable, the Soo Canal taps the rich Lake Superior country and is itself the improvement of a short river. Without this canal and the Welland Canal (wholly in Canada), the Great Lakes would have been much less important as a waterway. Both are now part of the Saint Lawrence–Great Lakes Seaway.

The New York State Barge Canal—once indispensable to the moving of crops and other cargo eastward during its days as the Erie Canal, greatly improved from 1910 to 1920, and now inadequately used—"canalizes" a portion of the Mohawk River and connects the Hudson River with Lake Erie.

The Illinois Ship Canal cuts through a low divide and reverses the direction of flow of a part of the Chicago River, leads to the Illinois River, and, thence, to the Mississippi. It becomes a part of the Mississippi River system which with the St. Lawrence Seaway and the Intra-coastal Waterway are the three waterway projects of greatest promise.

In addition to the Mississippi River system, which has been the scene of greatest study, experimentation, and development in river navigation, all the great river-valley projects include improvement of navigation as one of their objectives. On the Tennessee (independently from the Mississippi program), the Columbia, the Sacramento (Central Valley Project), and the Missouri (a part of the Mississippi program) navigation bids fair to increase in importance as a use of water.

The Inland Waterways. Corporation. This corporation should not be confused with the Inland Waterways *Commission* mentioned early in the text and having an important role in the early days of the conservation movement. The Inland Waterways *Corporation* was created by the Congress in 1924, some years after a study of needed increase in transportation made when the Federal government took over operation of the railroads as a war measure. This study recommended the building and operating of two fleets of modern river barges, one for the lower Mississippi and the other for the Tombigbee and Warrior Rivers in Alabama, from the Gulf to the steel center near Birmingham. At first the War Department was to acquire and operate these barges experimentally as a demonstration to private enterprise of the economic feasibility of river transportation; it functioned with some losses until the corporation came into being in 1924. This was one of the early Federal corporations now so common as administrative devices in a democracy.

The act creating the Corporation has this to say of its purpose: "to promote, encourage, and develop water transportation, service, and facilities in connection with the commerce of the United States, and to foster and preserve in full vigor, both rail and water transportation." As a means of implementing this policy, it has also recognized the need for interchange of water traffic with railroads through the medium of the establishment of "such joint tariffs with rail carriers as shall make generally available the privileges of joint rail and water transportation upon terms reasonably fair to both rail and water carriers."[22] In other words, whether a shipper or a buyer of a shipped commodity lives on a river bank or not, he is entitled to the benefits of lower-cost water transportation. This smacks of equitable distribution in this kind of water conservation.

With such joint rates, modern terminal facilities, and improved barge and tow equipment, the Corporation still had, up to 1953, a chance to demonstrate transportation as a beneficial use of river water, but its record to that date was somewhat disappointing. The Corporation, with an initial appropriation of 5 million dollars, had an investment of 24 million dollars by 1930, steadily saved money for the shippers but lost for the public, and still operates as an experiment, theoretically to be turned over to private enterprise when the demonstration is sufficiently convincing. During the war year 1944 the Director of the Office of Defense Transportation pointed out that the 5,000 barges operating on the improved channels of the Mississippi and its tributaries showed heavy traffic and that 95 per cent of the commodities carried were directly needed for war purposes. By 1953 the Corporation had proposed to Congress two alternatives for the future of the experiment. The first emphasized the insistence at hearings by certain shippers of bulk cargoes, such as steel, sulfur, and grain, and by numerous smaller shippers that the barge service was indispensable. It also pointed out that plans for modernization through barge design for integrated tow and other improvements would be possible with increased capital investment. Such capital if made available would definitely demonstrate the barge lines as a paying business and promote sale of the lines, with the Federal government retiring from the river-transportation business in favor of private enterprise. The second alternative offered was a recommendation that immediate sale without modernization be authorized.

The Congress, having created the Inland Waterways Corporation in 1924, had to choose what it would do with the experiment, which had

[22] *Annual Report,* Inland Waterways Corporation, St. Louis, Mo., 1944, p. 6.

demonstrated almost everything it was designed to do save some way of achieving joint rail-barge rates and other necessary types of cooperation from railroad carriers. Strangely enough, in deciding this the Congress needed to listen to the paradoxical argument from private enterprise which went something like this: "We oppose government in business on principle. This Corporation of yours is the only government corporation in competition 100 per cent with private enterprise. It has saved us money. Do not liquidate it." But the Congress in 1953, authorized sale of the facilities for 9 million dollars. The Corporation is continued.

Privately Operated Barge Lines. On the Mississippi and its tributaries, a number of privately owned barge lines are operated, and barge haul is important on the Tennessee River where modernized, articulated barge units are used for high-speed transportation of automobiles. Here terminal facilities are new and efficient, but absence of joint barge-rail rates is a drawback.

FLOOD CONTROL

Although floods are as old as the rivers themselves and their "control" sounds like flying in the face of providence, it is still profoundly true that the human race, through its abuse of the land and its invasion of the natural valleys and bypasses through which flood waters must flow, has served as a multiplier of, and a target for, the fury of flood waters. It is defeatist to conclude that nothing can be done to control the runoff when there are promising possibilities of accomplishment, first on the land from which the waters drain and finally in the river bed and its immediate valley. Up to 1936 the efforts to achieve control had the reverse emphasis, with little attention being paid to the source of flood waters.

Heavy and unseasonable rainfall and early or sudden melting of accumulations of snow have accompanied many of the great floods in the United States in recent years. These phenomena are recurring and inevitable. But overuse of watersheds for the grazing of livestock, deforestation, injudicious partial clearing for agriculture and later abandonment, unplanned drainage projects, and unplanned and thoughtless farming—all these occur not in the stream but back on the land. Every one of them contributes to the rapid runoff of rainfall and the certainty of flood conditions.

How Important Is It to Control Runoff? Human life and useful, well-distributed accumulations of human effort expressed in homes, businesses, and public works are regarded with more respect in a democracy than in any other form of government (Fig. 5-12). Floods destroy every one of these things, over and over, while in many places the people have short water supplies within the same year.

figure 5-12
What a flood can do to a railroad. (Photo by Tennessee Valley
Authority.)

Among the more spectacular floods it will be recalled that the Johns-
town flood of May, 1889, which took many lives, was increased in sud-
denness and destructiveness by the failure of the dam on the Conemaugh
River in Pennsylvania. The largest flood record in the Tennessee Valley
occurred in 1867, destroying a community and making 5,000 persons
homeless. Here for 70 years agriculture and lumbering had made only
modest headway, but had such a flood happened today, it is estimated
that the city of Chattanooga would have experienced 40 million dollars'
damage and its population of 130,000 would have suffered greatly. An
Ohio flood in 1913 took 400 lives and destroyed and damaged 100 million
dollars' worth of property. In 1927 the Mississippi flood drove 700,000
people from their homes and destroyed millions in crops and property.
The Pickens Canyon flood in Southern California in 1938 took lives,
homes, orchards, and public works, following a heavy rain over a burned-
out watershed. In August, 1945, a rainfall of high intensity following
grazing abuse of the contributing watersheds and a bad plant-cover fire
the previous year brought Salt Lake City a flood which damaged homes
and property to the extent of $347,000. The town of Lampasas, Texas,
northwest of Austin, after the worst drought in years, suffered a flood
on May 12, 1957, from failure of a levee along Sulphur Creek. Water is
said to have risen 1 foot a minute to a depth of 10 feet following a heavy
rainstorm. Five persons lost their lives. Ninety per cent of all businesses

were destroyed, and damage was estimated at 3 million dollars.[23] Serious floods of the Sun River in Montana in the spring of 1964 cost the lives of more than 30 people and caused damage running into millions of dollars. As floods receded in the winter of 1964-1965 in northern California, Oregon, Washington, Nevada, and Idaho, the stricken states listed forty-eight dead, 17,000 families homeless, and damage of more than half a billion dollars.[24] These examples, chosen at random from a tremendous list, indicate the importance of investing money and effort to save life and property.

Engineering Works for Flood Control. "Main strength and awkwardness," or what the English call "muddling through," has worked so well in freedom-loving democracies that early flood-control statesmen and builders may be forgiven for a stubborn policy of "levees only," a belief that whatever is done must be in the form of earth walls to confine the river to its channel. Up to 1927 this policy was seldom challenged.

Required in the grants by the King of France as a condition of holding land, the planters of Louisiana were building levees on the Mississippi as early as 1717. Everyone who lived within 7 miles of the river had to help, and not until 1850 did the levee districts—similar to irrigation, drainage, and soil conservation districts discussed earlier in this text—come to be common and to take over the increasing task of building and maintaining levees.[25] After the War between the States, during which levees were neglected and destroyed, the desperate extent of the flood problem led to the establishment by the Federal government of the Mississippi River Commission in 1879. This body concluded, partly on a cost basis, that levees were the best way to meet the flood menace, and it suggested no other remedies. These devices served remarkably well until the 1927 flood broke through disastrously in so many places with such loss of life and damage to property as to shock the nation into more constructive thinking (Fig. 5-13). In spite of convincing testimony, however, concerning the necessity of extending control measures back on to the land where the rainfall first becomes runoff, sometimes thousands of miles from the scene of flood damage, the Federal aid then granted and the Army Engineers' plans adopted *still* included only engineering work: levees, to be sure, as an indispensable defense; storage reservoirs to hold surplus water for later use, perhaps for power, irrigation, or maintaining depth required for navigation; retarding basins to be empty most of the year but available in times of flood to spread the flow temporarily and

---

[23] The disaster at Cameron Parish, Louisiana, a few weeks later was caused by a combination of hurricane and tidal wave. More than 500 lives were lost.

[24] *Life,* Jan. 8, 1965, pp. 22–23.

[25] Richard T. Ely and George S. Wehrwein, Land Economics, The Macmillan Company, New York, 1940, p. 352.

figure 5-13
Waters of the Quinebaug River wash away both approaches of
Pomfret Street bridge in Putnam, Conn., 1955. (Photo, courtesy of
U.S. Department of the Interior.)

cut down dangerous peaks; and spillways and bypasses to be coordinated with the levee system. Each one of these should be explained and its limitations emphasized.

STORAGE RESERVOIRS   Designed with flood control as the first objective, these lakes behind dams, unless of tremendous capacity, are useful for little else, are likely to depreciate rapidly by filling with silt, and usually present a sorry prospect for recreational use because of the changing and ugly shore line. Moreover, an enormous number are necessary to approach anything which can be called control. This does not mean that some control is not realized by existing and proposed storage dams, such as the Norris in the Tennessee Valley, which has enormous storage capacity over and above that needed for power production and other purposes; the Grand Coulee with its vast tributary watershed; the Shasta and other reservoirs which hold for the Central Valley's dry-season use the waters which would otherwise produce flash floods; and the Santee in South Carolina where the principal objectives served are power production and improvement of navigation. Only in terms of the cost of world wars could enough reservoirs be built and maintained to reduce the heights of flood levels at critical points by feet instead of inches. At best they can serve only as one of many measures which must be employed.

RETARDING BASINS   The word *basins* is used in this connection because dams are established so that the basins behind them shall be empty as often and as long as possible. In the Miami Conservancy District in Ohio, this is recognized and the public is kept advised. The loss of potential power production is paid for in prevention of flood damage. Useful on smaller rivers, these retarding basins would have to be on a vast scale throughout the Missouri and other tributary valleys if attempts were made to use them to control floods in the lower Mississippi. Moreover, if they were functioning in this particular, they would be out of service for controlling local floods just below their locations. When the roof leaks into the attic, the ceiling into the second floor, and on into the living room and the basement, there are likely to be basins enough only for the attic. Again, however, retarding basins *are* one means among many which can be employed in flood control.

CHANNEL IMPROVEMENTS   Straightening stream channels, clearing them of obstructions, and otherwise speeding up the flow of water are obvious advantages to land on which water is being backed up; and if such improvements extend virtually to the mouth of the stream, it means further rapid disposal of potentially destructive flood waters. Here, siltation, city dumps, and accumulations of uprooted trees and wreckage present constantly recurring obstructions to the river current which needs engineering help.

LEVEES AND SPILLWAYS   Such structures are built at varying distances from the actual river channel (Fig. 5-14). They have served to hold many streams within harmless paths, except when crests become too high and pressure brings about breaks or crevasses causing the inundation of occupied lowlands. Like many of the gadgets about which men become enthusiastic, levees are useful only within limits and must be supplemented in every way practicable. One of these ways which finds continuing favor is to construct a break or spillway in the levee, sending a part of the flood on a detour or bypass, which may be an old channel, a swamp, or a constructed floodway. Handling a part of the flow in this manner is sometimes spoken of as the *outlet method.* There are a number of these "detours" on the lower Mississippi.

Vegetative Cover and Floods. It does not tax one's mental powers to appreciate the fact that vegetative cover, from moss to redwoods, has some effect in retarding runoff of rainfall. Even sparse shrub and herbaceous growth on a steep slope exhibit a noticeable effect in reinforcing

figure 5-14
Levees on banks of Lake Pontchartrain, Louisiana, consisting of 3,057,000 cubic yards of hydraulic fill. (Photo by Corps of Engineers, United States Army.)

the soil and increasing *infiltration*—a term used for cutoff, or taking up of rainfall by the soil. Fortunately, quantitative figures are available on infiltration under vegetated and bare-soil conditions, and more and more data are becoming available for use in definite employment of revegetation for partial control of runoff. Some of these figures may be found on pages 37–40 under the discussion of soil conservation. Unfortunately for flood control, however, the purposes for which men want to use or to neglect much of the land in the vast watersheds of the country which furnish flood waters give the vegetative cover a round beating or keep it removed. Fire following logging or on brush-covered slopes of the arid Southwest, the destruction of all vegetation by smelter fumes, overuse of mountain lands for grazing domestic livestock, poorly planned construction of anything from a road to a subdivision, ill-planned cultivation followed or not by abandonment—all these tend to diminish the protecting cover with its shielding, absorptive, and infiltrating effects. But the plant-cover people have finally made their voice heard, and the 1936 Omnibus Flood Control Act requires that the United States Forest and Soil Conservation Services and the Army Engineers join forces in the study of flood control from the downstream works right back to the timber line on the highest mountain.

One example of the power of vegetative cover to retard flood waters in a limited area is worth recounting: the Pickens Canyon flood in Southern California, which was mentioned on page 138. It followed a fire which had consumed the chaparral cover on 5,000 acres. A few miles to the east lies San Dimas Canyon, one of the "experimental forests" of the Forest Service. Twelve inches of rain fell in 2½ days late in December, 1933, on both watersheds. New Year's Day saw the village of La Crescenta flooded, with 34 lives and 200 homes lost. The peak flow at crest was 100 cubic feet per second per square mile of watershed. The peak flow in San Dimas was 50 cubic feet, and no damage occurred.[26]

The Parrish Canyon flood in Utah exhibited a relatively small but convincing with-and-without-flood-control lesson in 1930 (Fig. 5-15). Overgrazed and underprotected for years, this canyon spilled the waters of a sudden storm on the village of Centerville, wrecking seven homes, crashing in the walls of a schoolhouse, spreading 1 to 7 feet of debris over orchard lands valued at $600 to $800 an acre, and requiring the expenditure of $100,000 to open and repair the damaged highways alone. Right beside it, Centerville Canyon, hit by the same storm but long protected and well covered, yielded no flood and accounted for no damage.[27]

[26] F. A. Silcox, Forests and Flood Control, in The Scientific Aspects of Flood Control, Supplement to Science 84, Science Press, New York, 1936, pp. 10–11.
[27] *Ibid.*, pp. 13–15.

figure 5-15
Parrish Canyon flood over village and farm lands of Centerville, Utah, in 1930 from overgrazed headwaters. Better cover at head of adjoining canyon took the same storm without damage. (Photo by United States Forest Service.)

Whose Business Is Flood Control? Historically, the landowner first, then the states, and finally the Federal government have recognized obligations in attempting to control floods, but all have thought of the problem and worked at it from the wait-until-it-comes and multiple-purpose-with-flood-control-incidentally approaches. Now the Federal government has something in the way of policy as far as responsibility is concerned: it is definitely committed to the increasing use and encouragement both of all useful works and practices on the land and of multiple-purpose river-development projects that include flood control as an objective.

The "pork-barrel" temptations in the requests for, and appropriation of, money for flood control are warned against in the recommendations of the Water Planning Committee of the National Resources Board.[28] Here the Federal appropriation of funds for flood control will be made under these conditions: (1) only where there is reasonable protection against maximum floods: (2) only when the total benefits justify the expense; (3) only where there are responsible and legally constituted authorities with which to deal; (4) to an extent not greater than 30 per cent of the cost of labor and materials where benefits are chiefly local; (5) to an extent greater than 30 per cent only in proportion to benefits applicable to recognized national interests; and (6) to a full 100 per cent only where the benefits are almost wholly of national interest. The application of these guides requires the wisdom of a Solomon, but it is well that they are set down somewhere.

In the final analysis, the user of the land as well as the rank-and-file taxpayer must support those to whom public office is assigned and the skilled engineers and scientists to whom the actual task is given. The better the voter understands flood control, the better will be the control. Only in this manner, too, may the public be assured of an accounting from its servants.

BIBLIOGRAPHY

Annual Report, Inland Waterways Commission, 1944.

Annual Report, 1962, Saint Lawrence Seaway Development Corporation, Government Printing Office, 1963.

Annual Reports of the Secretary of the Interior, 1946, 1962, and 1963.

BROWN, HARRISON, JAMES BONNER, AND JOHN WIER: The Next Hundred Years, The Viking Press, Inc., New York, 1957.

ELY, RICHARD T., AND GEORGE S. WEHRWEIN: Land Economics, The Macmillan Company, New York, 1940.

Estimated Future Power Requirements of the United States by Regions, 1955–1980, Federal Power Commission, 1956.

LANDSBERG, HANS H., LEONARD L. FISCHMAN, AND JOSEPH L. FISHER: Resources in America's Future, The Johns Hopkins Press, Baltimore, 1963.

An M.V.A. or Stagnation, National Farmers Union, Denver, Colo., undated pamphlet of about 1945.

National Resources Board Report, Government Printing Office, 1934.

Newsweek, May, June, and July, 1957.

Our Energy Resources, National Resources Committee, Government Printing Office, 1939.

SCHURR, SAM H.: Some Observations on the Economics of Atomic Power, *Reprint* 41, Resources for the Future, Inc., Washington, D.C., 1963.

SILCOX, F. A.: Forests and Flood Control, in The Scientific Aspects of Flood Control, Science Press, New York, 1936.

Statistical Abstract of the United States, 1963, U.S. Bureau of the Census.

Typical Residential Electric Bills, 1956, Federal Power Commission, 1956.

[28] National Resources Board, Report, Government Printing Office, 1934, p. 273.

6 THE ATMOSPHERE

PERHAPS NO NATURAL resource has been so ignored or taken for granted as the atmosphere. Only recently has any idea of managing it occurred to mankind as a possibility and a necessity. The one problem of smoke as an air pollutant, however, was recognized as far back as 1257, when Queen Eleanor was forced to move from Nottingham because she could not endure the coal smoke. Edward I was responsible for the first smoke-abatement law in 1273, and by 1306 the members of Parliament had gotten around to authorizing the first smoke-abatement agency. A proclamation was issued forbidding the use of coal in furnaces, and the following year an offender was executed.

London fought the smoke nuisance for 500 years before the industrialization of the United States brought about an attack on smoke. Several large cities in this country had smoke-abatement ordinances before the War between the States, and in 1893 Chicago formed a citizens' committee to help the city government with its effort to clean the air for visitors to the Columbian Exposition. Since that time and before the Los Angeles area realized what was developing, St. Louis and Pittsburgh, notorious as dirty-air cities, had made good progress in controlling visible air pollution. But the people of the Los Angeles area were the first to recognize the threat of contamination by gases and fumes often undetected before chemical reactions had given them irritating qualities. What they have done about it will be discussed later. Just now more than 308 urban areas in this country have air-pollution problems, and more than just smoke is involved.[1]

But air pollution is not the only problem presented to those who would manage the atmosphere. Climatic disturbances wreak tremendous damage. Winds, once the principal power used to move ships, both aid and delay air travel. Large amounts of air are required for all combustion processes; for plant growth; for obtaining fertilizers; for capture and compression of air to be released for mechanical purposes; for channels of transportation and communication; and, perhaps most important of all, polluted or not, for human and animal consumption in life processes.

Some of these uses and needs for control will be discussed briefly toward the end of this chapter, but the principal emphasis will be given to maintaining air quality as human activities increase.

What Is the Atmosphere? The atmosphere we are interested in is the layer of air surrounding the earth. And what is air? It consists of a number of gases and vapors, and in the lower portions of the atmosphere it contains a lot of particles or "particulate" matter. The most plentiful gas in the air is nitrogen, followed by oxygen and carbon dioxide. These three, with argon, constitute more than 99 per cent of dry air. Of course, there is always water in the form of vapor and traces of a number of other gases. The particulate matter in the lower atmosphere consists of volcanic dust

---

[1] A Study of Pollution: Air, Staff Report to the Committee on Public Works, U.S. Senate, Committee Print, 88th Cong., 1st sess., September, 1963, p. vii.

from eruptions; salt spray from the ocean; dust blown from the deserts; various products of human activity—erosion of metal, rubber, and building materials; and the products of combustion. On days when there is "smog," a word coined from smoke and fog, or "smaze" as it is sometimes called, there may be added to the above-mentioned constituents carbon monoxide, hydrocarbons, oxidants (mostly ozone), oxides of nitrogen, aldehydes, organic acids, and sulfur dioxide.[2] The latter comes from the burning of coal and fuel oil.

This, then, is the air which must serve millions of people as the breath of life, help to grow crops, support combustion, support animal life, and serve as a medium of transportation and communication. It is this particular part of the atmosphere which needs to be managed because it is the part near the earth's surface. We have by no means used it up, so the problem is not so much one of possible exhaustion as one of maintaining quality. This is a stroke of management.

Amount of Air Needed by an Individual. If one breathes sixteen to eighteen times a minute, he requires 500 to 1,000 cubic centimeters, or 0.3 to 0.6 cubic foot, of air per minute. This amounts to 30 to 60 pounds per day. Added to this, an estimated 1,000 pounds per individual per day is required for various combustion services such as light, cooking, and transportation. All of these but transportation are consumptive uses. The air exhaled daily by an individual contains several pounds of carbon dioxide, and that used in various services produces pollutants.[3]

AIR POLLUTION

Fatal Episodes. The furnishing of sufficient unpolluted air to inhabitants of large cities or industrial areas has broken down in certain instances. Six occurrences in 25 years have been responsible for the death and hospitalization of human beings from smog under the following conditions: lack of wind; presence of pollutants; presence of fog; and, in several instances, the occurrence of sunshine-caused chemical reactions which affected visibility. There is an inversion of temperature amounting to the formation of a layer of warm air over the area where normally the air would be cooler as it rises. This puts a lid on the lower atmosphere, preventing the escape of pollutants.

The first episode of which international note was taken occurred in the heavily industrialized Meuse Valley near Liége in Belgium. Here a 5-day smog attack in 1930 cost the lives of sixty persons who died from respiratory irritation. The second episode occurred near the town of Donora, Pennsylvania, along the Monongahela River, on October 28, 1948, and for

[2] Morris Neiburger, The Atmosphere, Chap. 5 in Natural Resources, Martin R. Huberty and Warren L. Flock, eds., McGraw-Hill Book Company, New York, 1959, pp. 112–113.
[3] Albert F. Bush, Air-pollution Control, Chap. 6 in *ibid.*, p. 133.

4 days thereafter. Here 20 persons died and 5,910 were desperately ill. The third episode occurred on November 24, 1950, in Poza Rica, Mexico, 135 miles northeast of Mexico City, in the heart of the largest oil-refining industry in the country. Some 22 persons died and 320 were hospitalized. Here fog was present from combustion in a wet gas stack, and the pollutant was hydrogen sulfide from a plant operated to recover sulfur. The acute period of the episode lasted only 20 minutes, from 4:50 to 5:10 A.M., and it ceased when the plant was shut down. The fourth episode occurred in a considerable area in and about London from December 5 to 10 in 1952, when a concentration of sulfur dioxide (coal gas) reached a high level; 4,000 persons lost their lives.[4] The fifth instance, also in London, occurred in 1962, when 136 (another figure claimed 750) persons died.[5] Sulfuric acid was actually present in the air. The loss of life in this instance would have been greater except for several years of educating people to be on the alert and training them to protect themselves. Also, more efficient practices in burning coal had been enforced. A sixth episode,[6] which was not determined to be due to smog until it was investigated 9 years after it occurred, probably took the lives of 200 more people than normal during a brief period of stagnant weather in November, 1953, in New York City, which recorded high levels of sulfur dioxide and smoke shade. (A serious airplane disaster over New York City, accounting for loss of 200 lives, took the headlines at the time, and *its* cause is thought to have been due to low visibility brought about by the same smoggy condition.) No seventh episode has been recorded, but Los Angeles had a scare in late August and early September, 1955, when 1,000 more deaths than normal occurred during a short and extremely hot period of heavy smog. Investigation however led to the conclusion that heat prostration caused the deaths.[7] About 50 per cent of the complaints recorded against smog in the Los Angeles area concern effects upon health.

Startling as these acute episodes may be, much greater significance is attached to the long term, low-level pollution which aggravates certain diseases. Those for which strong evidence is growing are listed in a Staff Report to the Committee on Public Works of the United States Senate as follows: (1) nonspecific, infectious, upper-respiratory disease; (2) chronic bronchitis; (3) chronic constrictive-ventilatory disease; (4) pulmonary emphysema; (5) bronchial asthma; and (6) lung cancer. The "common cold" is included in (1) above.[8]

[4] *Ibid.*, p. 135.
[5] The Polluted Air We Breathe, *Labor's Econ. Rev.*, February, 1964.
[6] A Study of Pollution, *op. cit.*, p. 13.
[7] John R. Goldsmith, Effects of Air Pollution on Health, *California's Health*, Oct. 1, 1960, p. 50.
[8] *Ibid.*, p. 14.

Damage to Crops. Only in recent years has damage to crops, other than to vegetation in general around smelters, been identified as coming from air pollution. Long known damage has occurred in the state of Washington, from a smelter across the line in British Columbia; in the areas around Copper Hill, Tennessee; in Kennett and Coram, California; in the upper Sacramento Valley; and in Anaconda, Montana. The damage has resulted in ugly and denuded landscapes. But in 1958 lesions on grape leaves in California were observed, caused by the pollutant ozone. A blight on white pine in West Virginia, known as *emergence tipburn*, is attributed by the Southeastern Forest Experiment Station of the U.S. Department of Agriculture to ozone contaminant associated with motor-vehicle pollution. In 1958 also, damages to certain crops were reported by the New Jersey Department of Plant Pathology. These include ozone injury to spinach, alfalfa, rye, barley, orchard grass, tobacco, petunia, radish, red clover, bean, parsley, grape and perhaps chicory, endive, broccoli, carnation, and pine.[9]

Livestock foraging on vegetation on which airborne fluorides have been deposited have suffered adverse effects. Certain plans have shown injury caused by concentrations of hydrogen fluoride as small as 1 part in 10 billion parts of air.[10]

The 1962 National Conference on Air Pollution had this to say: "The agricultural losses resulting from the adverse effects of all the presently recognized pollutants have been estimated to amount to hundreds of millions of dollars a year."[11]

Property Losses. While accurate data on property losses from air pollution are not available, one frequently employed estimate is $65 per capita per year. This represents a yearly cost to the nation of more than $11 billion dollars.[12] Materials, structures, machines, and property values —all suffer. Metals corrode, fabrics weaken and fade, rubber cracks and loses elasticity, leather weakens and becomes brittle, paint discolors, concrete and building stone discolor and erode, glass is etched, and paper becomes brittle. Complex and expensive control systems, which have become so commonplace in modern technology, can be ruined or seriously damaged by the corrosive action of gaseous pollutants or by deposited dust. And coming closer to the average citizen's daily life, air pollution occasions household expense in terms of necessity for more frequent painting and bigger laundry bills.

Safety Hazards. Travelers by land, water, and air face serious threats because of air pollution. Recent instances recorded in the news—one in

<hr>

[9] A Study of Pollution, *op. cit.*, p. 18.

[10] *Ibid.*, p. 19.

[11] National Conference on Air Pollution, 1962, *U.S. Public Health Serv.* Publ. 1022, 1963, p. 391.

[12] A Study of Pollution, *op. cit.*, p. 20.

Louisiana near a burning dump and another in Pennsylvania close to a smoldering culm pile—serve as examples in motor travel. Sudden application of brakes by a single individual in each instance led to a chain reaction which wrecked a number of vehicles and injured many of their occupants. Normal fog with added pollutants frequently grounds aircraft which are not equipped with blind-flying instruments, and visibility is slower in clearing. Back in 1946, a survey indicated that the number of hours in 1 year in which smoke, alone or in combination with other obstructions, at the Newark, New Jersey, Airport cut visibility to 6 miles or less totalled 4,359—almost half the number contained in one year. "Obstructions to vision" was given as the cause of six airplane accidents in 1962 out of 1,660 record cards reviewed by the Civil Aeronautics Board. Smoke, haze, sand, and dust were involved, and two of the planes were large ones. If this is a fair sample (and the number reviewed is one third of the total), fifteen to twenty plane crashes in 1962 could be attributed to this cause.[13] Moreover, pollution aids the formation of fog, and because harbors are often surrounded by industrial development, impaired visibility becomes a threat to shipping. Local atmospheric changes due to contamination also affect the weather.[14] Storms may increase in fury as the amount of carbon dioxide in the air increases and intercepts heat waves going into space from the earth. As the earth's atmosphere becomes warmer, air circulation is bound to be more violent. There is some evidence and much speculation about the effects of this increase in temperature.

Effect of Air Pollution on Recreation and Aesthetics. Fresh air is something associated closely with outdoor recreation, as are sunshine and natural beauty. All three of these requirements are bound to suffer from air pollution. Noisome odors, such as those near packing houses, chemical plants, oil refineries, and rubber-manufacturing plants, can take a lot of joy out of a drive, a golf game, or even watching one of the spectator sports. And while eye irritation caused by air pollution is not blamed with permanent injury, it limits the enjoyment of many recreations. Also, distant scenery is often screened by smog.

Aerosols in Air Pollution. Eye and throat irritations and, possibly, the spread of disease, involve tiny particles in the air known as aerosols. They may be bits of water or solids, the surfaces of which scatter light and destroy visibility. Their role aside from this is undetermined, but there is reason to suspect that they may furnish the needed surfaces on which the atmosphere's chemical reactions take place and may serve to absorb the irritating gaseous-reaction products and thus add to the discomfort of mankind.[15]

---

[13] *Ibid.*, p. 21.
[14] Sir Bernard Lovell, Does Our Space Research Threaten Life on Earth? *Saturday Evening Post*, Philadelphia, Feb. 22, 1964, p. 10.
[15] Bush, *op. cit.*, p. 141.

Attempts to Control Air Pollution. While smoke abatement effort has been going on in this country for more than a century, serious work on the total air-pollution problem dates from 1947 when the Air Pollution Control District of Los Angeles County was organized. This is similar in form to the irrigation districts and the soil conservation districts described earlier. The area concerned is probably the most perfect setup in the world for the development of the smog nuisance. Here is a metropolitan valley near the sea, partly surrounded by high mountains, and subject to an inversion factor which may cause an accumulation of smog at any time during the greater part of the year. Contributing to the problem in 1947 were 1½ million backyard incinerators (which have since been outlawed), a similar number of automobiles, and an increasing number of industries. By 1965 there were nearly 4 million motor vehicles, around 16,000 industrial plants including some of the largest oil refineries in the world, and a population of 7 million. Along with these contributing factors, winds from the ocean are too weak to disperse the polluted air but strong enough to prevent it from drifting oceanward (Fig. 6-1).

Over the years since 1947, some fifteen citizen committees have been organized to study causes and promote control of air pollution, and from 1953 to 1960 a Southern California Air Pollution Foundation was active.

figure 6-1
Cartoon used in Los Angeles area to bring about understanding of sources of smog. (Los Angeles County Air Pollution Control District.)

figure 6-2

Smoking vehicle is stopped on California highway. Driver is given notice of violation of ordinance, and this will be followed by a court citation. (Los Angeles County Air Pollution Control District.)

This was financed by private individuals and organizations. It enlisted the help of many business and university people, coordinated many of the research efforts, accomplished a lot of public education, and finally went out of business when the motor vehicle was proven to be the area's worst pollutor.[16]

But the Los Angeles County Air Pollution Control District, operating with a budget of more than 3 million dollars a year, had carried, up to 1959 when the state came into the picture, the burden of research, promulgation of regulations and rules which have the force of law, enforcement, (Fig. 6-2), cooperation with the management of stationary sources of pollution, and information and education of the public. On July 1, 1963, the state of California completed its assumption of responsibility for the pollution by automobiles through a Motor Vehicle Pollution Control Board established by law. Thus, as reorganized in 1963, the district was left with the responsibility of dealing with stationary sources of pollution and enforcing regulations as its principal duties. Monitoring the air for quality was also an important assignment. The California State Department of Public Health and the United States Public Health Service now

[16] California against Air Pollution: A Six-year Progress Report, 1955–1961, State of California Department of Public Health, Berkeley, Calif., 1962.

furnish research service utilizing data collected by the district over the years.

In 1963 the district reported that nearly 5,000 tons of pollution were being kept out of the air every day and that—in spite of an explosive increase in population, vehicles, and industrial operations—the atmospheric loading of pollution from stationary sources had been reduced significantly.[17] Los Angeles County still suffers from the world's most notorious air-pollution problem, photochemical smog. This is because there is still, as of early 1965, no effective control of exhaust emissions of the nearly 4 million motor vehicles. Solving this part of the Los Angeles smog problem, the report continues, depends upon the success of the efforts of the state of California, the developers of control devices, and the automobile industry. Reasonably effective exhaust controls have been developed and will be on 1966 models, out by September, 1965.

Meanwhile, six other air-pollution-control districts had been established in the state, one of which included six counties in the San Francisco Bay area.

AIR QUALITY STANDARDS The state Legislature and the California Department of Public Health had not been idle during this period. In 1959 legislation was passed requiring the Department of Public Health to set standards for air quality and motor-vehicle exhaust emissions. Thereupon the state Board of Public Health, after a number of studies had been made and hearings held, adopted standards for oxidant, carbon monoxide, sulfur dioxide, and particulate matter in *ambient* air. The standards are based on three levels of concern: "adverse," where sensory irritation, damage to plants or reduced visibility result; "serious," where impaired function of chronic diseases may develop in sensitive groups; and "emergency," where disease or death may result in sensitive groups.[18]

At the same time the state Board of Public Health adopted standards for the emission of hydrocarbons and carbon monoxide from motor-vehicle exhaust requiring an 80 per cent reduction in emissions to 275 parts per million of hydrocarbons and a 60 per cent reduction in carbon monoxide to 1.5 per cent. Standards now require a further reduction by 1970 to 180 parts per million for hydrocarbons and 1 per cent for carbon monoxide. Automobile manufacturers voluntarily equipped all new cars sold in California, from 1961 on, with crank-case devices which could remove approximately one-third of the hydrocarbons in emissions. From 1963 on, these were required by law in California and were being applied

[17] S. Smith Griswold, air-pollution-control officer, *Biennial Rept.*, 1961–1962, 1962–1963, Table V, Los Angeles County Air Pollution Control District, Los Angeles, Calif., 1963.

[18] John R. Goldsmith and John H. Maga, Development of Air Quality Standards in California, *California's Health*, Mar. 1, 1964, p. 154.

voluntarily to most cars sold in the United States. But manufacturers had not yet obtained approval of a tail-pipe device good enough to comply with the above motor-vehicle exhaust standards. These and other standards came to be known as CAS (California Air Quality Standards). The California Motor Vehicle Pollution Control Board awaited the testing of further exhaust devices in 1964. Two types of tail-pipe devices competed for approval by the board. One used a catalyst of materials over which the exhaust gases would pass and by which they would be converted into water and carbon dioxide. The other used a spark plug in the tail pipe which, with the addition of air, ignited the emissions and burned them up. Technical troubles dogged each of these devices. For example, the catalyst fouled easily by becoming coated with such things as the lead in gasoline, and in the other device sufficient air for burning was difficult to deliver. Overheating was also a problem. Slight modification of CAS gave promise of perfecting certain devices. Successful tests were reported in May, 1964, and four devices were approved for new-car installation in June 1964. Expense of installing these "tack-on" devices is of considerable concern to motorists, particularly on used cars. By December, 1964, it appeared doubtful that exhaust controls ever would be applied to used cars. And although most of the hydrocarbons and the carbon monoxide might be taken care of by crank-case and tail-pipe devices, experts pointed out that, even with these devices, nitrogen oxides might be increased and that these were more dangerous to health than carbon monoxide. This problem was next in line for solution.

THE WORK OF THE UNITED STATES PUBLIC HEALTH SERVICE   The program of the United States Public Health Service has been based on the philosophy that the primary responsibility for regulatory control of air pollution rests with state and local governments and that the Federal role should be a supporting one of research, technical assistance to public and private organizations, and training of personnel. There are three basic objectives: (1) to increase knowledge of the causes and effects of air pollution and the means of controlling it within acceptable limits; (2) to apply present and future knowledge to the actual control of air pollutants through technical assistance to states, communities, and industry; and (3) to stimulate all levels of government, industry, and the general public to devote increased attention and greater resources to the prevention and control of air pollution. A National Advisory Committee on Air Pollution, with representatives from industry, control agencies, and other public bodies, helps to guide the program.

Research under this setup has touched the fields of engineering, chemical analysis, meteorology, biomedical studies, population, laboratory and hospital facilities, and injury to animal and vegetable life. One of its most highly organized efforts is a monitoring system for sampling air in every

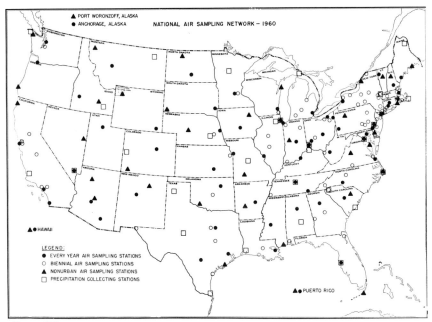

figure 6-3
Map of system of air-sampling stations maintained for monitoring purposes
by Public Health Service. (Division of Air Pollution, U.S. Department of Health,
Education, and Welfare.)

state, including Puerto Rico and the District of Columbia (Fig. 6-3).
Training and graduate fellowships have been assigned to twelve universities in nine states, and cooperation is maintained with many Federal agencies and with the states.

All of this activity is authorized by a group of laws, beginning with "An
Act to Provide Research and Technical Assistance Relating to Air Pollution Control" passed by the Congress in 1955 and supplemented by other
laws up to 1963.

THE "CLEAN AIR ACT OF 1963" This law, approved by the Congress in
December, 1963, summarizes and strengthens the provisions of the National Advisory Committee on Air Pollution, authorizes larger appropriations for cooperation with state and local agencies, and provides for the
organization of interstate compacts for dealing with air-pollution situations. A total sum of 95 million dollars is authorized for cooperative projects to be appropriated over a period of 3½ fiscal years ending June 30,
1967. Certain limits are specified for amounts of grants-in-aid of air-
pollution-control programs and for scholarships and training. Where a
state is suffering from a source of pollution in another state, the Secretary
of Health, Education and Welfare may request the Attorney General to

bring a suit on behalf of the United States to obtain abatement of such pollution. And if an air-pollution situation arises within any state where there is need for technical or other assistance in judicial proceedings to obtain abatement, such assistance shall be given at the request of the governor or, at his request, the Secretary may instruct the Attorney General to bring suit on behalf of the United States. Congress further declares that it is its intent that any Federal facility contributing to air pollution shall cooperate with the Department of Health, Education, and Welfare to control such pollution. It is not clear whether or not this provision applies to the Atomic Energy Commission and the Department of Defense. Some interesting situations may arise in connection with airplane spraying for pest control. The Secretary of Health, Education, and Welfare is authorized to prescribe such regulations as are necessary to carry out his functions under this act.

INDUSTRIAL ACTIVITY IN AIR-POLLUTION CONTROL   Almost every industry has a waste-disposal problem. For example, a study of air-pollution sources in the Los Angeles County area include sixty-seven industries, among which were such widely differing plants as deep-fat fryer and coffee roaster to phosphate-fertilizer and synthetic solvent dry cleaner. Among those over the nation which have the most difficult and costly tasks are oil- and coal-burning power plants, oil refineries, chemical industries, and steel mills. Industrial organizations rank second after Federal agencies in the support of air-pollution research, exceeding state and local expenditures combined (Table 6-1).[19] Sometimes the expense of actual control, aside from research, can be reduced slightly by the sale of by-products obtained. Fly ash, for example, precipitated electrolytically from the stacks of power plants, has been purchased and used in a number of the great dams in the West (Shasta, Hungry Horse, Bonneville) as an ingredient of concrete[20] (Fig. 6-4). In general, compliance with regulations and cooperation by the industries in air-pollution-control efforts has been of a high order.

STATUS OF STATE ACTIVITY IN AIR-POLLUTION CONTROL   As a result of replies to a questionnaire sent out on April 30, 1963, by the Chairman of the Senate Committee on Public Works, the following information on state consideration of air-pollution control was revealed: Of the fifty-one states and territories replying, thirty-three had some air-pollution-control laws and eighteen had planned new legislation; six had air-quality and emission standards; nineteen faced interstate problems; ten had authorized research projects; and thirty-eight desired help from the Department of Health, Education, and Welfare on formulation of air-quality standards,

---

[19] *Ibid.*, p. 37.
[20] C. T. Wanzer, Use of Fly ash in Concrete, reprinted from February, 1959, *Combustion*, by Bituminous Coal Institute, Washington, D.C., 1959, p. 4.

figure 6-4

The air of certain eastern cities is cleaner because this Hungry Horse Dam in Montana contains 3.09 million cubic yards of fly ash as an inexpensive and useful ingredient of concrete. This potential pollutant is electrolytically precipitated from the stacks of coal-burning power plants. (National Coal Association.)

TABLE 6-1. AIR-POLLUTION RESEARCH 1962

Organizations supporting air-pollution research	Number of projects	Funding, dollars	Per cent of total
Universities	17	548,000	4
Federal agencies	227	8,866,000	62
State agencies	18	1,027,000	7
Local agencies	11	640,000	5
Industrial	38	1,890,000	13
Private (nonindustrial)	11	386,000	3
Not classified	25	799,000	6
Totals*	347	14,156,000	100

* A total of 466 projects was reported in this survey, indicating that the total amount actually being devoted to air pollution research in 1962 may have been as much as 20 million dollars.
SOURCE: A Study of Pollution: Air, Staff Report to the Committee on Public Works, U.S. Senate, Committee Print, 88th Cong. 1st sess., September, 1963, p. 37.

thirty-five on formulation of emission standards, and eighteen on obtaining compliance with standards.[21]

The committee concluded that although the states appear to be wary of direct Federal action in air-pollution control, they admit their own inadequacy in the fields of research, including the development of criteria for standards of air quality, and seem to favor expanded Federal action in these areas.

Radioactive Air Pollution. No mention of radioactive fallout from the testing of nuclear bombs occurs in any of the laws cited in this chapter, although in 1955, the same year that the first law was enacted, Chairman Lewis L. Strauss of the Atomic Energy Commission admitted that contamination from the Bikini explosion of March 1, 1954, was so great downwind over an area of 7,000 square miles that survival might be questionable unless shelter were available. This may mean an added air-pollution problem within the boundaries of the United States for which the Federal government will be responsible and which may require further legislation. It is well that limits in testing have been set by the treaty signed with and ratified by the Soviet Union.

Concern was expressed by the United States Public Health Service in the summer of 1963 over the danger of air pollution from the firing of rockets using fuels containing toxic substances such as beryllium and fluorine. Beryllium can cause respiratory illness and skin disorders, and fluorine compounds affect mankind. Although these materials are ordinarily discharged safely in high atmosphere, ground testing is practiced and contamination can ensue. Cooperation between the United States Health Service and the military and civilian space agencies is expected to guard against accidental discharges at the launching pads, but control of private companies making ground-level tests was still to be worked out.[22]

Air Pollution with Destructive Noise. One kind of air pollution not considered in the Clean Air Act of 1963 is noise in general and the sonic boom in particular. Although the public has come to accept most of the sounds of construction, blasting, transportation (aside from jet planes), and manufacturing, there is plenty of evidence that it will not accept the opinion that the sonic boom, with its record of destruction, must be endured without modification. Already protests have been made in the courts by citizens of Oklahoma City. Sonic boom is the deafening report heard when a plane flying faster than the speed of sound compresses the atmosphere around it and leaves a thunderous cone of sound in its path. It may be produced by diving deeply, and booms so caused have broken windows

[21] A Study of Pollution, pp. 53–57.
[22] Robert C. Toth, U.S. Worries About Air Pollution from Rockets, in *Los Angeles Times*, July 1, 1964, p. 12, part 1.

and even dislocated door and window frames in the area over which the flight is made. The Federal Aviation Agency in doing some "research" looking toward developing a plane with a speed of 2,000 miles an hour actually hired jet pilots to break the sound barrier across the heart of a city several times a day from seven o'clock in the morning on, for a period of 6 months.[23] On the second day of this program, property-damage claims began coming in, and in the first week there were 655 complaints. Two citizens, who were unimpressed by FAA's suggestion that they take tranquilizers, went to court with their claims only to have their complaints dismissed by a judge in the United States District Court. Only when the complaint reached the Oklahoma State District Court was an order issued to cease the production of sonic booms, and this order was soon violated. Proven damage and even personal bodily injury had not impressed the Air Force officials, but at least the public's refusal to tolerate this kind of air "pollution" was registered. All of this occurred in 1964, and even in October, 1963, the American Association of Airport Executives stated before the United States Senate Subcommittee on Aviation that "the noise emanating from the present jets is in many areas not acceptable to the general public."[24] Local pride in the prospect of having America's first supersonic airport was a factor in getting a temporary injunction against it quashed, and the experiment of the FAA continued in spite of the filing of a total of 5,655 damage claims in about 3 months.

NATIONAL CENTER FOR ATMOSPHERIC RESEARCH

Just what can man do to manage the weather? Well, a group of scientists is attempting to find out at a great national center in Boulder, Colorado. The National Center for Atmospheric Research was established in 1961 by fourteen universities, with its budget provided by the National Science Foundation. It has a staff of some 500 scientists and technicians. Its program seeks to create a better understanding of all the many events, trigger mechanisms, and natural processes—subtle or powerful—that create our weather. The program involves providing research tools too large and expensive for a single university to supply such as a scientific balloon flight station now operating at the Center's branch in Texas or the most improved and complex computers capable of figuring out the significant implications of billions of bits of information. The scientists at this center want to know more about the effectiveness of cloud seeding in producing rain, and even to determine what kinds of space research and activity may affect living conditions on this planet.

[23] John Lear, The Era of Supersonic Morality, *Saturday Review*, July 6, 1964, pp. 49–50.
[24] *Ibid.*, p. 49.

So far as actual management techniques are concerned, the men who study the atmosphere at this great institution realize that they are dealing with an international resource and that radical experimentation in our locality may have widespread effects.[25] It would be interesting to know what they think about atmospheric changes that may be brought about by attempts to reach the moon.

Although a vast number of things are still to be learned about the atmosphere, actual management of it as a natural resource is bound to come. First attempts in this direction will no doubt be dominated by doing everything possible to control air pollution. But, as observed earlier, the air is used as a medium of transportation and communication, both of which are now subject to certain kinds of management as to how the air is used.

AIR-TRAFFIC REGULATION

The use of the atmosphere as a medium of travel is becoming more and more important, and its regulation through the Federal Aviation Agency is as much a matter of conservation as the keeping open and improving of inland waterways for traffic by the Army Engineers. In its spatial sense, for such service as it may afford to transportation, the atmosphere is a natural resource.

An expert, reporting to the President of the United States upon request for advice on aviation-facilities planning, observed in 1957:

> We have developed 158,000 miles of airways over continental United States, and our aircraft population has grown from 29,000 in 1936 to 90,000 today. By 1975 we expect the U.S. aircraft population to increase to 125,000. . . . During peak hours on busy days in 1956 there were 270 aircraft simultaneously airborne in the Los Angeles area (which generates the largest volume of general aviation in the world). It is estimated that by 1975 this number will have grown to 730. . . . So intense is the pressure, especially around major metropolitan centers, that a drastic rationing of air space will soon be inescapable unless we install a more efficient system of traffic control. . . .
>
> By 1975 the airport capacity of the country must be doubled, and the number of aircraft under traffic control will increase by ten times.[26]

The final statement here emphasizes the growing need for ground space, possibly at the expense of cropland and potential subdivision areas. This ties conservation of the atmosphere in with conservation of land in a spatial sense (Fig. 6-5).

[25] Alton L. Blakeslee, Giant Research Effort Seeks Weather Control, in *Los Angeles Times*, Feb. 16, 1964, Sec. A, p. 16.

[26] Edward P. Curtis, Traffic Control in Crowded Skies, copyright by *Atlantic Monthly*, vol. 200, pp. 118–119, October, 1957. By special permission of the publisher.

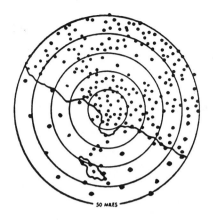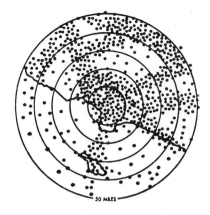

figure 6-5
Simulated radar display showing distribution of airborne craft in the Los Angeles area. The circle on the left shows the peak load on a busy day in 1956–about 270 aircraft. The circle on the right shows estimated load forecast for 1975–about 730 aircraft. Necessary regulation of air traffic constitutes conservation of the atmosphere. (Copyright by Atlantic Monthly. Used by permission.)

REGULATING THE ATMOSPHERE FOR COMMUNICATION

Calling the work of the National Communications Commission a business of dealing with the air as a natural resource seems pretty farfetched, but allocating frequencies and channels amounts to the regulating of one use of the atmosphere. If the privilege of using it thus is kept in order and equitably distributed, such regulation may be called an angle of conservation.

BIBLIOGRAPHY

Air Conservation: How to Shift from Air Pollution to Conservation of Our Atmospheric Resource, *Vital Issues*, vol. 13, no. 8, Center for Information on America, Washington, Conn., April, 1964.
Air Pollution Control in the County of Los Angeles and Six Other Metropolitan Areas, Report to Board of Supervisors, Oct. 11, 1954. (Mimeographed.)
Air Pollution Control through Proper Coal Utilization, National Coal Association, Marketing Department, Washington, D.C., 1962.
BLAKESLEE, ALTON L.: Giant Research Effort Seeks Weather Control, Associated Press item in *Los Angeles Times*, Feb. 16, 1964.
BROWN, HARRISON, JAMES BONNER, AND JOHN WIER: The Next Hundred Years, The Viking Press, Inc., New York, 1957.
BUSH, ALBERT F.: Air-pollution Control, Chap. 6 in Natural Resources, Martin R. Huberty and Warren L. Flock, eds., McGraw-Hill Book Company, New York, 1959.
California against Air Pollution: A Six-year Progress Report, 1955–1961, State of California Department of Public Health, Berkeley, Calif., 1962.
CURTIS, EDWARD P.: Traffic Control in Crowded Skies, *Atlantic Monthly*, vol. 200, pp. 118–119, October, 1957.

DIXON, JAMES P.: Air Pollution, Report of Meeting of the Air Conservation Commission of American Association for the Advancement of Science, *Science*, vol. 143, pp. 1349–50, Mar. 20, 1964.

———— AND JAMES P. LODGE: Air Conservation Report Reflects National Concern, *Science*, vol. 148, pp. 1060–1066, Washington, D.C., May 21, 1965.

Emphysema: A Growing Menace, *Changing Times*, Washington, D.C., April, 1964.

GOLDSMITH, JOHN R., AND JOHN H. MAGA: Development of Air Quality Standards in California, *California's Health*, vol. 21, pp. 153–155, Berkeley, Calif., Mar. 1, 1964.

GRISWOLD, S. SMITH: *Biennial Rept.*, 1962–1963, Los Angeles County Air Pollution Control District, Los Angeles, Calif., September, 1963. (Mimeographed.)

LOVELL, SIR BERNARD: Does Our Space Research Threaten Life on Earth? *Saturday Evening Post*, Feb. 22, 1964, p. 10.

Meteorological Research in Air Pollution, Robert A. Taft Sanitary Engineering Center, Cinncinnati, Ohio, U.S. Department of Health, Education and Welfare, 1960.

Motor Vehicles, Air Pollution and Health, A Report of the Surgeon General to the U.S. Congress, U.S. Department of Health, Education, and Welfare, 1962.

National Conference on Air Pollution, 1962, *U.S. Public Health Serv. Publ.* 1022, 1963.

NEIBURGER, MORRIS: The Atmosphere, Chap. 5 in Natural Resources, Martin R. Huberty and Warren L. Flock, eds., McGraw-Hill Book Company, New York, 1959.

A Study of Pollution: Air, Staff Report to the Committee on Public Works, U.S. Senate, Committee Print, 88th Cong., 1st sess., September, 1963.

WANZER, C. T.: Use of Fly ash in Concrete, reprinted from February, 1959, *Combustion*, by Bituminous Coal Institute, courtesy of National Coal Association, Washington, D.C., 1959.

WEST, WALLACE: Clearing the Air, Committee on Public Affairs, American Petroleum Institute, New York.

Where We Stand on Smog Problem, What's Been Done, What's Ahead, reprint from *Los Angeles Times*, Jan. 8, 1961, Government Printing Office, 1961.

7 FORESTS

A FOREST IS A community of living trees and associated organisms covering a considerable area; utilizing sunshine, air, water, and earthy materials to attain maturity and to reproduce itself; and capable of furnishing mankind with indispensable products and services (Fig. 7-1). But what is a tree, and what are these other organisms? And are the benefits mentioned expected to keep coming from a forest automatically? Unless the answers to such questions are reasonably well understood, both by the people who make their living from the forest resources of the country and by the individuals to whom the forest is significant only in terms of shade, beauty, and a source of wood for whatever purpose, or of maple sugar, game animals, clear water, Christmas trees, and turpentine, there can be little understanding and less performance in conserving the forest as a natural resource.

Trees for purposes of this discussion may be thought of as woody plants that usually grow upright with single stems. Standing close to each other, their roots form a network deep into the soil. Their trunks, or boles, have usually shed twigs and branches for most of their lengths, but their upper branches, twigs, leaves, and buds form a crown where the raw materials of growth from air, moisture, and soil meet for manu-

The forest—indispensable natural resource because of its many products and services. (Photo by A. E. Wieslander, United States Forest Service.)

figure 7-1

facture through the action of sunlight and for distribution to all parts of the plant. This process which we call growth appears to occur very slowly, but the total year's wood increment may vary from one cord per acre in the southern pines with their long growing season to less than one-quarter cord in the spruce swamps of the Lake states. Meanwhile the forest, wherever it may be located, is improving the scene; protecting the soil from blowing and washing; furnishing a home for useful wild animals; developing a number of minor products useful in food, medicine, and the arts; increasing the water-holding capacity of the immediate surface cover and the soil; and, like as not, exerting some small influence on the local climate.

So far, the flow of "indispensable products" sounds as though it were all set to be automatic. But even before men have started to help themselves to the benefits available, storms, lightning fires, insect attack, decay, and possibly drought are at work; and when harvesting of products by men starts in earnest all these troubles are likely to increase. Some of the beneficial organisms in the soil may have a hard time adjusting to the commotion or may stop operations completely.

It may be said then of the forest, as of every other renewable natural resource, that its productivity in use depends considerably upon the way its benefits are reaped by men and that a continuing flow of these benefits demands skillful, scientific management. This, in the case of forests, is called the science and art of forestry. Whether or not it is invoked and made to bring about conservation is also a matter of business management and of public policy. In these two particulars, understanding has been halted by the vast extent of the original resource, the fact that it was a crop that did not appear to require cultivation, and the fact that it was often in the way where agriculture seemed to be a land use of pressing need.

With these characteristics of the forest as a resource in mind, some attempt to measure its importance is appropriate.

HOW THE FOREST RESOURCE IS USED

In 1962 the people of this country consumed the equivalent of 68 billion feet board measure of products from their forests.[1] Not all of it was in the form of lumber. Indeed, only 37.3 billion feet of it was sawed into boards, dimension stock, and heavy timbers. The remainder was in the form of pulpwood, fuel wood, miscellaneous products including those representing new uses. To get some idea of the magnitude of the above

[1] Adapted from Timber Trends in the United States, *U.S. Forest Serv., Forest Resource Rept.,* 17, 1965, Tables 47 and 48, p. 220. (Converting factor of 6½ feet board measure to cubic feet, selected from R. D. Forbes, ed., Forestry Handbook Society of American Foresters, The Ronald Press Company, New York, 1961, Table 32, pp. 1–47.)

amount of lumber, one can go back to the playing area of a football field, which covers about 1 acre, and imagine such a field covered over with 1-inch boards. The gigantic total of 37.3 billion would cover more than 860,000 such fields. Or one may reduce the total to six-room cottages of average size, each of which would require about ten thousand feet board measure of lumber in its construction, and some 3½ million of them could be built. If these comparisons are not enough and the reader is ambitious statistically, he may calculate one of those mythical to-the-moon or around-the-world-at-the-equator examples.

Per-capita consumption of lumber for 1962 in this country amounted to about two hundred feet board measure, which would more than cover the floor of a room 11 by 18 feet in area with 1-inch-thick boards.

From the viewpoint of variety, wood is used for not less than 4,500 purposes[2] in the United States. Its properties give it a versatility possessed by almost no other material. Among these, workability, combined strength and light weight, color and grain, insulating ability, response to sound vibrations, bending strength, and odor have been appreciated and used for centuries. Today, new uses in the fields of plywood, plastics, and chemical derivatives give wood from the forest added importance.

Far smaller in volume than wood, actual tree products help to make up a long list of materials indispensable in modern technology and trade. Among these may be mentioned rosin and turpentine (known in the trade as "naval stores"), quinine, cascara, charcoal, acetic acid, rubber, maple syrup and sugar, Christmas greens, and nuts. These products are significant aside from their intrinsic usefulness because of the part they play, often unrecorded, in local economies.

Thus the use of the products of the forest alone would appear to make this natural resource indispensable. But services rendered mankind by the forest, while more difficult to appraise, may overshadow values in the form of products and dictate exclusive use of the resource for protection, scenery, or management of wild-animal life. As in the field of river-valley development and water use, these producing and serving functions of the forest resource may or may not proceed simultaneously and on the same area in a multiple-purpose program.

The public values of forest cover in erosion control have been touched on under Soil Conservation and Flood Control on pages 61 and 124. It should be repeated here, however, that quality of water, steadiness of its flow from natural storage, and resistance of the soil to the erosive power of rainfall dictate the permanent maintenance of the forests in headwater areas of river systems and smaller streams and that restoring of

[2] J. Alfred Hall and T. J. Mosley, *Products of American Forests*, U.S. Forest Service, 1946, p. 5.

forest cover frequently offers the only hope of arresting soil erosion in abused hilly country. Furthermore, a large proportion of the national forest area in the White and Appalachian Mountains has been acquired under the Weeks Law of 1911, in which authority for purchase is based on control of water in navigable streams under the commerce clause of the Constitution.

Perhaps no use of the forest as a resource appeals to the average citizen more than recreation. Campers who enjoy activities from the simplest hike or family picnic to a canoe trip or highly organized deer hunt head for the woods and capitalize on its beauty, solitude, and mystery. Literally millions of persons use the national and state parks and forests for recreation, and more and more the parks are becoming indispensable for this purpose. Devoid of forests it is hardly too much to say that most of their attractiveness would be gone. Hunters and fishermen, whether they are after big game or small, use forests and waters, seeking big game particularly in the forests as such or in the openings and fastnesses surrounded by forest growth. To a remarkable degree, the necessary safe breeding places appropriate to the special needs of a particular animal, the places of temporary refuge from predatory enemies while foraging and during both day and night, and the sources of food that are adequate and suitable for use of the animal[3] are found in forests and their openings.

Forage from the forest and its openings, important as it is to the larger game animals, also supports great herds of domestic sheep and cattle during the milder months of the year. Some 1.3 million head of cattle and 2.3 million sheep in 1963 were grazed under permit on the national forest ranges alone, and an additional 2.4 million calves and lambs were grazed without charge.

More than one-half of the total commercial forest area of the country and about three-fourths of the privately owned area are in the hands of 4½ million owners. Only 2 per cent of these own more than 500 acres. Many of the tracts are part of farms and are coming more and more to be handled as crop-producing areas. Fuel, repair material, and miscellaneous products are counted into farm income, and their harvesting furnishes profitable employment during slack farming periods. These facts, as well as the fact of wide distribution of farm-woods ownership, put the forest resource squarely into the agricultural economy of the country. Planted strips of "forest" in the form of shelterbelts, as discussed on pages 45 and 46, hold the soil, conserve snowfall, and temper drying and freezing winds. Similar services are rendered by natural tracts of woods on many farms.

[3] Joseph Grinnell, Wild Animal Life as a Product and as a Necessity of National Forests, *J. Forestry*, vol. 22, pp. 840–841, 1924.

In addition to those who work only a part of their time on the smaller forest areas, more than a million men were employed in 1950 in the lumber and pulpwood industries, including the mills, and something like a million more worked in the fabricating industries and others using wood.

EXTENT AND NATURE OF THE FOREST RESOURCES IN THE UNITED STATES

The United States is rich both in the distribution of its forest volume and in the number of usable species of trees represented in its forests. Some 100 varieties are valuable enough to find their way into the lumber trade over a considerable territory. More than 200 are used locally, and many species once discarded have come into regular use as demand has grown. Eastern hemlock, for example, was formerly considered valuable only for the bark, which is used in the tanning industry. Now it holds a respected position in lumber markets. Balm-of-Gilead and aspen, two of the widely distributed and fast-growing poplars, were formerly good at best for pulpwood and excelsior. Now they command good prices as saw timber in certain localities. The better species, among which are the pine, Douglasfir, redwood, oak, birch, maple, hickory, and walnut, are large in size and produce wood of high quality. But whether they are the giant firs, pines, or redwoods on the Pacific coast; the pines or cypresses of the Deep South; the jack pines, birches, and aspens of the Lake states' plains; the pinyons and junipers of the Southwest; or the oaks, hickories, elms, and maples of the Appalachians and the Northeast—products and services are taken from them as if they would always be there. They stand as forests unique among those of the entire globe.

Before taking up geographical distribution, it is well to go over some of the terms used in describing the forest resource: A *hardwood* tree, whether it produces a wood of peculiar hardness or not, is a broad-leaved tree. This is an established lumber-trade term which has persisted in forestry literature. Likewise, a *softwood* is a needle-leaved tree which may be evergreen, like the pines or spruces, or deciduous, like the tamarack or bald cypress. Then, too, a *hardwood forest* is sometimes contrasted with a *coniferous* forest—the latter being made up of cone-bearing needle-leaved trees and those with scalelike foliage. The term *commercial forest* means, as one would suppose, a forest from which merchantable wood products can be taken in paying quantities. *Protection forests* are chiefly dedicated to watershed protection, *park forests* or *scenic forests* are those in which no cutting is done, and miscellaneous scattered areas which bear trees but are relatively unproductive are known as *noncommercial forests*. The terms *national forest, state forest,* and *municipal forest* signify more than just ownership classification, for these are usually definitely organized and managed areas.

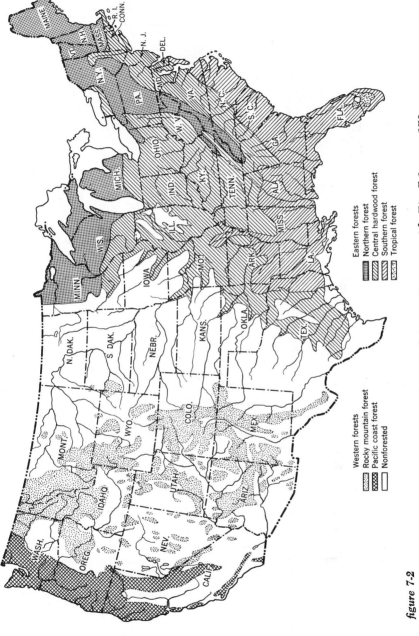

figure 7-2
Generalized map of the forested area of the United States. Compare with Fig. 7-3, page 170.

Eastern forests

▦ Northern forest
▨ Central hardwood forest
▧ Southern forest
▨ Tropical forest

Western forests

▨ Rocky mountain forest
▨ Pacific coast forest
☐ Nonforested

169

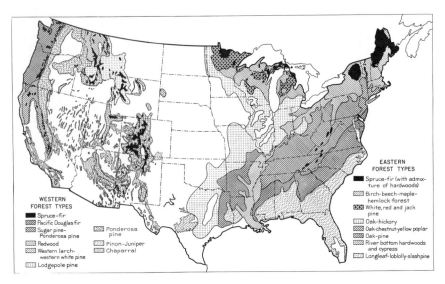

figure 7-3
Principal forest types of the United States. (United States Forest Service.)

FOREST REGIONS

It takes a good forester and a better student to keep abreast of the ways in which the other foresters and the botanists divide the country into forest regions. The authors believe that the older generalized division shown on the map[4] (Fig. 7-2) is both convenient and logical, and will follow it in briefly describing the forests of the United States. Another map designed to show specific features of distribution is shown in Fig. 7-3.

The Northern Forest. It will be observed that the Northern forest (Fig. 7-4) extends pretty far south in Appalachian highlands. Otherwise it is mostly along the northern border areas of the northeast quarter of the country. It is characterized by soils generally better adapted to forests than to agriculture. Although dairy farming and the raising of short-growing-season crops are common and widespread, a large part of the region is in forests of white, red, and jack pine; white, red, and black spruce; paper and yellow birch; maple; beech; elm; ash; and aspen. Eastern hemlock is also found in mixture with hardwoods; and white or balsam fir, white cedar, and tamarack are found in the swamps. Miscellaneous hardwoods are found throughout the region. White pine growing in this region, prized and marked for the king's navy in colonial times, dominated lumber production for the first 250 years of the country's

[4] Wilbur R. Mattoon, Forest Trees and Forest Regions of the United States, *U.S. Dept. Agr. Misc. Publ.* 217, 1936, pp. 34–35.

figure 7-4

The Northern forest. White pine, hemlock, and associated species.
(Michigan Department of Conservation.)

settlement, and the region still figures importantly in the production of
pulpwood and, to a lesser extent, other round products and lumber.

The Central Hardwood Forest. Stretching almost from the Rio Grande
River to Cape Cod and including the southern half of Minnesota, Wisconsin, and the Lower Peninsula of Michigan, the Central hardwood
forest (Fig. 7-5) still grows some of the world's largest and finest hardwoods, although its richer soils have been the occasion for much clearing
for agriculture. Here, white oak, hickory, white ash, walnut, and tulip or
yellow poplar (well named except that it is not a true poplar and it is
a soft "hardwood") reach their maximum development and highest
quality. More than a dozen hardwood species in this region are of com-

171

figure 7-5
The Central hardwood forest. Oak, yellow poplar, and hickory. Anne Arundel County, Md. (United States Soil Conservation Service.)

The Southern forest. Typical stand in Arkansas of loblolly and shortleaf pine, about 80 years old. (Photo by C. L. Lockard, United States Forest Service.)

figure 7-6

mercial value and extent. Flying over this area, one is impressed with the vast amount of cultivation throughout still heavily wooded areas. Hardwood lumber, railroad ties, cooperage stock, and piling are characteristic products of this forest.

The Southern Forest. Following the coastal plain from southeastern Maryland to eastern Texas, the Southern forest (Fig. 7-6) is characterized by four pines—longleaf, shortleaf, loblolly, and slash. Also in the swamp and river bottoms cypress, gum, and other lowland hardwoods—including river birch, laurel, live oak, and swamp chestnut oak—are found in great abundance. Pecans and other hickories are common in better-drained locations with good soil. Pine lumber, naval stores, and, more recently, pine pulpwood are leading products in this region, and huge volumes of wood are produced in record time because of the long growing season and abundant rainfall.

The Tropical Forest. Interesting botanically but small in size, without commercial value, and characterized by scrubby hardwoods, mangroves (helpful against wave erosion), and palms, the tropical forest occupies the southern tip of Florida and a small area in southeastern Texas.

The Rocky Mountain Forest. More far-flung but less continuous than any other forest region, the Rocky Mountain forest (Fig. 7-7) extends in large and small spots from Canada to Mexico and from the Black Hills in South Dakota and southeastern Colorado to the eastern slopes of the Sierra and Cascade ranges. Ponderosa pine, western white pine, Douglas-fir, and Engelmann spruce are the principal commercial species in this region. Western larch, magnificent in size and quality, must in its limited range in the North compete with western white and ponderosa pines and has not yet come into its own. Lodgepole pine in heavy stands is of great local importance, and Engelmann spruce, long important only

figure 7-7
The Rocky Mountain forest. Old growth of Engelmann spruce in Colorado. (Photo by Richard W. Mosher, United States Forest Service.)

locally, is now finding its way into paper manufacture, with promise of increasing demand. The growing season which is relatively short and large stretches of low-rainfall area introduce real handicaps to timber growing in this region. Grazing, water conservation, soil protection, and recreation—all depending heavily on the forest—are highly developed in the Rocky Mountain forest.

Pacific Coast Forest. Smaller in area but producing greater volumes per acre and larger single specimens than other regions, the Pacific Coast forest (Fig. 7-8) yields lumber from Douglasfir, Sitka spruce, and western hemlock in the Northwest; redwood along the northern half of the California coast; and ponderosa and sugar pine in the Cascade and Sierra ranges at higher elevations and extending to the drier eastern

The Pacific coast forest. Old growth of Douglasfir in Washington. (Photo by Ray M. Filloon, United States Forest Service.)

figure 7-8

slopes. Species of great value but of lesser volume include Port Orford cedar along the Oregon and Washington coast and western red cedar and alder in the moist heavy-rainfall Northwest. The size and weight of these giant specimens in virgin stands has required powerful logging equipment, and only in the heavy rainfall and productive forest soil is there the best hope for adequate regeneration. Logged forests do, however, come back rapidly, forestry practices yield good results, demand for products is high, and the Pacific forest will continue, as has the Southern forest, to be a major forest-growing region. Scenic and recreation values are high and are increasingly recognized in management.

Forests in the New States and Puerto Rico. Most important among the forests in the outlying areas of the United States are those of Alaska, the commercial portion of which is at low elevations and extends only a short way inland. Western hemlock, Sitka spruce, and Alaskan red cedar are the important species. The principal product is lumber for packing cases used by the salmon industry. Prospects for a great paper industry, which is just getting started, are bright.

Charcoal burning is the only important forest industry in Puerto Rico, with its "wet forest" in the north and its "dry forest" across the range to the south. Small areas of saw timber of various tropical species are included in a small national forest, but most of the needed lumber for a crowded population must be imported. Such unfamiliar names as mountain palm, muskwood, and bullet wood designate species important in the wet forest.

The wet and dry forests of Hawaii have suffered from fire and overgrazing and while in Federal ownership in a national park or state forest add more to the scene than to the economy of the islands. *Koa,* one of the acacias prized as a cabinet wood, and *ohia lehua* are used commercially.

PROBLEMS AND NEEDS IN FOREST CONSERVATION

Some measure of the productive ability of the existing forest resource is needed to match actual growth and estimated demand for products and services. Heavy utilization of products combined with minor dedications to noncommercial uses hasten the time when most of the forests will be "second growth" rather than "virgin." Growth under these circumstances should be faster on the same area basis because fewer trees will have reached the old-age period during which they mark time rather than grow in wood volume.

This sounds as though everything were neatly arranged and that demand for products and services will be met automatically. But in the words of the song, "It ain't necessarily so." Again, therefore, one may ask, "What do we know of the productive capacity of the forests of the country?" "Can it be made to meet the probable demand?" "What are the technical and economic hurdles to be cleared?" "How well are we doing?" and "What more is necessary?"

Productive Capacity of Forest Resources. In appraising the ability of forests to continue their important services to humanity, a short historical summary is in order.

The early settlers in this country were too busy to philosophize much about future flow of products and services from a forest that seemed always to be in the way. They did turn its products into early cash commodities of trade such as lumber, staves for casks, and naval stores, and they used it for buildings and fuel. There is little evidence that up to 100 years ago any thought had occurred to the people concerning the forest as yielding any important benefits save wood products. The fur trade and game for food figured to some extent in the economy of the times, but surely water conservation was not a recognized service. The Rip Van Winkles who hunted and fished and the Thoreaus who explored for recreation were considered time wasters. Skis and toboggans, if any, were for the serious purposes of travel. The necessity of burning the resulting forest waste in clearing for agriculture may have influenced an attitude of fatalism toward forest fires. "Waste" had less to do in the thinking of the times with natural resources and more to do with the precious results of long hours of labor in terms of actual items of food, clothing, and shelter. Land given away to railroad, canal, and wagon-road companies and to the states (see Fig. 1–3) was expected to be settled and worked by an agricultural population to whom it would be sold in relatively small parcels. A little later the settler could acquire land, whether timbered or not, by living on it and "homesteading" it, taking certain areas for timber and stone, planting trees on a "claim," or taking land for other alleged purposes off the hands of the states, which had acquired it by various grants from the Federal government. If he wanted to be a miner, he was given a rather free hand to claim, and later acquire, land whether timbered or not. All this led to forest destruction and to concentration of forest ownership on a grand scale in a rather free and easy interpretation of the laws and customs and the duties of citizenship in a democracy. The logger in his natural haste to meet a demand for lumber used the old device of making one factor of production carry the other two. Capital and labor were scarce; "land," or natural resources in the shape of forests, was abundant and took the heaviest beating. The logger left inflammable "slash" from the unused portions of the trees and abandoned his camp structures. These frequently caught fire at once, or as the settler followed the logger. Burned-out soils refused to "blossom as the rose" with new forests or, if they did grow up, exhibited inferior types of forest. Meanwhile insects and disease were beginning to take toll.

Mild interest, early expressed by President John Quincy Adams and others, in reforestation by planting had died down. Trespass on Federal lands was severe in the Lake states. No legal way of purchasing standing timber apart from the land or of timbered lands for purposes of utilizing the forest had been worked out. The states showed even less interest in the forests than the Federal government. There were no trained foresters in the country. The American Forestry Association, a group of public-spirited citizens interested in adequate forest resources, had not yet been organized, and even informed scientists paid little attention to the march of forest exploitation. People were probably not saying, as many conservation writers insist, "Our forests are inexhaustible." They were saying nothing. The nation was a busy, toiling people bent on "developing" the natural resources in terms of transportation, trade, settlement, and agriculture, with even the interest of the nation's early years in forests for building and maintaining a navy pretty thoroughly forgotten up to 1876. Although there was then an awakening, to be discussed later, the exploitation of forests for the next 30 years has probably not been duplicated anywhere in the world. A historical summary of this period will be given later in this chapter, but against the background so far, productive capacity may be discussed.

PRODUCTIVE CAPACITY OF ORIGINAL FORESTS It is not difficult to figure out that white pines, large and straight enough for the king's navy in colonial days, had been growing for hundreds of years before the Atlantic seaboard was settled. Giant oaks, chestnuts, and elms 200 to 400 years old were no doubt standing in the Ohio Valley. The larger trees dominated the stand except where lightning fires had exposed the soil and younger forest was coming on. Productive power was there on a grand scale from the viewpoint of growing conditions, but the forest was stagnant because crowded. Had the spectre of timber famine disturbed their rest, the early settlers might have kept 1 acre out of every 6 in forest and drawn upon it as need arose. Indeed this is what William Penn required of those to whom he assigned land. As older trees were removed, young ones would have taken their places through natural reproduction. A sort of crude forestry would thus have been practiced and a part of the forest area actually cultivated by skillful harvesting. Two hundred to five hundred or more board feet might have been made to grow per acre per year, and local demand would have been met with much shorter haul and less expenditure of energy. But the productive capacity of forests decreased rapidly because of the favor given to agriculture and lumber production during this period, both through rapid reduction of commercial forest area and through abuse of the forest soils by fire. Justifiably in many respects, but surely at a considerable reduction of productive capacity, the area of forest has shrunk from its original 822 million acres to about 650 million acres, plus 16.5 million in coastal Alaska, with only about 509 million acres of commercial importance or promise, in less than 350 years of settlement.[5]

PRESENT PRODUCTIVE POWER OF FORESTS Local scarcities of forest products still plague many localities in the United States, but on the whole the remaining forests retain the necessary productive power to serve the needs of the nation both for wood and for other services. Yet it will have to be fully used and so handled as to step up present rates of growth 50 per cent or more. With moderate overcuts for a few years from remaining virgin forests in the West and from rapid-growth Southern forests, demand could probably be met until the time the majority of commercial forests, public and private, could be brought under good management and be protected well enough to make them permanent.

The United States Forest Service estimates that, with the expected increase in population and in improved living standards and with the price of wood rising faster than that of competing materials, demand for timber products in 1975 and the corresponding growth necessary are likely to be 24 per cent greater than today and, in 2000, 67 per cent greater. On the other hand, if the price rises no faster than that of competing materials, we may expect an increase in demand and needed growth for timber products of 44 per cent in 1975 and of 122 per cent in 2000.[6] The prospect for meeting these demands on the largest holdings is good. It is not so good on the small areas which comprise more than one-half the total, although it is improving slowly.

How Forest Productivity Is Maintained. Fire, insects, disease, storms, overgrazing, overcutting, and waste in utilization are the depleting forces which must be held in check if forests are to produce the returns which people demand. This particular problem may be stated as that of assuring for the use of mankind the forest products and services which would otherwise be wasted.

FIRE Fire is one of the greatest of discoveries. Certainly it serves men in enough ways to brand it a blessing. Only when it is out of control does it turn into an enemy, and a forest is no place to let it get out of control. To its credit in forest management, fire can be used conservatively to expose mineral soil in some forest areas and so promote better germination of seed and natural reproduction of the forest. It is also available as a weapon against itself in "starving out" a destructive fire by backfiring, so that the area ahead of the main fire will have nothing to burn and may be controlled; by disposing of debris which

---

[5] Figure for acreage of commercial importance is from Timber Trends in the United States, *op. cit.*, p. 102.

[6] Timber Resources for America's Future, *U.S. Forest Serv., Forest Resource Rept.* 14, 1958, p. 107.

constitutes a fire hazard in a forest; or by consuming trees in which insects are "trapped."

In a general sense, moreover, fire as an industrial servant makes possible the manufacture of tools and equipment used in forest management and furnishes comfort to forest workers. And what would recreational camping amount to in the forest without the campfire? Uncontrolled, on the other hand, fire destroys trees as potential wood products. It injures and weakens trees which may not be consumed or killed and so joins forces with insects and diseases which can attack more destructively. It consumes the duff or ground cover of leaves, twigs, and decayed wood and frequently burns into the soil itself, changing its physical character, reducing its water-absorptive capacity, and destroying beneficial soil organisms. It exposes the soil to the erosive effects of rainfall. It destroys the peculiar habitat necessary for many valuable wild animals and frequently the animals themselves. It ruins forest scenery. It destroys buildings and other structures, and every year it takes a toll of human life.

Forest fires which burn principally in the ground itself—consuming roots, peatlike soil, and other organic matter—are known as *ground fires.* Those which consume only the duff and low herbaceous and brushy growth are called *surface fires.* The forest fire usually pictured, and the most terrifying and destructive, burns in the branches, sweeps everything in its path, and is known as a *crown fire* (Fig. 7-9). The word "crown" is also used as a verb in describing the behavior of a forest fire. The surface fire is the least destructive of the three and the commonest, but all three must be prevented or controlled if productive power is to be maintained.

For uniform statistical purposes, seven causes of forest fires are recognized. Ranked from highest to lowest incidence in 1963, these are: incendiaries, 41,429; debris burning, 38,756; smoking, 24,521; miscellaneous, 17,223; lightning, 11,565; machine use, 8,208; campfires, 4,218— a total for the United States of 145,355 forest fires, some 92.07 per cent having been man-caused.[7] These figures are for the 97.07 per cent of all land needing protection on which organized forest-fire-control forces are maintained. "Machine use" is a new classification including lumbering and railroad fires formerly reported separately, as were those from unknown causes. The latter are now included with the most likely causes.

Grouping the fires which occur according to their causes is helpful in planning prevention work. Smokers may be warned, restrained by laws and regulations, and punished when apprehended for violation; informed of safety measures which they themselves can use; and even

[7] 1963 Forest Fire Statistics, United States Forest Service, p. 5.

figure 7-9

Observers from both airplanes and towers are on the watch for forest fires during hazardous season. This tower is in Michigan. (Michigan Department of Conservation.)

appealed to with some success during dangerous periods. The incendiary —who sets fire deliberately from a variety of motives rooted in ignorance, desire for thrill, grudge, or for personal gain and convenience—is a hard forest-fire causer to deal with. His record persists in spite of the work of psychologists, of law and its enforcement, and of efforts to enlighten his self-interest. Campers may be warned, furnished safe places for building campfires and directions and tools for safely extinguishing them, apprehended and punished for violation of laws and regulations, and even excluded from forest areas by proclamation in dangerous periods. Debris burners may be required to obtain permits stipulating care and are sometimes offered assistance when burning is to be done. Railroads are regularly required to use safety devices on locomotives operating in hazardous forest regions, are required to reduce inflammable hazards on rights of way, and frequently are proceeded against for damages to forest cover and physical properties. Fires from miscellaneous causes, such as an exploding plane in a crash, an automobile wreck, or various freak accidents, are unpredictable and may be prevented only by steady

figure 7-10
*Lightning during storm in Oregon. Eight fires occurred from this storm.
The photo was taken about 10 P.M. (Photo by John B. Smith, United
States Forest Service.)*

progress in safety education. Lightning fires (Fig. 7-10) cannot be prevented but can sometimes be outguessed and controlled by prompt and
vigorous attack. Unknown causes become yearly a smaller group as
vigilance in fire protection and control improves. There is, however, a
disturbing increase in the number of man-caused fires.

FOREST-FIRE CONTROL   Somewhat oversimplified, the steps in forest-fire
control, assuming a skeleton organization and service of supply, are
detection, reporting, dispatching, travel, attack, control, and mop-up.
Practically every forest fire is a potential conflagration. Observers from
towers (Fig. 7-11)—and to some extent from airplanes, homes, resorts,
mines, logging camps, cattle headquarters, ranches, vehicles on public
highways, and any other available spot—are definitely employed or enlisted for detection service by cooperative agreement or informally.
Instruments and maps of special accuracy are used in towers and other
equipped and manned observation posts. Telephone and radio both are
employed for reporting and dispatching, radio being the more common.
A recent development in detection involves the use of an airborne infra-
red scanning device which can penetrate smoke and reveal the perimeter
of a fire, the hot spots, and spot fires occurring outside the main fire area.
Thus the fire boss can receive information which otherwise would require hours to obtain.[8] Elapsed time from detection to attack is counted
in minutes and seconds. Transportation of men and equipment and
supplies employs fast motorized equipment, boats, railroad, saddle and

[8] *Report of the Chief of the Forest Service*, 1963, p. 21, 1964.

figure 7-11

Minnesota crown fire—a real danger to human life. (United States Forest Service.)

pack animals, airplanes and helicopters at times, and "shank's mare," or foot travel, in wild and rough country. "Smoke jumping" by individual fire fighters dropped from airplanes is used to reach isolated fires. (Fig. 7-12). Attack resembles actual combat in war. It uses water from back packs, tank trucks, natural bodies tapped by portable motor pumps, or shallow wells driven by special equipment in appropriate territory in as little time as 15 minutes—all applied in the form of stream, spray, or "fog" to cool down or "knock down" the fire so that men can work on it. Dirt is also used to deprive the flame of oxygen and knock down the fire and is applied by a mechanical scattering device or by shovel and hand power. Depriving the fire of something to burn is the secret of control. This involves direct attack at the edges, clearing a line or break to mineral soil to which the advancing fire may approach and die, or burning out the space intervening between this line and the advancing fire. The latter method, called *backfiring*, is risky and inadvisable except in the hands of skilled men. Control is achieved in a technical sense when the spread of the fire is successfully checked. Extinguishing of islands of fire within the burned-over area and particularly near the extinguished edge both on the surface and underground constitutes mop-up. Long patrol is frequently necessary before abandoning the area.

Through all this "battle"—depending on weather and on character, amount, and arrangement of cover, slope, and local air currents—from one individual to several thousand men may be working on the fire itself (Fig. 7-13). Skilled direction, ingenious equipment, and highly organized systems of communication, transportation, and supply are the results of long workouts. Lives, not only of travelers and residents in the area but of fire fighters, are occasionally lost. Damage is usually appraised in terms of value of merchantable timber, young growth projected into the future, physical improvements, and repair costs to the public works. Scenic, game animal, and other recreation values, formerly not usually included in damage figures, are now considered.

In broad terms, then, fire control has one objective and that is maintaining the productive power of the forest. It accomplishes this by preventing waste in a physical sense, to be sure, but most significantly in

Smoke jumpers drifting toward a remote forest fire in Alaska. Bureau of Land Management fire fighters are responsible for protecting the unreserved public domain. (Photo by Jim Lee, Bureau of Land Management, Department of the Interior.)

figure 7-12

figure 7-13

Plane dropping borate on a California chaparral fire. Frequently this treatment "knocks down" a fire so that men can work close to it. (Los Angeles County Fire Department.)

protecting a growing forest from one force which curtails its growing power. A recently adapted term for the damage incurred by forest fires is *growth impact*, which includes both mortality and growth loss.

FOREST INSECT DAMAGE AND CONTROL Insects no doubt have their rights, but in arguing as to whether men or insects shall get the forests, it is important that men should win by preventing insects from curtailing the productive power of the forest. It is no easy task, for trees are subject to trouble in this direction from the time the weevil finds an edible tree seed right up to the day when a pine-bark beetle cooperating with others of his kind has successfully girdled a great tree under its bark. In addition to these two forms of insect attack, the grub of the June bug, or May beetle, feeds on the roots of small trees, particularly the stock in forest tree nurseries and that just planted for reforestation purposes; the larvae of numerous moths attack the leaves and buds of many forest trees; certain weevils and larvae of moths attack terminal shoots and buds and thus deform trees; scale insects get in their work on the sap of twigs and branches; borers injure trunks and branches mechanically; and finally the wood products, having safely escaped the forest insects, invite termites and powder-post beetles.

Prevention of insect attack is a matter of strictly quarantining insects which may be brought from abroad and moved into uninfested domestic regions; maintaining the forest in healthy, growing condition; and avoiding the logging and fire injury which expose live trees to insect attack. Threatened epidemic attacks can be halted to some extent by felling and barking the tree and exposing grubs and adult beetles to the sun or cold or by burning the bark or the trunk itself, sometimes with the tree still standing. A modification of this method is used in removing large jack pines of certain bushy form which support the staminate flowers upon which spruce budworm attack is concentrated. (The bark beetle is a girdler; the spruce budworm is a leaf eater, or defoliator.)

Planning on a broad scale, generous public financing, and employment of highly trained scientists as well as extensive survey and work crews make the control of insect attack a major undertaking as one means of maintaining the productive power of forests.

Recent years have been marked, both in the control of forest insects and diseases, by the use of airplanes spraying and dusting with poisons. Costs have been reduced, so that much of this work may be done by contract (Fig. 7-14).

CONTROL OF FOREST-TREE DISEASES Attacks on the forests by diseases are subject to the same principles, to a large extent, as those governing insect attack. Various rusts, cankers, and rots must be made subject to quarantine so far as is practicable, and, here again, the attack may start at the seed and may occur in some other form at all stages of growth and on all parts of the tree. In control of diseases, however, the most difficult so far encountered have come to America from other countries, and one, the chestnut blight, has so far proved too much for scientists. Its life history is well understood, but because it can be carried by birds and because of the rapidity of its spread after reaching this country from China, the American chestnut—valuable for its wood, tannin, and nuts —appears to be doomed. Only with the development of blight-resistant strains will the chestnut be reestablished.

Aerial war on tree-killing insects. Here the spruce budworm, which threatens vast areas, is subject to an average kill of 98 to 99.5 per cent with a DDT solution, at a cost of around $1 per acre. (Photo by Donn Bonham, American Forest Products Industries, Inc.)

figure 7-14

Another baffling disease is the white-pine blister rust, brought to this country from Germany on nursery stock. It has spread until it now reaches the Pacific coast, attacking any of the "white," or five-needle, pines. This disease selects what is known as an *alternate host,* maturing on the pines but starting all over again from them on currant and goose-berry bushes (*Ribes* sp.). It sounds simple, then, to catch it at a vulnerable point in its life history by destroying the bushes which serve as alternate hosts, but these form a host in another sense. There are vast numbers of them scattered throughout the range of these valuable pines. After an infected area is discovered and surveyed and its control is fully planned, the work of destroying the bushes, both domestic and wild, must be done with a "fine-tooth-comb" thoroughness. The citizen's garden is sometimes invaded in the interest of conserving forest resources, and the owner loses his currant bushes. A mountainside of scattered bushes or a deep rough canyon with junglelike growth of *Ribes* is attacked with digging tools, by the gloved hands of the worker who pulls the thorny plants, or by another worker carrying a heavy back-pack spray rig—all these activities are part of the control task (Fig. 7-15). Vast expenditure of funds and of energy has held down, but not eliminated, this disease. Certain hybrid white pines have exhibited resistance to attack from blister rust and offer some promise of control.

Still another disease which threatens the elms of the country, valuable

Spraying skunk currant, one of the alternate hosts of the white pine blister rust, in Franklin County, N.Y. This disease is widespread on five-needle pines. (Photo by L. R. Strickenberg, United States Forest Service.)

figure 7-15

in the veneer and other wood industries and outstanding as shade trees, is the so-called Dutch elm disease, which reached this country in imported logs from Holland. Here an insect reinforces the attack of the disease by helping to spread it. Control dictates the location and destruction of infected trees.

Along with all this there must be more "barn-door-closing-after-*one-of-the-horses*-has-been-stolen" in the form of quarantine enforcement, and the over-all program is just another necessary contribution to the maintenance of the productive power of the forest resource.

DEALING WITH DAMAGE TO FORESTS BY THE ELEMENTS   Men have not yet found a way to reduce hurricane damage to the forests (Fig. 7-16), lightning hazard, breakage from ice and snow, frost damage to reforestation stock or to alleviate, on an economic scale, the effects of drought. Yet every one of these natural phenomena may set back the productivity of a forest for years. Windfall in a managed forest can be lessened by care in the distribution of the removal of mature and "crop" trees (those designated for growth and eventual removal for a definite market) and to some extent by streamlining the windward edge of a forest by allowing it to grow or shaping it or by using giant fences so that destructive winds will be deflected upward. The latter procedure is expensive and rarely used in this country. Salvage of fallen timber, cleanup of potential fire

Blowdown from Columbus Day storm in the Northwest, 1963. The national forests of this region suffered loss of around 2 billion board-feet of timber, and the total loss in Oregon and Washington was much greater. This scene is on the Siuslaw National Forest in Oregon. (Photo by United States Forest Service.)

figure 7-16

hazards, encouraging natural reproduction of "wind-firm" species, or growing a crop of smaller trees on a shorter rotation are the alternatives to the prevention of storm damage. Avoiding low "frost pockets" with sluggish air drainage is indicated where frost damage has appeared in forest-planting projects. Drought can be combatted only in an immediate and local situation such as with the establishment of shelterbelt forests in prairie country. Here actually watering the trees until they are established is sometimes justified because of the great values inherent in them in addition to wood production.

Once more, whatever can be accomplished is aimed at maintaining the productivity of the forest.

So far various efforts to defend the forest from depleting forces have been discussed from the viewpoint of *maintaining* productive power and preventing waste of resources (Fig. 7-21) and products so that men instead of destructive forces should take them over. But certain manipulations of the forest are desirable, and these will often amount to a rude cultivation practice keyed largely to careful harvesting of products and, to a lesser extent, to artificial replacement, or reforestation. Out of such practices an actual *increase* of productivity is possible, and such an increase is one of the essentials of "conserving" the forest.

How Forest Productivity Is Increased. Due attention and effort having been given to maintaining productive power, that power should be kept at work. Arrogant as it may appear, the cooperation and skill of men can bring about increased yields of forest products, and they can do it with much less intensive and backbreaking methods than farmers have used for centuries in obtaining progressive increases in soil productivity. The forester calls his art of growing timber *silviculture* and his application of this art to a forest business, *management*. Harvesting, or cutting and removing trees for market, figures strongly in these practices. A ship or vehicle, however it may be supplied with power, cannot be steered unless there is some place for it to move and unless it is moving. A forest does not move from place to place in a physical sense, but it moves in the sense of growth: having once been established, it cannot grow unless it has room. Periodic harvest of increment furnishes this room. How is all this planned and brought about?

First of all there must be a forest. Bare ground or grassy or brush areas sometimes yield slowly to the spread of natural forest from wind-blown seed; from seed carried by birds, rodents, or large mammals; or even from seed or twigs floated on a stream or by temporary runoff. When a forest must be established artificially, men usually grow in the forest nurseries large numbers of small trees about the size of the tomato plants purchased by the home gardener (Fig. 7-17). These are planted on the selected sites, using special tools or, more recently, motor-powered ma-

figure 7-17
State-forest nursery in Michigan. (Michigan Department of Conservation.)

chinery (Figs. 7-18, 7-19), and are placed in a more or less definite pattern of rows to assure proper spacing (6 by 6 feet or 6 by 8 feet is frequently decided upon). Technically this is known as *afforestation* if on a previously treeless site and *reforestation* if it is to reclothe a logged-off area or any other area recently occupied by forest (Fig. 7-20). After the plantation or new forest is thus started, it must, of course, be protected

figure 7-18
Reforestation by machine on Michigan cutover land. Note the two planted trees in furrow at lower right center. (Michigan Department of Conservation.)

figure 7-19
Reforesting by hand in a 19,000-acre burn on the Apache National Forest in Arizona. (Photo by Daniel O. Todd, United States Forest Service.)

from the depleting forces mentioned earlier. When it reaches a growth sufficient to supply marketable products, the manipulation mentioned above is employed, first by thinning for small products—fence pickets, Christmas trees, cheap ornamental stock, greens for floral purposes—or by thinning without using the material removed. Next, in rare instances where it will pay and where natural dying off and shedding of lower branches is not satisfactory, pruning may be employed. After this there may be a thinning of larger trees with a yield of fuel, posts, pulpwood, chemical wood from which charcoal and distilled products are obtained, or Christmas trees of larger size. In this thinning, "crop trees" are selected to be left and encouraged to grow for the main yield and to reseed the area. Things do not proceed so neatly as this, of course, except on relatively small planted forests located close to good markets or where the forestry, or silviculture and management, described, is more intensive than usual. Once a new forest is established, with not only an increase in productivity of the original bare site but also of an artificial and tended forest, the immediate objective, as in management of natural forest, is *sustained yield*. By this is meant the growing of as great a volume of wood and the assuring of as much other service during any given harvest period as it is proposed to cut and lose by damage or to enjoy during the same period. Stated in a different way and with respect to wood harvest only, sustained yield means seeing to it that growth in volume balances removal in volume over any given period—be it year, decade, or 100-year rotation. (It is important that the emphasis be put on growing rather than on cutting.)

figure 7-20

An unusual example of reforestation on a spoil bank of a strip-mine area in Indiana. The trees are yellow poplar. (Indiana Coal Producers Association.)

Starting with a natural forest "fully stocked" (as a forester would say), hoping that all productive ground was growing trees or serving its main purpose otherwise, or starting with any kind of promising natural stand of timber, silviculture and management have an immediate chance to show financial return. The need to await the first few years' growth (as in the planted forest) does not arise. The program of heading for sustained yield starts right off. Protection and periodic cuttings designed to maintain and increase productive power and yields may be much more difficult and costly in a natural forest because of terrain, distance from markets, legal restrictions, and extent of area which make control of trespass and other depleting forces hard to achieve. But the same general

figure 7-21
Patches of clear-cut Douglasfir in Oregon. Because of size and weight of trees, this logging practice is standard in both public and private forests in the Northwest. Seed must reach mineral soil, and young trees must have light to grow. These patches, ordinarily, will be re-seeded naturally from remaining timber after logging. (Photo by American Forest Products Industries, Inc.)

program is indicated. Any one of several systems of management may be used in harvesting and in so employing the soil, light, and moisture through spacing of trees left that natural reproduction rather than artificial reforestation will take place (Figs. 7-21, 7-22). A selection of specimens may be made and they may be marked for removal; entire strips or blocks may be cut clear (all trees removed); small groups may

figure 7-22
Selectively logged area in loblolly and shortleaf pine in Arkansas. Reproduction occurs from trees left standing when larger ones are taken. (Photo by C. R. Lockard, United States Forest Service.)

be completely cut; species peculiarly adapted to the particular site may be favored in the cuttings and left to increase; and certain portions may be dedicated for game cover, grazing, or scenic use and either left undisturbed or "man-handled" as far as timber production is concerned. The reader should understand that in the process of "management" a forest may at times look like a bedraggled beauty, just as one might view an ugly, waterless retarding basin in a flood-control project, a field ready to be plowed and redolent with manure, or a farm pond full of fish but the color of dirty dishwater. Maybe after all this *is* beauty—the beauty of the laborer's muscle. For the labor of productive forces is increasing the flow of natural resources and, characteristic of our country's possibilities, making life more abundant in a democracy.

CONSERVING FORESTS ON A NATIONAL SCALE

Although the ownership of the forests of the country involves a large number of individuals, the problem of conserving forest resources on a national scale differs in one marked respect from that of conserving the soil: large ownerships require a different kind of attention than those, for example, located on farms. And so while an important part of the task is to influence individuals to practice good forestry, Federal, state, and local governments and large corporations must deal with forest resources directly, as proprietors, in a manner almost unknown in managing agricultural soil resources.

The Federal Government as a Forest-land Proprietor. In the public lands the Federal government has long been the proprietor of large tracts of forest. In its use of lands of all kinds—among them forest lands of great value—to subsidize the building of railroads and other international improvements and to encourage education, the Federal government has made possible, unintentionally, the ownership by operating and nonoperating corporations of great concentrations of forest land. To a lesser extent, but with a similar effect, this Federal proprietor—through such laws as the Homestead Act, the Timber and Stone Act, and the mining laws, sketchily administered—followed democratic theory in attempting to distribute land ownership among large numbers of its citizens. Corporations did rather well in accumulating these individual "claims" into large timberland ownerships. Grants to the states frequently, though not always, were sold off as promptly as possible in order to obtain cash for education and other state expenses. Frequently the land bounced back into state ownership after being gutted of its timber and becoming no longer worth the taxes which the owner was called upon to pay. Thus the states accumulated large holdings and found themselves saddled with obligations of proprietorship once held by the Federal government.

But with all this shifting of ownership, the Federal government in 1876, as thought on forest conservation was being revived, found itself still the proprietor of vast tracts of public timberland in the West, with no legal way of operating the timber separate from the land or disposing of it on that basis. Selling the timber alone, to be cut under conservative regulation, had hardly been thought of. One "national park and forest reserve," the Yellowstone, had been withdrawn from entry under the various land laws and was eventually put under the superficial police protection of the cavalry of the United States Army.

More will have to be said later about the Federal government's showing as a forest-land proprietor, but here a short historical summary is in order.

Events Leading to the National Forest Movement. As was mentioned in the introduction, the memorial sent to the Congress by a committee of the American Association for the Advancement of Science in 1874, under the chairmanship of Dr. Franklin B. Hough, emphasized not only timber values but the importance of public forest lands in maintaining favorable water conditions. The recommendations included the withholding from sale and the protection of public forest lands. They brought about the establishment of a Division of Forestry in the Department of Agriculture the principal activities of which were publishing forestry bulletins and, later, offering assistance to forest-land owners in the practice of forestry. Appropriations were scant, and this division had no jurisdiction over the forest reserves for many years.

In 1890 the American Association for the Advancement of Science persisted with another report to the President of the United States, again recommending the withdrawal of forest areas in the public domain from sale, settlement, and entry for timber and water-conservation purposes "until a permanent system of forest administration be had." Impressed by this memorial, Secretary of the Interior J. W. Noble, during the administration of President Benjamin Harrison, recommended action to the Congress. This resulted in the enactment of a law in 1891 authorizing the President to establish by proclamation reservation of public lands whether heavily timbered or not, but it contained no provision for their protection or administration. Therefore, some 13 million acres, promptly reserved by President Harrison in the Western states were for many years unattended.

By 1896 the Federal government had raised some money for one of its early "brain trusts," the National Academy of Science, to make a study and to recommend a national forest policy. Its report outlined a policy and plan for administering the existing reserves and others which it recommended be established. The latter recommendation received the prompt attention of President Grover Cleveland, who in 1896 withdrew as new reservations 20 million acres. Apparently this action impressed certain interests in the West as anything but democratic, and out of the criticism and debate on the President's action came the important Organic Forestry Act of 1897 for administering the "forest reserves" (since 1907 called "national forests"). With authority in this act to regulate occupancy and use of forest-reserve lands, to sell timber separate from land under proper cutting restrictions, and to protect the forest resources, the Federal government was beginning to roll up its sleeves as a proprietor.

Actual progress in organizing the reserves for administration was somewhat slow until 1905. At this time the responsibility was transferred from the Department of the Interior to the Department of Agriculture, and the Bureau of Forestry, which had been clothed with little authority and fewer duties since its creation as a Division in the Department of Agriculture in 1887, came into its own. By 1907 it was the "Forest Service," the forest reserves were "national forests," and the Federal government was taking its task as a proprietor seriously over a part of its domain. But this is only a part of the public-land story, featuring principally the forest reserves.

Forest Lands Other Than National Forests. Considerable areas of forest land remained unreserved in the public domain, including millions of timbered acres of Indian reservations, for which the Federal government as guardian had certain responsibility, and vast railroad land grants bade fair to be back on the government's hands because of the refusal of the railroads to abide by the terms of the grants.

Also during this 30-year period the forest lands in the hands of the states suffered continuing neglect in many instances (Fig. 7-23), although Maine, Michigan, and Wisconsin had started some studies in the 1860s. In all, fourteen states had initiated some sort of forestry programs between 1885 and 1891, most of which had to do with protection and sale of state-owned timber.

Corporations showed an occasional spark of interest, a few in the Eastern and Southern states accepting help from the Bureau of Forestry in planning forest management on their lands. Little actual forestry, however, was under way on private lands, and there was a real exhibition of diligence in discussing why the private owner could not afford this new luxury on account of unfair taxation practices.

Federal Leadership from 1905 to 1933. As the Bureau of Forestry assumed its role in the Department of Agriculture and became the Forest Service in 1905, the dynamic interest of President Theodore Roosevelt, influenced by his Chief Forester, Gifford Pinchot, was reflected in the creation of new national forests, more generous appropriations for their administration, and the beginnings of a forestry profession.

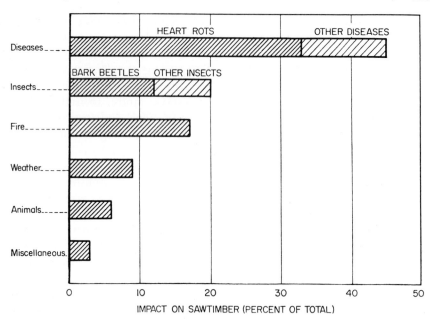

figure 7-23
Impact on saw timber by destructive agencies as per cent of total impact on United States, including coastal Alaska. (Graph by United States Forest Service.)

The entire forestry movement received a real impetus from the White House conference of governors called by the President in May, 1908, and from the report of the National Conservation Commission (see pages 10 and 11). Research in forestry and forest products was inaugurated, states became increasingly interested, and a series of important Federal laws were enacted. The latter will be listed for convenience.

THE WEEKS LAW OF 1911   Urged for many years, the Weeks Law, enacted in 1911, established two important principles: (1) the purchase with Federal funds of lands to be managed as national forests at the headwaters of navigable streams and (2) the cooperation in terms of finances and technical advice and assistance between the Federal government on the one hand and the states and private forest-land owners on the other in forest-fire control in the watersheds of navigable streams. Under this act considerable area was purchased and organized in the next decade in the White Mountains of New England and in the Appalachians. Definite cooperative agreements for fire control were entered into with most of the states, and Federal appropriations for the latter purpose had greatly increased by 1923. Fire and damage records were improving.

THE CLARKE-MC NARY LAW OF 1924 Following heated discussion throughout the country on the subject of Federal regulation of forestry practices (usually meaning timber cutting) on private lands, this compromise act was passed in 1924, dismissing the idea of enforced Federal regulation in favor of cooperation after the pattern of the Weeks Law. Emphasis was still on fire control, authority for which was broadened. Land for forest-demonstration purposes in growing timber, rather than for watershed protection only, and particularly cutover lands, could be purchased and organized into national forests (but no financial program for these purchases was authorized). Federal cooperation with states in support of extension work in farm forestry and the distribution of forest-tree seed and reforestation stock was provided for. A study of the effect of taxation on forest perpetuation was authorized. Fire control was definitely strengthened as a result of this act, and farm forestry was stimulated. It has also produced better working relations between the Federal government and private owners of forest land. It no doubt also cleared the way for a tremendous expansion of the forest-purchase program.

THE MC NARY-MC SWEENEY LAW OF 1928 Although it had been recognized as important since 1908 by the Forest Service, no policy on forest research, as such, had been adopted until the enactment of this law. In it a financial program authorizing forest research, having in mind particularly a scientific and thorough inventory of the country's forest resources, was set up. Under it this survey has been pushed and a system of regional forest experiment stations had been planned (Figs. 7-24, 7-25).

Northern Institute of Forest Genetics at Rhinelander, Wis.—one of the numerous forest research centers in the United States. (United States Forest Service.)

figure 7-24

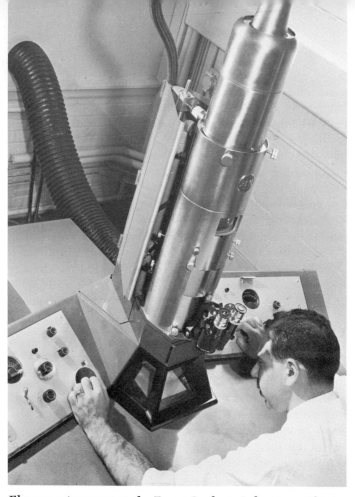

figure 7-25

*Electron microscope at the Forest Products Laboratory. This in-
strument permits study of the basic structure of wood in relation
to impregnation with preservatives, the interaction of wood
surfaces and paint films, and investigation of the size and structure of various cell constituents. (Forest Products Laboratory,
United States Forest Service.)*

KNUTSON-VANDENBERG ACT OF 1930 A financial program authorizing
funds for reforesting national forest lands was set up in this act. This
followed long effort by the Forest Service to get adequate support for
this work, and it carried another interesting provision: the earmarking of
certain additional proceeds levied on the purchaser of national forest
timber for reforesting or otherwise improving the particular sale areas
after cutting. This was significant because the Civilian Conservation
Corps with its wealth of labor, later to figure importantly in this work,
had not yet been created. The program still continues.

OTHER LAWS AND STUDIES FROM 1905 TO 1933   Not all the policy making and progress in public forestry concerned the Forest Service during this period. Agricultural lands within national forests could be homesteaded under an act of 1906. This led, in 1912, to a complete classification and listing of such lands. Two Supreme Court decisions in 1911 sustained the contention of the Forest Service that it was authorized to charge for and to regulate the grazing of domestic livestock on national forests. In 1916 the Oregon and California Railroad grant lands to the extent of 2 million acres were repossessed by the Federal government for violation of the grant terms, and the sale of land and timber was authorized under conditions inviting exploitation (this was corrected in 1939). The National Park Service was established in 1917 under an authorizing act passed in 1916. A study of the lumber industry by the Secretary of Commerce and Labor appearing in 1913 disclosed the startling concentrations of private timberland ownership and emphasized the speculative character and lack of forestry interest in the businesses of the holders. This led to the agitation for Federal regulation of timber cutting on private lands preceding the enactment of the Clarke-McNary Act of 1924. President Hoover's Commission on the Conservation and Administration of the Public Domain, appointed in 1930, recommended in 1931 the turning over of vast Federal areas to the states and ignored anything but forest cover as an appropriate characteristic of land to be added to national forests. His Timber Conservation Board concerned itself with wasteful overproduction in the lumber industry and with competition of national forest timber with that privately owned and marketed. In March, 1933, the so-called "Copeland Report" was issued as a result of a congressional resolution, and it concluded among other things that, since most of the forestry problems in America center in or grow out of private ownership, public ownership of forests should be greatly increased. It recognized the need for private enterprise and ownership in the forestry picture but pointed out that such management was not enough.

Other events, laws, and reports affecting forest policy figure in the history of this period from 1905 to 1933, but this summary brings the general story up to March, 1933. Then with the inauguration of President Franklin D. Roosevelt, circumstances combined with the President's leadership brought about a fast and far-reaching increase in all natural-resource conservation. Forest resources received marked attention.

Further Progress in Maintaining and Increasing the Productivity of Forest Resources. The reader must here pause to remind himself that, throughout an account that seems to be endless historical summary, the discussion is still concerned with ways in which maintenance and increase of forest productivity is brought about. He should also remember that, although accumulating and disseminating scientific knowledge and information on the techniques of forest management are vastly important, the way in which a democracy and its people make possible and get to work at the job of management determines whether or not it will be done. For this reason, the burst of physical accomplishment in all natural-resource conservation during the administration of President Franklin D. Roosevelt, mentioned in the introduction, merits further discussion strictly from the viewpoint of forestry.

Three considerations should be noted concerning the Civilian Conservation Corps (and, to a lesser extent, the other emergency labor organizations) (see pages 13–14): (1) the long-planned, time-consuming, labor-consuming program of reforestation, timber-stand improvement work, and building of fire-control, recreation, and other administrative facilities on public lands, both Federal and state; (2) the almost sudden granting of authority to use constructively, in both a social and a physical sense, the labor of millions of unemployed young men who were in distress through no fault of their own; and (3) the need for stimulating heavy industry and other business by furnishing a wartime-like market for their products.

We will pass over the inevitable question of why millions of young men should be unemployed in a rich democracy, ever; but their accomplishments in forestry during this period may be listed briefly. Public forest nurseries were greatly expanded, and many acres of Federal and state lands were reforested. Promising young-timber stands on 2,504,808 acres were thinned, released from overshading species, and otherwise set to growing faster. Forest-insect and forest-disease attacks were combatted on 13 million acres. Fire-control facilities—including observation posts, cleared firebreaks, low-grade roads for moving heavy equipment and men, water sources, airplane landing fields, warehouses, and headquarters for fire-control forces—were, in almost every instance, completed far in excess of anything that had appeared in all the preceding years. Recreation facilities in terms of camp grounds, water bodies, shelters, winter-sports areas, and improvements to hunting and fishing grounds received their first major attention in a physical sense. Grazing areas on the national forests were improved by the development of stock-watering facilities, fences to keep cattle from drifting off the assigned ranges, and control of damaging rodents. Terracing and revegetation of certain small, but important watersheds were made possible. Certain forest research projects requiring large forces and vast physical effort were completed. And cutting across these activities, the defense of the forests from fire was handled by a skilled force never before or since available.

Similar but very much smaller contributions were made by other labor organizations, including the WPA (Works Progress Administration).

Frequently unappreciated too, is the fact that this chance to get needed work done operated to increase the purchase of lands for national forest purposes and, to a lesser extent, to increase the areas of the national parks. Exchange of private, state, and Federal lands for the blocking up of the three types of forest holdings also went forward more rapidly than usual under a law of 1922 which authorized the trading of land or standing timber to state or private interests for lands owned by them in and along the border of national forests.

Still other unappreciated features of "emergency" work performed by the Civilian Conservation Corps and other public-work agencies are the capital-investment character of the properties developed and the increase in productivity of the forest resources that were brought about. These will pay off to a much greater extent than is assumed in the calculation of actual returns measurable only in money. The vast gain in human welfare has already been evident. The "Job Corps" camps, which are being established as a part of the "War on Poverty" program as this book goes to press, have similar objectives to those of the CCC with more emphasis on education.

In attempts at industrial recovery after the Crash of 1929, the various natural-resource industries learned a great deal about cooperation in trying to help themselves through the National Industrial Recovery Act with its "Codes of Fair Competition," of which the "Lumber Code" was one. It is hardly too much to say that the regional "rules" of forest practice which had a short tryout during the life of this act hastened a consciousness in the industry which has resulted in remarkable progress toward a sound industrial forestry program on the part of many large-timberland owners (Figs. 7-21, 7-22).

Curtailing Waste in Forest Utilization. When a tree is cut for lumber, only about 66 per cent of it, on the average, is utilized. Getting heavy logs to a mill is ordinarily too expensive, whatever the transportation system used, to allow the kind of close utilization which would salvage tops, large limbs, or broken and cull logs. Certain unavoidable waste also occurs in milling. The sawdust, slabs, edgings, trimmings, and cull lumber accumulate much faster than they can be used for fuel by the mill's power plant or by the local community. The unused part of the pulpwood cut amounts to 4 per cent; of veneer and plywood logs, 25 per cent; and of the cut for other purposes, 11 per cent. Even in the harvesting of farm-forest crops considerable waste occurs, and the owners of a portable sawmill faced with an uncertain market for their products and with limited mechanical equipment at their disposal cannot be bothered too much with the unprofitable business of guarding against waste. Finally the fabricating industries experience losses in seasoning and storing stocks of lumber and other wood items and in manufacturing

figure 7-26

Wood distillation plant of Cliffs-Dow Chemical Company in Northern Michigan using low-grade wood for manufacture of charcoal and chemical products. (Michigan Department of Conservation.)

processes. The parts of the tree, therefore, that finally land in a residence or a finished manufactured article represent anything but full utilization.

All along the line from logger to builder or manufacturer this problem of inefficient utilization of the forest crop is a daily puzzle, and in recent years much has been accomplished toward finding economic use for greater amounts of the tree. In fact many larger companies look to the waste pile for a part of their business.

Integration of wood-using industries is one way to improve utilization practices. The same company or group of enterprises may set up at one place a sawmill, a pulp mill, a wood-distillation plant, a post and pole yard, a fuel yard, and a woodenware or furniture plant—or a less complete combination. Cull logs and other logging waste might then find their way economically to the pulp mill or to the wood-distillation plant for use in the production of charcoal and chemicals (Fig. 7-26). Small-diameter waste would find outlets as pulpwood, chemical wood, or fence posts to be treated for prevention of decay and then marketed; and mill waste, including even bark, might come out finally as wallboard or insulating products. Even logging waste has recently been attacked with considerable vigor in the big timber regions of the West through (1) using portable sawmills set up at the logging site and salvaging much of the smaller-diameter material left by power logging of the larger and more valuable cuts; (2) "prelogging," in which the lighter material which would otherwise be abandoned is removed ahead of power logging; and (3) "relogging," which is a salvage operation using lighter machinery and following the regular removal of heavy logs.[9] Peeling of logs before sawing yields clear slabs which may be worked into chips for use in the manufacture of paper. This is a significant waste-prevention accomplishment.

Among the more interesting products obtainable from wood waste which are promising as the results of conservation in the wood industries are roofing felts and building papers from cull wood; cork substitutes from bark and useful linoleum manufacture; ethyl alcohol and yeast from wood sugars, the latter showing promise as human and animal food; turpentine extracted by steam and solvent processes; and briquetted waste for more efficient use as household fuel. Besides these, the possibilities of a greater demand for charcoal in the fast-growing light-metals industries is encouraging as an outlet for wood waste.

Continuing and intensive research in the field of wood-waste utilization is important. Growing interest in this line throughout the lumber and paper industries is significant. Any prolonging of the life of wood in service, through skillful construction and protection from decay and insect attack, such as termite damage, amounts to waste prevention and to real conservation.

THE FUTURE OF FORESTRY

Because demand for the products and services of forests is predicted to increase rather than level off in the next 2 decades, the program ahead becomes a matter of concern to everyone. Protection and management of existing forests, reforestation of denuded areas with high potential productivity, reconciling the several uses of the total forest resource, progressive control of waste in utilization, and research and straight thinking on ways and means to accomplish such purposes—these are the directions in which effort must be stepped up and maintained.

Protection and Management. Assurance that fire, insects, disease, and storm shall not rob the people of too large a part of the products and services cannot now be given by either public or private forest owners. Losses, however, have been reduced, more and more area is under organized protective effort, and salvage procedures are increasingly effective. While no completely new procedures are indicated in forest-fire control, two items need more attention: (1) definite local, regional, and international coordination of plans, forces, and equipment to meet conflagrations such as the one which hit New England in 1938 (three such compacts have been authorized by the Congress in recent years—the Northeastern Interstate Forest Fire Protection Compact in 1949 and one each

[9] Wood Waste in the United States, Report 4, *Reappraisal of the Forest Situation*, 1947, United States Forest Service, p. 21. (Mimeographed.)

for the Southeastern and the South Central states in 1954); and (2) increased analysis, study, and effort in preventing fires. More than 92 per cent of the fires recorded in 1952 were preventable in theory because they were man-caused. It is perhaps safe to say that half of them can be prevented in practice as the years go on, even though the *number* of fires has not yielded encouragingly to effort so far. Hazards can be reduced; precautions can be made easier and can become matters of habit; and appeals, while they have the help of the advertising industry, can and must at the same time compete with the most universal and effective commercial advertising that the world has ever known. Use of forest-fire information in public-school teaching holds real promise in preventing forest fires. Even the comic strip is being used effectively. The annual "Smokey the Bear" campaign in cooperation with the National Advertising Council and the "Keep Green" organizations of the various states are making themselves felt.

Insect and disease control promises to gain effectiveness from the Forest Pest Control Act of 1947, through which prompt action may be obtained in the event of sudden outbreaks. Injury of forests by animals may eventually be considered also under this act (Fig. 7-27). Appropriations under this act, however, must be increased; more entomologists and pathologists must be trained and employed; and modern methods, insecticides, and fungicides must be made fully and safely available as life histories and control programs are worked out. Airplane dusting and spraying is becoming effective and economically feasible (see Fig. 7-14). Continuing research is particularly important in these fields in order to

The porcupine feeds on the bark of forest trees, and injury from this and other animal sources must be taken into account in forest management. (Michigan Department of Conservation.)

figure 7-27

determine the need for proclaiming and enforcing quarantines, recommending use of insect- and disease-resistant species for reforestation, and cutting practices which will amount to biological control through timed removal or reduction in number of host species preferred by various insects and diseases. Finding uses for and developing economical methods of salvaging fire- and insect-killed forests and those felled by storms require more study in line with present work on the Tillamook burn in Oregon and on the beetle-killed Englemann spruce in the Central Rocky Mountain country.

All this will require heavy investment of public and private funds, but it should be *considered an investment* in the permanent productivity of an indispensable resource.

Management of existing commercial forests is improving, and there need be little worry about the relatively small proportion of such areas that is in the hands of the public agencies. Larger private holdings, too, are lining up as "tree farms" (Fig. 7-30), and well-organized corporations are making a good showing in their cutting practices, in the control of fire and its use as a forest management tool, and even in tree breeding to develop more productive forests. A disproportionately large acreage in small private holdings presents a less encouraging picture and a tougher problem. A considerable amount of improved practice on such lands has been brought about through the wood-purchasing policies of large operating companies. Some public regulation of cutting practices is appropriate, for the ax can be a destroyer or a builder and maintainer. Federal laws in this direction have long been opposed by the lumber industry. Self-regulation had a trial under the NRA (National Recovery Administration), but state laws, although they are rare and weak, perhaps offer the best approach. Until these are perfected, and along with their operation, the Federal forest experiment stations offer valuable advice to the industries. Many of the latter employ trained foresters, and increasingly enlightened self-interest becomes an incentive to better private forest management. Farm holdings receive better management through the work of Federal and state agencies. Such help was speeded up by the Cooperative Forest Management Act of 1950. In 1955, 35,000 woodland owners were furnished assistance on 5,762,008 acres of land, or 2.2 per cent of the nation's small-forest acreage. Gross returns to the owners from the sale of forest products amounted to 3.7 million dollars. More than 9,000 small operators also were assisted.[10] Demand for help is brisk.

Reforestation. Contrary to much popular belief, tree planting is not our top forestry job in this country. But to bring an estimated 52 million acres of barren or poorly stocked forest land into production, the present effort, at which rate the job will not be completed for 75 years, must be stepped

[10] *Report of the Chief of the Forest Service*, p. 27, 1964.

up. And progress is being made. In 1962 forty-nine tree nurseries in forty six states produced and distributed 1,008,398,000 trees that were used to reforest 1,141,182, acres. State-owned and industrial forest nurseries produced most of the stock. Direct seeding by hand, machine methods, or airplane was accomplished in thirty nine states on 221,517 acres, of which 65 per cent was private land; 29 per cent, Federal; and 6 per cent, non-Federal public land.[11] Direct seeding is increasing each year.

Reconciling Various Uses of Forests. There is nothing automatic or magic about the phrase "multiple use." It works only when worked at. The same forest can produce timber, game, fur, forage for livestock, water, beauty and restful atmosphere, and even maintain itself with mining in operation underneath it. Such a combination of objectives, however, is bound to present conflicts. Priorities must be decided upon and regulations recognizing such priorities enforced. One of the most baffling things currently is the conflict between the desire to keep certain areas in the forest as dedicated wilderness and the increasing pressure to harvest from such areas any resource that will contribute to local economy. The United States, as the richest democracy in the world, has not yet decided firmly that primitive and inspirational wilderness values have much of a bid to priority except in rare instances. Legislation that was designed to obtain definite dedication of public wilderness areas, in which such values should be given priority, was enacted by the Eighty-eighth Congress in 1964 after long debate. Even though this legislation creates no new administrative agency, its opponents argue that it challenges the authority of the present agencies to practice a multiple-use land policy in the over-all management of public lands. And, of course, others oppose the idea on the grounds that *any* such dedications constitute a waste of natural resources. Another conflict arises in umpiring the competition between animals, wild and domestic, on the one hand and trees and water on the other. Rabbits, porcupines, cows, deer, pine trees, farm-woodland sprouts, sheep on the range, and city water systems all get into the picture. And the forest usually takes the beating before the unscrambling is effected. Techniques are important in multiple use and so are policies. River-valley and interbureau programs offer a real chance to work out equitable priorities.

Increasing Control of Waste in Utilization. The information on waste in harvesting and manufacturing forest products on pages 201 to 203 points to the need for continuing research to find uses for parts of trees now discarded in logging and for mill wastes such as sawdust, small-dimension slabs and edgings, and bark (Fig. 7-28). Research alone, however, is not

[11] *Ibid.*

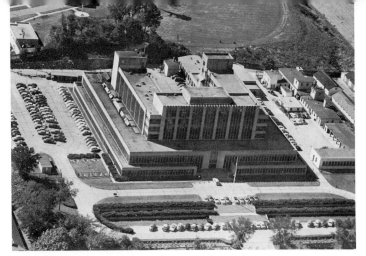

figure 7-28
Aerial view of the Forest Products Laboratory maintained by the United States Forest Service in cooperation with the University of Wisconsin. Along with studying the fundamentals of forest products, the staff of this station works to curtail their waste. (Forest Products Laboratory, United States Forest Service.)

the answer. The adoption of waste-prevention practices requires demonstration and "selling" to operators, many of whom are not in business on a scale large enough to make such practices attractive. Opportunities for the "sales engineer" or the "research missionary" will no doubt increase. Perhaps the most notable development in reducing waste is the use of chips from slabs and other formerly waste wood for the manufacture of paper. This practice is widespread in the South and in the Northwest (see page 203).

Incentives and Policies to Meet Future Forest Yields. Whether or not the practice of forestry at the hands of private industry contributes its share to future needs of forest products and services is to a considerable extent in the hands of the public. Exploitation of natural resources is not usually too risky a business. Conservation through intensive management, on the other hand, may be risky. This brings questions of ownership, credit, insurance, and regulation into the picture. At present, ownership of commercial forest lands (those which actually produce our timber crop) lines up with public agencies, accounting for 137 million acres; and private companies and individuals own 367 million acres, almost 300 million of which are in the hands of owners of considerably less than 5,000 acres each.[12] To assure good management of the latter is a real problem and is tied in with size of holding, available markets, and the dispensing of needed advice and help. Private owners are, in a sense, trustees of the forest resources in their hands. So long as they can do

[12] Timber Trends in the United States, U.S. Forest Serv., Forest Resource Rept. 17, 1965, p. 102.

the combined jobs of supplying the public with products and keeping their lands productive, their good stewardship entitles them to continue as owners (trustees). Such an arrangement is the only one fair to the people as a whole, and it should govern the action of public agencies in acquiring extensive increased holdings. It should also constitute notice to owners that the public expects good management on their part *and* that the public will cooperate in regard to grants-in-aid for protection, research, and advice on management problems and help on credit and insurance. Credit is particularly important to small owners. Insurance not now available is needed by all owners, and that part of the public engaged in banking and insurance has considerable responsibility in these directions. Some public help may be necessary and appropriate.

How the Forestry Program in the United States Goes Forward. Activity in the field of forestry in this democracy demands organization and leadership. These rest in four bureaus and groups, of which the United States Forest Service in the Department of Agriculture is the busiest. Its line-up of work is seen in the diagram (Fig. 7-29) on page 209. In addition to administering more than 150 national forests, some of them more than a million acres in area, its cooperative relations with the states and other bureaus and with the owners of private forest land are far-flung and effective.

Another Federal bureau which is active is the Bureau of Land Management in the Department of the Interior, which has the responsibility for some 110 million wooded acres of the public domain including 46 million acres of commercial forests. Certain lands belonging to the Indian tribes are also administered in trust by this Bureau.

A third group of agencies which figures large in the forestry picture is the state forestry departments. No less than thirty-three states engage in forest-fire control, reforestation, and in the administration of state forests of varying size and importance.

The fourth group, which is growing in importance, is the owners and operators of forests on private lands. These owners may be large or small lumber or paper companies or individual farmers and landowners of small, but important, timberlands. In the last 3 decades these forest owners have come largely under the leadership of the lumber and paper companies as "tree farms" dedicated to sound forest management and registered under the American Forest Products Industries which cooperates with the public agencies. Owners sign up to give their lands protection and management for the production of timber with certain specified practices which will assure this objective. Certificates, which are revocable for noncompliance, are issued. This movement is highly successful, having signed up 28,455 owners representing 65,501,143 acres as of May 1, 1965, and involving every form of ownership from small patches of woods

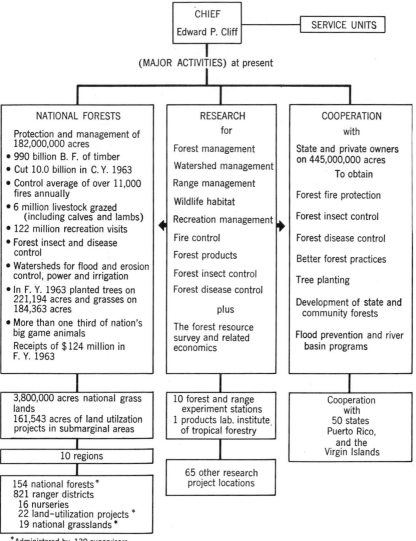

FOREST SERVICE
U. S. DEPARTMENT OF AGRICULTURE

CHIEF
Edward P. Cliff

SERVICE UNITS

(MAJOR ACTIVITIES) at present

NATIONAL FORESTS

Protection and management of 182,000,000 acres
- 990 billion B. F. of timber
- Cut 10.0 billion in C. Y. 1963
- Control average of over 11,000 fires annually
- 6 million livestock grazed (including calves and lambs)
- 122 million recreation visits
- Forest insect and disease control
- Watersheds for flood and erosion control, power and irrigation
- In F. Y. 1963 planted trees on 221,194 acres and grasses on 184,363 acres
- More than one third of nation's big game animals
Receipts of $124 million in F. Y. 1963

RESEARCH
for

Forest management

Watershed management

Range management

Wildlife habitat

Recreation management

Fire control

Forest products

Forest insect control

Forest disease control

plus

The forest resource survey and related economics

COOPERATION
with

State and private owners on 445,000,000 acres
To obtain

Forest fire protection

Forest insect control

Forest disease control

Better forest practices

Tree planting

Development of state and community forests

Flood prevention and river basin programs

3,800,000 acres national grass lands
161,543 acres of land utilzation projects in submarginal areas

10 forest and range experiment stations
1 products lab. institute of tropical forestry

Cooperation with
50 states
Puerto Rico, and the
Virgin Islands

10 regions

65 other research project locations

154 national forests*
821 ranger districts
16 nurseries
22 land–utilization projects *
19 national grasslands *

*Administered by 130 supervisors

figure 7-29
Major activities of the United States Forest Service as of June, 1964. (United States Forest Service.)

figure 7-30

An owner posts his tree farm which has been certified by the
Regional Committee of the American Tree Farm System. He
is one of some 27,500 participants. (American Forest Products
Industries, Inc.)

located on farms to the forest holdings of some of the largest corporations (Fig. 7-30).

Three other Federal bureaus should also be noted. The Fish and Wildlife Service manages timberland contained in Federal wildlife refuges
and other wildlife reservations. The Soil Conservation Service offers help
in the management of farm plans involving timberlands. The Tennessee
Valley Authority manages the timberlands on its reservoir sites and
assists farmers in its territory.

Situation Surveys by the Forest Service. Under the title *Timber Resources for America's Future* the Forest Service published in 1958 the
most complete survey ever undertaken of the nation's timber situation
and prospective future demands for timber products.[13] It was conducted
in collaboration with states, forest industries, and other Federal agencies.
Briefly, the study shows that there has been considerable progress in
many phases of forestry, that growth is increasing, and that productivity
is moderately high on industrial and publicly owned forests. But it also
indicates that growth will probably have to be doubled in the future
if it is to keep pace with the demands of increasing population. In spite

[13] Timber Resources for America's Future, *U.S. Forest Serv., Forest Resource Rept.*
14, 1958.

of the fact that industry was involved in the study, certain of the spokesmen for industry have shown a tendency to be complacent and to question the conclusions.

In 1965, *Timber Trends in the United States,* published by the Forest Service, appeared and for the first time announced that timber growth in the country had come to exceed timber harvest. The reservation was made, however, that this increase was unsatisfactory inasmuch as timber of large size and special quality was not included in this increase of growth.[14]

Highlights of this report include the following statements:

> Demand for timber products are projected to increase about 80 per cent by the year 2000.
> Continued expansion in population and economic growth are anticipated.
> Continued technological improvements in production and marketing in the forest industries will be essential to achieve projected demands for timber.
> Imports of timber products are likely to increase somewhat, but most of the timber required to supply future U.S. markets is expected to come from domestic forests.
> Timber supply-demand relationships in the United States have generally improved over the past decade.
> Prospective timber growth and inventories in the U.S.—with recent levels of forest Management—appear sufficient to meet projected demands for the next two or three decades, but not in later years of this century.
> Declining quality of timber resources represents a major problem for wood-using industries.
> The timber supply outlook is relatively favorable for the pulp and paper industry, but not as encouraging for the lumber and plywood industries.
> Projected timber demands to the year 2000 could be met with more intensive forest management and utilization.
> Forest industries depend on farm and miscellaneous ownerships for half of their material requirements.
> The long-range outlook and uncertainties of projections must be considered in formulating forestry programs.

The future of forestry in this democracy can be assured only as its citizens demand it. The strongest public agencies, and the most powerful members of the industry as well, need the support of a public that understands the indispensability of forests.

BIBLIOGRAPHY

ALLEN, SHIRLEY WALTER AND GRANT WILLIAM SHARPE: An Introduction to American Forestry, 3d ed., McGraw-Hill Book Company, New York, 1960.

[14] Timber Trends in the United States, *op. cit.*

American Forest Products Industries, Inc., Letters and magazine, Washington, D.C., 1965.

American Forests, magazine of the American Forestry Association, Washington, D.C., 1930–1965.

Annual Reports of the Chief of the Forest Service.

Annual Reports of the Secretary of the Interior (particularly those sections relating to the Bureau of Land Management), 1949–1964.

DAVIS, KENNETH P.: Forest Fire: Control and Use, McGraw-Hill Book Company, New York, 1959.

Forest Fire Statistics for 1963, U.S. Forest Service, 1964. (Mimeographed.)

Forestry Handbook, R. D. Forbes, ed., for the Society of American Foresters, The Ronald Press Company, New York, 1961.

GRINNELL, JOSEPH: Wild Animal Life as a Product and as a Necessity of National Forests, *J. Forestry,* vol. 22, pp. 840–841, Washington, D.C., 1924.

HALL, J. ALFRED, AND T. J. MOSLEY: Products of American Forests, U.S. Forest Service, 1946.

LANDSBERG, HANS H., LEONARD L. FISCHMAN, AND JOSEPH L. FISHER: Resources in America's Future, The Johns Hopkins Press, Baltimore, 1962.

Quest for Quality, U.S. Department of the Interior Conservation Yearbook, 1965.

Resources for Freedom, vol. I, Report of the President's Materials Policy Commission, 1952.

Timber Resources for America's Future, *U.S. Forest Serv., Forest Resource Rept.* 14, 1958.

Timber Trends in the United States, *U.S. Forest Serv., Forest Resource Rept.* 17, 1965.

8 GRASSLANDS

MAN'S BASIC BREAD grains—wheat, rice, corn, rye, barley, and oats—are grasses. This large plant family includes about 3,500 species, 1,500 of which occur in the United States. In addition to these cereals the family includes the bamboos; sugar cane; ornamental grasses used for lawns and parks; and the many species of sod crops which provide forage or pasture for all types of farm animals, as well as for deer, elk, antelope, and rodents such as the prairie dog.

At one time the natural grasslands covered two-fifths of the entire land area of the United States. The climate is one controlling factor in the development of natural grasslands: rainfall is usually insufficient to support the growth of forests but sufficient to prevent the formation of deserts. The tall, medium, and short grasses reflect the varied amounts of rainfall in the areas. Three kinds of grassland areas are recognized: the short-grass land; the tall-grass land, or prairie; and the savanna. In the United States the most extensive grassland regions are the short-grass areas of the Great Plains. Rainfall in this area is light but sufficient to support the shallow-rooted short grasses. The tall-grass land, or prairie, is found in regions of heavier rainfall in central North America. These areas do have sufficient rainfall to support trees, and why grass instead of forests grew in this climate has been a matter for speculation. Savannas are the grasslands of the tropics. They are widespread, exceed the prairie in extent, and equal in extent the short-grass areas of the world. They cover large areas of Africa and Brazil.

The Uses of the Grasslands in the United States. The breeding and pasturing of domestic livestock for the purpose of producing meat, leather, and wool are two of the oldest industries known to mankind and ones which have long depended largely upon publicly owned or very extensive privately owned grasslands. The early colonists in the United States seem to have taken grass for granted. They turned their livestock loose to graze on unoccupied land in the colonies and were unaware of the variation in the nutritional value of plants and of the need to care for and develop pastures. As farming expanded, it became necessary to protect the crops from the free-grazing livestock and this was done with fencing or by employing herdsmen or shepherds. The practice of allowing cattle to graze on unfenced land persisted as pioneers moved to the Great Plains, where, shortly after the Civil War, a thriving cattle industry developed. Presence of suitable natural vegetation, increased population and the demand for more meat, accessibility of markets provided by completion of the transcontinental railroad, the slaughter of the buffalo, and the subjugation of the Plains Indians—all contributed to the rapid increase of this industry. By 1880 the range was fully stocked. The land was mostly government land, and it was freely used by the stockmen on a first-come–first-served basis. Without regulated grazing, the supply of tall grass was soon exhausted and the short-grass supply was threatened. Man's long history as a herdsman seems to have taught him little about overgrazing; so it may not be surprising that overuse both of enormous areas of privately owned grassland and of the vast public acreage under the stewardship of government agencies has created a grasslands record more of destruction than of sustained yield.

In the United States today, approximately 889.1 million acres, both public and privately owned, are used for grazing. Nearly three-fourths of this area lies west of the Mississippi River, and an entire new discipline known as range management has been developed to deal with it. In 1959 about 4.1 million cattle and 9.3 million sheep grazed on about 242 million acres of federally owned range lands administered by the Department of Agriculture through the Forest Service and by the Department of the Interior through the Bureau of Land Management.[1] This number of animals should keep nearly one-fifth of our population supplied with a generous yearly ration of beef and mutton, to say nothing of accompanying amounts of wool and leather. These figures emphasize the need for conserving every available acre of range and for putting a stop to the traditional abuse of the grazing lands.

As is true with other natural resources, the range and its forage form the material foundation for an important segment of our economy. It is not to be taken lightly that nearly 2 million farm and ranch families obtain a considerable portion of their living from the range-livestock business or that businesses closely related to the industry add perhaps 5 million to 10 million more people whose living is geared to whether or not the livestock enterprises prosper.

Nearly every acre of range has other uses and values besides forage production—to protect watersheds, produce timber, give wildlife a home, and provide a place for recreation. Responsible projections indicate that demands for outdoor recreation will intensify very rapidly within the foreseeable future, and Federal range lands will certainly get their share of attention. The increase in number of big-game hunters, for example, may jump from 6.3 million in 1960 to about 12 million by 1980—an increase of about 90 per cent.[2] These are the "other" values of the range. If grazing is properly managed, the various uses are usually compatible with the use for forage by livestock.[3]

The Nature of the Forage Resources. Natural pasture or range vegetation is more than just grass, although the stockmen would probably be happier if brush species, weeds, sedges, and even small trees did not

[1] Prospectus to Trial Program of Public Land Range Appraisal, *S. Doc.* 119, 87th Cong., 2d sess., 1962.
[2] *Ibid.*
[3] Charles A. Connaughton, Grass and Water and Trees, *Yearbook of U.S. Dept. Agr.* 1948.

figure 8-1

Sheep grazing in high mountain meadow, Plumas National Forest, California. (Photo by Daniel O. Todd, United States Forest Service.)

complete the forage picture. One well-defined range of considerable area may serve to feed the herds or flocks of several owners and may include vast open tracts of grass, patches of sagebrush, mountainsides of chaparral (a term used to designate a type of brush involving many species), areas of open timber and mountain meadow (Fig. 8-1), and finally old burns or forest-fire areas which have come back to grass, weeds, and brush rather than to forest. The food or, as the stockman says, the "feed" value of species other than grass may vary with the class of stock which graze upon them, and this fact is naturally considered in assigning stock to any given locality. Goats, for example, can do well on leaves and twigs of brush- and dwarf-timber species. Horses need grass. Sheep sometimes do well on weeds. Cattle will take a certain amount of "browse"—or leaf, twig, and seed of brush species—in addition to grass, which they prefer (Fig. 8-2). Hogs, of which relatively few are grazed in the West, seek the "mast" or fallen acorns and other nuts from foothill hardwood forests. Larger wild animals, depending upon species and haunts, feed on everything from water plants to twigs and foliage of cone-bearing trees.

Use of the range lands is limited to a considerable extent by the distribution of water as well as by types of vegetation and nearness of grazing grounds to home ranch properties. These among other things have affected the ownership pattern which makes it hard to find large unbroken blocks under single ownership, public or private. Quantitatively, about one-half the area of Western range is privately owned, and of the remainder, one-sixth is state land and five-sixths Federal.

Difficulty in reaching agreement on range management is often increased by these complex patterns of land ownership. A given large-size

<figure 8-2

Cattle grazing in Sawtooth National Forest, Idaho. (Photo by Bluford W. Muir, United States Forest Service.)

unit of range may well include any or all of the following ownerships: Federal, state, railroad grant, mining claim and patent, homestead, timber corporation, Indian reservation, and ranch. Moreover, it has seemed good business to the stockmen to allow large stretches of grazing land to remain in public and corporation ownership. In the early days large livestock owners fought, literally, attempts by small farmers to fragment the range, and cattlemen and sheepmen engaged in notorious feuds. So long as range land was there for the taking, free of charge, and so long as control of the watering places could be gained, there was no need to acquire title or to assume the obligations of proprietorship. These might include payment of taxes, maintenance of improvements, revegetation and protection of over-grazed areas, eradication of poisonous plants, and even reduction in numbers of animals grazed on favorite ranges.

Why the Range Resource Is Depleted. Estimates by the Conservation Needs Inventory made between 1957 and 1960 indicated that of privately owned Western range 50 per cent was in poor condition and only 5 per cent could be rated excellent.[4] The basic cause of unsatisfactory range condition is overgrazing. Hungry animals feed so heavily that the sod becomes broken and the grasses are eaten down so that no seed is produced. Seed from the less palatable weeds and brush species are then likely to take over and produce a poorer forage, if any. Because the grass cover is broken and because of restless trampling of exposed soil, erosion is likely to set in (Figs. 8-3, 8-4). Such rainfall as occurs in the drier range country is likely to be torrential at times, and runoff water aggravates the erosion. Even wind erosion occurs when the native sod has been broken by cultivation.

[4] Soil and Water Conservation Needs, *U.S. Dept. Agr. Misc. Publ.* 971, 1965.

figure 8-3
Severe gully erosion on overgrazed high-elevation summer range.
Note bare ground. Nez Perce National Forest, Idaho. (Photo by
Walter F. Mueggler, United States Forest Service.)

Setting the Use of the Range in Order. Until the national forests (then called "forest reserves") were established and put under management, no attempt at regulation of grazing on public lands had been made. Even then, in the first years of this century, the only legal basis for such regulation was contained in the law of 1897 which authorized the Secretary of the Interior to make rules and regulations for the administration of the reserves. This authority was later extended to the Secretary of Agriculture with the transfer of the reserves to that department and their later designation as national forests. Finding itself faced with a grazing occupancy on the national forests, the Forest Service, a bureau of the Department of Agriculture, worked out regulations which the

figure 8-4
The light soil on many Western mountain lands is subject to
gully erosion from overgrazing. Mono National Forest. (Photo
by United States Forest Service.)

Secretary approved and published, and these still apply on national forest land. They define preferences in the allotment of grazing privileges to former users who are bona fide settlers and who operate dependent ranches; they set grazing fees on a per head and seasonal basis; they define range-management practices required of the permittee and provide a basis for cooperative improvement of the range properties and use of intermingled private land; and, finally, they define and provide penalties for trespass on the ranges. The courts have upheld the Secretary's authority to make and enforce grazing regulations, and their operation through the years has resulted in beneficial use of the forage on the national forests and in perceptible improvement of the grazing conditions.

Not until 1934 was legislation enacted which would bring about regulation of unreserved grazing lands of the public domain under the jurisdiction of the Department of the Interior. Then the Taylor Grazing Act, which really started working in 1935, brought about the establishment of grazing districts, the adoption of moderate fees, the allotment of range to local users, and actual management of a considerable part of the lands in the Western public-land states. The administration is similar to, but somewhat less intensive than, that of the Forest Service. The control of water figures largely in the allotment of range to various stockmen, and certain administrative powers are delegated to boards of users. It is fair to say that long neglect of these so-called "Taylor grazing lands" and the far-flung extent of the open-range livestock business have made the task of regulation extremely complex and difficult. Furthermore, some of the unorganized public lands outside the grazing districts are used on a lease-of-area basis, and others are without even a lease agreement. Trespass on these lands, which along with the grazing districts are administered by the Department's Bureau of Land Management, is difficult to control. The Bureau's manpower is scant, and the areas are vast and scattered. On public-domain grazing lands in Nevada, for example, there is one technical range man for every 2 million acres.[5]

Certain large private holdings in checkerboard pattern, where land grants were made to railroads and wagon roads, share in the good management of the alternate square miles of Federal range. Livestock, of course, pay little attention to survey lines, and these are frequently the only boundaries between private and public lands. Permits are issued to stockmen who have obtained leases on the alternate railroad sections and whose stock graze a part of the time over Federal lands. The stock of other owners in turn graze over the railroad lands, and in adhering to the numbers of stock which Federal land will carry, the same formula must be applied to the intermingled private lands. This practice extends, to

[5] *Conservation News,* National Wildlife Federation, Washington, D.C., March, 1904.

lesser degree, to any areas of intermingled public and private ownership. Moreover, it should be understood that the Agricultural Conservation program, administered by the Department of Agriculture, provides extensive financial help for conservation practices on private range lands. These include deferred grazing (which amounts to resting the land) and reseeding and have affected about a million acres of privately owned range lands.

A specific program aimed at improving management of federally owned range is represented by the creation of the national grasslands. These lands first passed to public ownership through the Resettlement Administration, which, starting in 1934, bought and retired from cultivation many submarginal farms and ranches. As these areas underwent rehabilitation they were called Land Utilization Projects, and in 1960 some 3.8 million acres of them were designated as national grasslands to be administered by the Forest Service.[6]

The impressive part of the picture is the activity, to whatever extent, found in conserving large blocks of both public and private range.

The Demands and Possibilities of Range Conservation. It has been pointed out that range lands have suffered depletion from overgrazing and subsequent deterioration of forage and, finally, from erosion. With this succession of damage, the indicated conservation steps usually included are given in the following order: (1) reducing the numbers of grazing animals using the particular range; (2) preventing further erosion and repairing erosion damage, (3) reseeding the range where necessary; and (4) adopting a definite set of good management practices, which may include such requirements as development of water, confining stock to appropriate range by drift fences (usually crude fences which supplement natural barriers), systematic salting, eradication of poisonous plants, careful observance of grazing seasons, and using special driveways instead of highways for putting stock on the range and bringing it off.

This sort of program cannot be successfully carried out either by public or private effort alone and certainly not without expert advice and service based on dependable research.

Fortunately experiment stations combine grazing research with forest research (Fig. 8-5), and findings are shared by all public and private interests. Investigations are constantly being made covering such questions as the carrying capacity of certain types of range, best methods of reseeding spent range properties, improved methods of herding and of removing marketable stock to avoid shrinkage in weight, improvement of strains of grazing animals, and eradication of insect and plant pests.

---

[6] The National Grasslands Story, U.S. Forest Service, PA-607, March, 1964.

figure 8-5

Recovery of overgrazed area after 6 years of protection by fence in foreground, Tonto National Forest, Arizona. (Photo by Leland J. Prater, United States Forest Service.)

Recently published results of the Conservation Needs Inventory (page 217) have provided an excellent overview of land capabilities, uses, and conservation needs as these problems pertain to non-Federal lands.[7] Also, in 1962, the Senate Committee on Appropriations directed the Secretaries of Agriculture and of the Interior to undertake a trial program of range appraisal on lands administered by the Forest Service and the Bureau of Land Management. The resulting report[8] demonstrated that a full-scale appraisal of federally owned range lands could lead to greatly improved use of this far-flung resource.

An excellent summary of the nation's grazing-land needs has recently appeared:[9]

> The prospective need for pasture and rangeland in the decades ahead is in sharp contrast to that for cultivated cropland. More, not less, grazing land will be needed to keep up with the increasing demand for animal products.
>
> If the population increases by 45 per cent by 1980, as expected, the need for livestock production will increase 50 to 55 per cent over the 1959 level (USDA-LWP, 1962, p. 36) and the demand for meat from grazing animals probably will increase 70 to 80 per cent.[10] The grazing capacity of existing range and pasture cannot be expected to increase rapidly

[7] Agricultural Land Resources, *U.S. Dept. Agr., Agr. Inform. Bull.* 263, May, 1962.
[8] Trial Program of Public Land Range Appraisal, *S. Doc.* 119, August, 1962.
[9] Soil and Water Conservation Needs: A National Inventory, *U.S. Dept. Agr. Misc. Publ.* 971, 1965.
[10] Unpublished data, U.S. Department of Agriculture and U.S. Department of the Interior, compiled for President's Message on National Resources, January, 1962.

enough to accommodate such an increase in livestock. Some of the additional production will depend on new land added to the grazing resource. It is also important that full conservation treatment be applied as rapidly as possible to bring land now in range and pasture to a high level of productivity.

Existing pasture and rangeland is ill-prepared to supply the rapidly expanding needs for meat. A recent USDA study showed that grazing lands are producing forage at no more than half their potential.

For the past half century or more, continued overuse has seriously depleted forage resources. Brush, weeds, and other unwanted vegetation have encroached upon millions of acres that once were good grazing land; tons of topsoil are being eroded from them to pollute streams, fill reservoirs, and damage domestic, agricultural, and industrial water supplies. A long and costly effort will be necessary to halt the deterioration, even if the task is begun immediately; the longer it is delayed, the greater will be the ultimate cost of restoring grazing land to the level necessary to meet forage needs in the years ahead.

Forage and range problems are particularly critical in the eleven Western States where water shortage is also a chronic problem. Conservative estimates indicate that half the sediment being carried into major streams of the Southwest comes from land where grazing has upset the delicate balance between plant cover and the soil mantle. Steeply sloping land with scant plant cover and excessive erosion is being grazed in conjunction with better land with which it is interspersed.

The objectives of pasture and rangeland conservation are: (1) to stop deterioration of grazing resources; (2) to rehabilitate and repair those resources that have been damaged by overuse and neglect; (3) to create public understanding that will give appropriate consideration to forage resource problems; and (4) to coordinate the forage resource programs with other conservation programs on public and private land.

Forage resource problems play no favorites with the different land ownerships, geographic areas, or managing agencies. Neither the Federal Government nor private interests alone can be expected to assume the responsibility for correcting these problems.

Since over two-thirds of the grazing land is in private ownership, voluntary action by producers must be depended on for most of the improvements to be made on pasture and range. Thousands of private land operators have already made substantial improvements in grazing land. Greatest achievements have occurred where there has been a combination of: (1) active local leadership such as through soil conservation districts and grazing associations, (2) inspired and sound technical assistance, (3) rational cost sharing, and (4) informed and inspired producers.

All problems and treatments considered in the Conservation Needs Inventory (CNI), except management of excess water, require attention every year to attain conservation on pasture and rangeland. In this respect, the conservation job is never complete.

Farmers and ranchers must realize the importance of the management and cultural practices needed to keep their grassland productive and to furnish quality forage throughout the grazing season.

Basically, these measures center around growing forage species that are adapted to the soil and climate; supplying needed amounts of fertilizers and soil amendments, especially on tame pastures; using grazing management that favors desired plants; and controlling weeds, brush, and other undesirable plants.

Grassland is the most neglected part of many farms and ranches, yet on many it can be made to produce more net income per acre than many other crops.

The Citizen and the Range Resources. As has been pointed out earlier in this chapter (page 215) about one-fourth of the nation's grazing pasture lands lie east of the Mississippi River. However, to the average American weaned and nurtured on television, the range is synonymous with the West, and he tends to think of range problems in Western terms. The stockmen who make their living and serve the rest of us by using natural forage resources are in a tough business, fraught with everything from drought and disease to blizzards and occasional ruinous markets. These stockmen are essential to the local and national economies. They are, indeed, the trustees of the range, whether they are users or owners. However, even though raising livestock is a beneficial use of the Western range, it is not the only one. The ordinary citizen has a real interest in range conservation in terms of the price of meat, wool, and leather and the availability of these things. But he is also interested in terms of the scenery he wants on his vacation; in terms of wise expenditure of the taxes he pays for irrigation and power reservoirs that should not be silted full by soil eroded from overgrazed lands; and, just possibly, in terms of the picturesque segments of American culture which he does not want to disappear.

BIBLIOGRAPHY

Annual Report of the Director of the Bureau of Land Management for 1956 (*Statistical Appendix*), U.S. Department of the Interior, 1957. (Mimeographed.)

Annual Reports of Chief of Forest Service, 1949–1963.

Annual Reports of the Secretary of the Interior, 1949–1963.

CLAWSON, MARION: Western Range Livestock Industry, McGraw-Hill Book Company, New York, 1950.

Grass, Yearbook of U.S. Dept. Agr., 1948.

HUMPHREY, ROBERT R.: Range Ecology, The Ronald Press Company, New York, 1962.

LANDSTROM, KARL S.: Conservation of the Public Range in Our Public Lands, U.S. Department of the Interior, 1951.

Long Range Agricultural Policy and Programs, *U.S. Dept. Agr. Sup. 4,* 1947.

Resources for Freedom, vol. I, report of the President's Materials Policy Commission, 1952.

SMITH, GUY HAROLD, AND ASSOCIATES: Conservation of Natural Resources, John Wiley & Sons, Inc., New York, 1950.

STODDART, LAURENCE A., AND ARTHUR D. SMITH: Range Management, 2d ed., McGraw-Hill Book Company, New York, 1955.

WELLS, GEORGE, AND IRIS WELLS: The Handbook of Wilderness Travels, Harper & Row, Publishers, Incorporated, New York, 1956.

The Western Range, S. Doc. 199, 74th Cong., 2d sess., 1936.

9 WILD ANIMALS[1]

WHILE IT IS possible to group certain animal forms on the basis of their usefulness for given purposes, many animals sought as the quarries of the hunter or as the producers of coats or hides that may be sold for profit represent other values which are easy to establish though often difficult to measure. Among these animals are those which control harmful insects and rodents. Also included are those which have aesthetic and spectacle value for the attraction of money-spending tourists and the less easily appraised value for human observation and enjoyment, study, and photographic stalking. On the other hand a grouping such as "game and fur animals" fails to suggest the important fact that many of the fur species are predatory upon game species and constitute real nuisances to the poultry raiser and the livestock grower. By the same token the game species displaced by encroachment of human settlement and activity frequently become destructive of crops if not of other animal species. Here they are said to be guilty of depredations. One must also bear in mind that a lot of so-called game animals are producers of valuable hides and furs and that fur predators furnish hunters with some of their most exciting targets. The examples chosen for discussion under the above heading will attempt to point out these overlapping benefits and nuisance features. Game birds and miscellaneous animal forms will be included. Further discussion in another chapter will cover fisheries and certain ocean species, including seals, which are important fur bearers. The role of each grouping in its natural-resource aspects will be emphasized.

As compared with soil, water, air, sunshine, and vegetation, wild animals sought principally for sport, wild meat, and furs are perhaps less essential for the survival of mankind, except for certain primitive peoples. The place of these resources in the happiness of men and in that part of our economy of which they are the basis, however, indicates that men have no intention of getting along without them. Americans who buy more than 33 million licenses to hunt, fish, and trap and those who hunt without license on their own lands and elsewhere include more hunters right now than can find something to shoot at. And the grumble of the disappointed fur trapper is growing louder. In 1963, a total of 13,994,375 hunting licenses brought in a gross income of $68,106,023 for that year, and the number of hunters increased by 245,012 over the 1962 total.[2]

A recent study by the Fish and Wildlife Service indicates that, during 1955, 1 in every 5 men in the United States hunted (Fig. 9-1); 1 in every 128 women hunted; 1 man in every 4 and 1 woman in every 11 fished; 1 in every 5 persons aged twelve or more, fished; and 1 in every 3 households

[1] At the risk of attempting the impossible in the task of directing thought to an entire field, the term *wild-animal life* will be used in the discussions that follow rather than the looser term of many meanings, *wildlife*.

[2] *Conservation News,* National Wildlife Federation, Washington, D.C., May 1, 1964, p. 7.

figure 9-1

Bringing in the kill. These Michigan hunters have a doe shot during a special "any deer" season in a crop-damage area. (Michigan Department of Conservation.)

contained a hunter or a fisherman. The study indicated, further, that the average hunter in 1955 drove 515 miles on 13.1 hunting trips, hunted 14.5 days, and spent $79.49.[3] From 1955 to 1960 the number of hunters increased 24 per cent.[4]

Original Abundance of Game and Fur Bearers. In the stories of early abundance, one reads relatively little about the forms of wild-animal life now commonly hunted and trapped. Rather, the passenger pigeon, now extinct, and the American bison, found only in specimen herds at present, are cited as examples. Frequently this is done without comment on the question, "Which shall we accommodate, people or wild animals?" For certainly few people would be happy in southeastern Michigan or like territory if passenger pigeons still maintained, as they are reported to have done at one time, 100 birds in a single tree and nested over a wooded area of 100,000 acres. Neither would the farms and ranches of the Middle and Far West be in existence if the 15 million bison estimated to have constituted the population in colonial days were still roaming at large. Even the waterfowl of which there are never enough today to satisfy the hunters are said to have occurred in masses of 50,000 on single limited areas of water and may have perplexed our forefathers in their plans for the next grain crop (Fig. 9-2).

Fur-bearing animals of some dozen or more species constituted significant parts of the fur catch as late as 1821, after almost 2 centuries of trap-

[3] National Survey of Hunting and Fishing, *U.S. Fish and Wildlife Serv. Circ.* 44, 1956.
[4] *Michigan Out-of-doors*, January, 1962.

figure 9-2

Ducks flying over Kentucky Lake. (Photo by Tennessee Valley Authority.)

ping by Indians and of trading by the French and British. One early white hunter and trapper in the Upper Peninsula of Michigan has left us as an estimated list of his catches over a lifetime: 100 bears, 1,000 deer, 50 wolves, 500 foxes, 100 raccoons, 25 wildcats, 100 lynxes, 150 otters, 600 beavers, 400 fishers, "mink and marten by the thousands and muskrats by the tens of thousands."[5] (Deer hides are included in the early fur lists although they were used almost exclusively as leather.) All the animals listed are predators except deer, beaver, and muskrat; and only muskrat, mink, skunk (Fig. 9-3), fox, raccoon, and otter persist in farming localities at present.

Perhaps it is enough, then, to say that no portion of the globe contained more of the useful wild animals than were to be found in what is now the United States. Certainly the traveler and explorer of those early days must have wondered if mankind could ever challenge the complete possession of the land by animals. Indeed it is said that the French and English had no wish to see the land settled so long as the yield of furs from trading with the Indians and the few pioneers constituted a source of easy profit.

But animals are a product of the land, and in spite of much loose talk about multiple use in land management, the production of *one* crop or the use for *one* activity must usually dominate. More human encroachment and more intensive growing of grain, hay, tobacco, cotton, fruit, truck vegetables, and other cultivated crops mean less wild land, which all but a few game and fur species must have if they are to prosper. To a lesser

[5] Quoted by James K. Jamison in his book, This Ontonagon Country, 3d ed., The Ontonagon Herald Company, Ontonagon, Mich., 1948, p. 32.

figure 9-3

This fur animal, the skunk, has a lovely coat but a bad reputation as a predator on domestic poultry and because of a highly odoriferous means of self defense. Nevertheless, he represents a valuable natural resource. (Photo by Rex Gary Schmidt, United States Fish and Wildlife Service.)

extent also the ranch-livestock business invades the natural habitat of big-game animals and larger fur bearers and aggravates, particularly, the problem of winter range for such forms as elk and deer.

And so, if one considers the numbers of hunters and trappers and the values, whatever they may be, of the game and fur animals, the natural-resource problem might be stated, "How can we restore and maintain a supply of these animals sufficient to meet the demand without too much interference with those human activities which conflict with such a program?"

It is surprising to find that quite a satisfactory solution to this problem would be possible if the expressions "sufficient" and "too much" could be agreed upon. That happy situation has not yet been reached, but the following examples of game and fur-bearing wild-animal resources and their handling will throw light upon the long struggle.

Factors Which Deplete Wild-animal Resources. It seems appropriate here to consider the reasons for scarcities and for present distributions of game and fur species. Depletion of original stock may be excusable or inexcusable, depending upon whether one thinks of man as just a factor of environment or as the lord of creation. There is not much doubt as to how the average American, if indeed we could find such a person, feels about these alternatives. He would probably list the following as excusable:

Encroachment on wild-animal habitat by settlement, agriculture, successful drainage projects, industry, and transportation

Breaking game laws without getting caught, particularly if the bag or catch is not wasted

Water pollution, if his own acts or business causes it or if it seems too expensive in his opinion to abate

Mosquito control attempted in good faith

Natural disasters, such as droughts, floods, blizzards, and fires

The automobile

Still hoping we had picked the average American, he would no doubt list the following as inexcusable:

Market hunting, particularly to supply early slave forces and construction crews

Water pollution, if it was caused by someone else than himself or his business

Overhunting and overtrapping in the past

Badly planned drainage projects

Predation, by animals he does not like

Difficulties and laxity in law enforcement

Use of poison baits, insecticides, or herbicides without assurance that they are harmless to the animals he wants around

Man-caused disasters, of which forest and grass fires are the best examples

Each one of these causes, whether excusable on any grounds or not, deserves some explanation. There is not much chance to argue against encroachment features if the expanding-economy idea is valid, and most Americans believe that it is and that our standard of living must be steadily improved. Luxury furs and hunting trips are a part of that standard, but they, in turn, can be acquired only by making a living with something extra to spend. New factories, roads, airfields, farms, golf courses, military installations and testing grounds, and real-estate subdivisions challenge the right of wild animals to occupy the land, and the owners in turn challenge the hunter in his pursuit of whatever game remains. Encroachment upon habitat is a most serious depletive of game and fur-bearing species.

Sportsmen of the better class are law-abiding and sometimes even militant against the game-law violator, but too common an attitude toward law is that the crime consists of getting caught. Game and trapping laws are hard to enforce, and sometimes the laws themselves are not based on complete knowledge of the need for protection and management of the species concerned. Law violation is a cause of depletion and a serious one.

It was pointed out in the first chapter on water that waste transportation is one of the inescapable and important uses of water. Moreover, it is so well established that this use has occurred without general protest or regulation until recent years. Pollution may result from untreated sewage; from industrial, shipping, and mining wastes, many of which are actual poisons; or (less frequently designated as pollution) from soil washing. Stream and other types of pollution are particularly destructive to fisheries, but they also affect the fur animals, many of which occupy marsh and stream-bank areas. Waterfowl also suffer through the destruction of food and cover and from actual poisoning.

Anyone who has suffered the tortures of a mosquito-infested area will be likely to believe in heroic methods to abate this nuisance. Yet the oil films, sprays, and other devices used may well make water intolerable to fur animals and to waterfowl and might on occasion pollute the only source of water available to larger game animals.

The destructiveness of droughts, blizzards, floods, and fires on game and fur-bearing animals is evident not only in their effects on food and cover but in the actual toll taken of the animals themselves, All forms suffer.

Our average American is likely to consider an automobile a necessity and whatever interferes with its operation, a nuisance. Safety in driving usually precludes taking care to avoid hitting slow-moving or suddenly appearing animals. Rabbits, muskrats, opossums (Fig. 9-4), and skunks are often killed on the highways. Even larger animals get into the list now and then, and they may wreck the car and the driver as well as themselves. In the neighborhood of and within the national parks of the West, officials make the interesting statement that automobiles have the combined forces of bobcats, coyotes, and foxes beaten in the toll taken of small mammals. Anyone who travels will remember pavements strewn with mangled woodchucks or marmots, squirrels, chipmunks, jack rabbits, and cottontail rabbits. By actual count the patrolmen of the Ionia County (Michigan) Road Commission for 1963 recovered 2,537 dead animals and birds from the area's major highways. Included were 66 muskrats, 229 opossums, 140 pheasants, 79 woodchucks, 203 turtles, and more than 400 each of squirrels and rabbits. In addition, cars and trucks killed 32 deer during daytime in the county.[6]

[6] Michigan Department of Conservation, News release, Mar. 19, 1964.

figure 9-4

This slow-moving "critter" with her hitchhiking family frequently gets in the way of an automobile. Her coat is only moderately valuable as opossum fur, and she is harmless and interesting. (Virginia Commission of Game and Inland Fisheries, photo by L. G. Kesteloo.)

Market hunting is now universally outlawed in this country, but formerly, it was probably a principal cause of depletion of birds and the larger game animals. To a greater extent than our American can imagine, the meat fed to early slave labor was usually wild, and the buffalo should be credited with a considerable part in the building of the transcontinental railroads. The size and weight of the buffalo made mass killing of these food animals for workers a regular occupation around the construction camps.

Mountain lions, foxes, coyotes, wolves, minks, and bears take their toll of their game and fur animal brothers and are particularly severe on the young. These predators, however, do not constitute an important factor of depletion and are themselves a part of the fur and game resources (Fig. 9-5).

Drainage projects are not always undertaken with full knowledge of the soils to be reclaimed or the full effects of lowering water levels over large areas. Thus, waterfowl and fur animals such as the muskrat are frequently robbed of necessary conditions for life and reproduction. Drainage for mosquito control may produce similar results.

Use of poison baits and insecticides may bring about the death of large numbers of birds and rabbits instead of the pest species for which they are intended. This is an important factor of depletion. Because many of the poisonous sprays find their way into streams, their use has wide-ranging effects on water quality.

Man-caused disasters are rare except in the case of forest fires, which are obvious destroyers of food, cover, and animals. Controlled use of fire

The coyote is an outcast and is generally considered a predator. He does, however, contribute something as a scavenger and a controller of small rodents on the Western range. (National Park Service, photo by Marler.)

and cover types resulting from fires may, on the other hand, benefit certain game animals eventually.

Finally overhunting and overtrapping in the past should be set down as one of the greatest of depleting factors. Of course, it overlaps market hunting and has been most common in areas where people live off the land rather than raise enough for their needs.

Big-game Animals. Deer, elk, antelope, moose, bear, bighorn sheep, mountain goat and mountain lion (also called panther and cougar) are the big animals pursued by the hunter at present in this country (Fig. 9-6). By far the most plentiful of these are deer, and so naturally they are the most commonly hunted. Those herds persisting or restored in the Northeastern part of the country and extending through the Lake states of Michigan, Wisconsin, and Minnesota range over forested and cutover lands and spread to some extent over farms and orchards. They "yard up" in winter, concentrating in cedar swamps if available, and they have their troubles as their populations increase and browse species become overgrazed. Restrictive hunting laws have usually spared too many does and resulted in a deer population beyond the carrying capacity of the land in winter. In a milder climate such as that found in the Piedmont and mountain country of the South, the problem of food is not serious (1) because the

figure 9-6

Michigan whitetail deer. The herd is still too large for its range, and in spite of special "any deer" seasons, considerable starvation occurs. (Photo, courtesy of National Park Service.)

population of deer is small as the result of years of overhunting and (2) because the winter feeding problem does not bring about harmful concentrations. In the Western timbered plateau and mountains, deer find refuge and food during the warmer months in the high areas but must seek the foothills when heavy snow comes. This is painfully true of elk also. Crowded out of their winter range of open grasslands by fenced ranches, they have reached numbers which are not yet held down appreciably by hunting or systematic slaughter. Antelope seek more open and usually lower country and must win their battle with fences or die (Fig. 9-7).

In all these situations the history of the herds and their management is similar. First there is a period of heavy depletion from overhunting. Then there occurs a long stretch of scarcity of animals for the hunter whose demands eventually bring about expensive and usually fruitless attempts to restock the areas artificially or to use restrictive measures only. Finally, in desperation, more range is made available at public expense and food and cover conditions are improved to care for a limited game population. The latter can be achieved only by population control with kill quotas and flexible regulation on season, sex, and number allowed to each hunter. What needs to be done can be determined by research. How to get it done is another matter running squarely into pressure for questionable practices in order to keep plenty of animals immediately available to hunters and into political and law-enforcement difficulties of administration.

Hunters probably bag bear more often when hunting deer or elk than when on organized bear hunts. Bear have had so little legal protection (outside the national parks) that no complaint of scarcity as game animals is heard. Rather, the predatory and marauding habits of these interesting animals often lead mankind close to practices of persecution.

figure 9-7

Pronghorn antelope on desert game range, Las Vegas, Nev. He seeks open lower country and has his troubles with fences. (Photo by E. P. Haddon, United States Fish and Wildlife Service.)

Hunters do go on trips particularly to get mountain lion, and it is likely that these stealthy predators will not always be available to sportsmen. The livestock industry will see to that (Fig. 9-8).

Small Nonmigratory Game Animals. Quail, grouse, pheasant, wild turkey, rabbit, and squirrel are sought principally by the small-game hunter and constitute the bulk of the take in farming country (Figs. 9-9, 9-10). Both open fields and wooded areas are essential for these forms, and brushy vine-grown fence rows are especially needed as cover and protected travel ways. Except for the nut- and edible-seed-bearing species, trees are less essential to these animals than shrubs and young forest reproduction which comes into open spaces and edges. Logs and hollow trees are used for dens and nests, and brush piles after logging get plenty of use by rabbits. Enforced seasonal and bag limits have put these game resources in less danger than big-game species, although there is much speculation over population cycles. These have not yet had sufficient study.

Migratory Birds. By far the most talked-of game species are ducks, geese, and other migratory waterfowl. Many of our song and insectiv-

figure 9-8

Mountain lion, also called panther or cougar. Apparently he is saying something unpleasant to the dogs. Hunted by stockmen as a predator and for sport, he is one animal, along with the grizzly bear and rattlesnake, that should stay in the wild-animal scene. (Photo, courtesy of Texas Game and Fish Commission.)

figure 9-9
Rabbits need places to hide and nest. These are just now in clover. (Photo by L. G. Kesteloo, Virginia Commission of Game and Inland Fisheries.)

figure 9-10

This gray squirrel and his lesser cousin the chipmunk are noisy and mischievous, but interesting to watch. The squirrel is widely hunted. Both deserve protection. (Photo by L. G. Kesteloo, Virginia Commission of Game and Inland Fisheries.)

orous birds are also migratory, but few figure in the hunter's plans. Migratory waterfowl have no unusual food, cover, and breeding-ground requirements except water. However, these essentials must be spread out over long fly ways, and lack of them has put the birds at the mercy of habitat changes and of hunters who were abroad before essential restrictions were in force. Even today one seldom hears of a hunter coming home with one duck. However figures obtained by the Fish and Wildlife Service in 1956 indicated an average daily bag of 1.34 ducks to the hunter who was out on the average of 4.4 trips a season and who, with his kind, accounted for a total kill of 16½ million waterfowl. This total involved principally mallard, pintail, and black ducks.[7]

Improved transportation, ingenuity in the manufacture and sale of arms and ammunition, increasing numbers of hunters, baiting, drainage

[7] 1957 Status Report of Waterfowl, U.S. Fish and Wildlife Serv. Spec. Sci. Rept.. Wildlife, vol. 37, August, 1957. By special permission.

and other types of habitat destruction, diseases such as botulism and fowl cholera, water pollution, lead poisoning from the ingestion of lead shot from the bottom of heavily hunted areas, and just plain overhunting within and without the law—all these have had their part in reducing the numbers of migratory birds and in the problem of keeping the present-day hunters happy. That the practice of overhunting has persisted in late years is attested to by the arrest and conviction of three persons in California in 1949 who possessed and were endeavoring to sell 800 wild ducks. This number is the equivalent of the combined daily bag of 200 sportsmen.[8] Even as late as 1956, twenty-eight market hunters were apprehended in Tennessee, forty-four in Texas, and six in Maryland.[9]

And while the hunters worry about ducks and geese, those who love the antics and calls of such nongame waterfowl as herons and loons know that these forms also have their feeding, hiding, and breeding troubles. Smaller forms, either of waterfowl or of songbirds, appear to have fewer difficulties although certain of them, such as snipes, curlews, meadowlarks, woodcocks, and doves, have suffered in the past from over-shooting.

Fur Animals. Some thirty kinds of animals are taken for furs in the United States proper, not counting as more than one kind the various species of any particular form. Among these the most frequently captured include muskrat, raccoon, mink, beaver, fox, skunk, otter, marten, fisher, weasel, rabbit, hare, coyote, wolf, opossum, badger, wildcat, lynx, and bear. In addition to these, Alaska yields furs from seal and blue fox principally.

The fur bearers as a class have a fine, soft undercoat for warmth as well as a crop of longer guard hairs useful for shedding water. These hairs are plucked or sheared when the hides are processed as furs. Some furs, such as those of rabbits and hares, mat easily and are more useful for the manufacture of felt of the sort used in hats. Other furs are not subject to matting and find their way into fur garments and trimmings. Once used extensively for male garments, furs are now more often luxury items in coats, capes, and separate pieces for women. Prices vary with style, but some idea of persisting values may be obtained from the fact that Alaska, purchased in 1867 from Russia for $7,200,000, had produced up to 1947 fur crops worth $100,000,000. During the fiscal year 1963 ending June 30, 1963, 54,820 United States–owned sealskins were sold for $3,566,764.[10]

---

[8] Wildlife Conservation Activities of the Federal Government, 1949, Hearings before the Sub-Committee to Investigate Wildlife Conservation, Committee on Expenditures in the Executive Departments, U.S. Senate, 81st Cong., 2d sess., 1950, p. 3.
[9] *Annual Report of the Secretary of the Interior*, 1956, p. 287.
[10] *Ibid.*, 1963, p. 346.

The muskrat, a small water-loving vegetarian, is the most commonly captured fur animal in the United States proper. It inhabits most of North America except the Southeast coast and is of one species except for the Louisiana and Texas forms. The muskrat inhabits stream banks and builds "houses" or "cabins" consisting of cone-shaped piles of cattail stalks and other vegetation, the tops extending a foot or two above water level in swamps and shallow water (Fig. 9-11). Three to five, and sometimes as many as eight, young are produced in a litter. Good muskrat localities will yield five peltries (skins) to the acre each year. The muskrat's enemies are the mink and the otter, both valuable fur bearers themselves. Throughout the northern part of the Middle West, particularly, muskrats are trapped in the swampland on and surrounding marginal farms, and the crop is counted on to furnish a part of the yearly farm income.

Raccoon and mink rank next in number taken annually in the United States and, along with otter and beaver, require much the same waterway habitats as supports their more plentiful neighbor, the muskrat. The raccoons, however, use hollow trees rather than waterfront accommodations for housing. The other fur bearers listed are likely to range over wider territory. Seals, a distinctive and important source of fur, are migratory animals herding a part of the year in the Pribilof Islands, off Alaska, and are not subject to trapping under license. Their management is discussed on pages 295–298.

MANAGING WILD-ANIMAL RESOURCES

Conserving the wild-animal resources of the country is a matter of understanding and management. Excellent progress has been made in both directions in late years. Every wild animal experiences stages in its development where it needs help in terms of food, shelter, protection, or some other service amounting to manipulation of environment or assurance of temporary freedom from capture. Providing this service to wild animals, based on knowledge of life history and habits, is the business of management. Discussions of it appear in the literature under such head-

A heavily inhabited muskrat marsh. Maple River region in Michigan. (Michigan Department of Conservation.)

figure 9-11

ings as Game Management, Wildlife Management, and Fisheries Management. Certainly considerations of cover, food, and water figure heavily in the picture, while restriction of the kill and controlled increase in the take of surplus animals are matters of cost and management which are difficult to enforce and which call for flexibility in policy. Ownership of wild animals, residing as it does in the states, complicates the business of management, because the animals furnishing some 75 per cent of the game and fur harvest in the United States spend most of their lives on farms. If the public assumes the task, public agencies must work on private land. If the private landowner takes over, he is dealing with animals which he does not own.

Specific Practices in Wild-animal Management. *Protection.* Historically, the attempts to conserve wild-animal resources have usually started with regulation of the kill, and this has usually meant restrictions in the form of laws or administrative regulations affecting bag limits on the number which any hunter or trapper may take in a day or season; on sex, particularly as regards big-game animals and certain game birds; on age and size; season; time of day; on arms, traps, and other gear; on length of time the captured animal may be in possession; on sale, shipment, and importation of game; and on areas where hunting, trapping, and fishing are permitted. All these restrictions are designed to protect animals from constant pursuit and capture by men. Properly worded and enforced, many of the regulations have worked well, but, at best, their principal positive effect is to give the animals a chance to catch their breath, breed, and grow without being under continual bombardment. The restrictive approach to conservation here is largely negative. Improvement of environmental conditions in such an approach is ignored.

IMPROVEMENT OF COVER Wild animals require many types and arrangements of vegetation for purposes of shelter and hiding while nesting, breeding, feeding, and even migrating. Edges of forests, marshes, and waterways are most commonly needed on wild land. Added to these, on cultivated land, are brush- and vine-grown fence rows, unharvested patches of grain and hay, shocked corn, brush piles, irregularly planted patches of shrubs and evergreens, and reflooded areas which have once been drained and abandoned. These happy (for the animals) combinations of cover are not always sightly. Frequently their maintenance is contrary to clean farming, roadside maintenance, the development of golf courses and landing fields, and other large space requirements. Here, as in all conservation efforts, the questions of priorities arise. Only by the most careful planning can the needs of animals, space users, intensive agriculture, and sometimes even forestry be reconciled. Actual planting of trees, shrubs, and vines for cover as well as food purposes has been promoted successfully for the past few years on farms throughout the

figure 9-12

Bull elk at Jackson Hole, Teton National Forest, Wyoming. This large game animal has lost much of its winter range to ranching operations and presents a problem of overpopulation. (Photo by H. L. Schantz, United States Forest Service.)

Eastern half of the country. This practice was undertaken first through cooperation of states, farm owners, and sportsmen's groups, with the universities and state colleges doing much of the necessary research work. The plans worked out by the soil conservation districts also include frequently a section on improvement of food and cover resources.

IMPROVEMENT OF FOOD CONDITIONS While food and cover problems overlap and are tied in to control of game populations, the question of food for wild animals is perhaps of greatest popular interest (Fig. 9-12). Starvation among big-game animals serves to dramatize the problems, and heavy winter storms are bound to interest large numbers of people in artificial methods of supplying food, such as scattering hay for big game and grain for game birds and songbirds. Not so well understood is the constant necessity of tailoring animal population to the food supply and of acquiring and improving wild lands to support the number of animals demanded by hunters. Efforts at improving food conditions vary all the way from raising hay for Wyoming elk and synchronizing cedar logging with season of greatest need for deer browse in the Lake states to planting of food patches of soybeans, berry bushes, and small grains or influencing farmers to leave unharvested crops. The judicious use of fire is said to have helped the quail in the South and is finding favor elsewhere as a stimulator of the growth of food-bearing vegetation. Chemical treatment of low-value forest cover, with various herbicides, has also been successful in inducing sprout growth. Putting the brakes on indiscriminate drainage so that marsh food plants as well as water levels can be maintained is a good stroke of management applying to fur bearers. But it may be generally said, and the statement defended, that artificially supplying food to wild animals is less successful in the long run than controlling population and extending natural food areas. In either case a vast amount of information on food habits and populations of the animals and on the carrying capacity of the land must be constantly sought through research.

ASSURING A WATER SUPPLY   Aside from the indispensability of water for waterfowl and marsh-inhabiting mammals (Figs. 9-13, 9-14) in the humid portion of the country, upland game birds and big-game animals must have water provided in arid regions. Thus the Chukar partridge, introduced from Hungary and first released in central Nevada, appears to be well adapted to hot desert areas but must have water developments to be assured of survival. Nevada sportsmen and the state game officials are cooperating with the Bureau of Land Management in water development for these birds. Similarly, the states of California, Arizona, and New Mexico have constructed numerous quail-watering projects under permit from the Bureau of Land Management. These facilities consist of small fenced areas with paved catchment basins for impounding small quantities of water for game birds, principally quails and doves. Some effort also is made to locate stock-watering developments to serve the needs of range game animals.

OBTAINING CENSUSES OF WILD ANIMALS   It is obvious that any allowable kill of wild animals should be based on the numbers constituting the resource at any time and place. But animals do not care to be inter-

Beaver dam on Pike National Forest, Colorado. Water is essential in wild-animal management. Big-game animals and waterfowl use this pond. (Photo by C. C. Spencer, United States Forest Service.)

figure 9-13

figure 9-14
Canada geese attracted to a farm pond. (Photo by United States Soil Conservation Service.)

viewed, and ingenious methods of counting them have to be worked out. Actual counts of both big game and smaller forms are made by sending trained observers over the land afoot in systematically covered routes, by supplementing such efforts through using well-trained dogs, by airplane surveys, and by analysis of figures on the season's licensed kill. Censusing is, of course, a kind of research and an important one.

Closely related to censusing is the study of movement and feeding of deer and elk during winter. Michigan is employing electronic equipment to "bug" various animals with tiny transmitters which are attached to collars, harnesses, and leg bands on specimens when they are captured. After the animals are released, field workers will man directional receivers to tune in on travel.[11] Fire observation towers and airplanes will be employed in the work. This study recalls the newspaper story of a dead whale floating in the Pacific off Sitka, Alaska, carrying a Russian-made harpoon equipped with radio transmitter and a trailing radar reflector. A Bureau of Commercial Fisheries spokesman figured that this was an extra kill beyond a whaling boat's capacity which was equipped so that it could later be found.[12]

CONTROLLED HUNTS TO REDUCE OVERPOPULATIONS A dependable census will sometimes indicate need for reduction of populations of big-game animals, and the controlled hunt will frequently accomplish the necessary kill. It works like this: The number to be removed is decided upon. A

[11] Michigan Department of Conservation, News release, June 4, 1964.
[12] Associated Press item in Los Angeles Times, June 18, 1964.

figure 9-15

It is 4 A.M. in the Pisgah National Forest in North Carolina. These hunters are being issued numbers and safety-red shawls in a controlled deer hunt. (Photo by United States Forest Service.)

hunt for which drawings will be held is publicly advertised, or dependable licensed sportsmen are notified. An appropriate number of names are drawn and the fortunate hunters report to a specified entrance point at a given date. They are checked in (Fig. 9-15), transported to various points in the area, and picked up with their kill later in the day. Successful hunts of this sort have been held in recent years for deer on the Pisgah National Forest in North Carolina, on the San Andres Mountain Game Range in New Mexico, and in Plumas County, California.

A variation of the controlled hunt is used by the National Park Service to reduce the numbers of elk in Grand Teton and Yellowstone National Parks. Elk-hunting permits are issued cooperatively with the Wyoming Game and Fish Commission, and hunters who receive them are deputized as park rangers. A satisfactory annual kill has not been achieved in the 11 years the plan has been in force (1951 to 1964 except for 1959 and 1960), although a considerable number of elk have been taken. An advisory board appointed by the Secretary of the Interior, has recommended that the required number of animals be shot by national-park personnel with the possible help of specially trained and supervised outside helpers. This would be strictly a management procedure, not recreation hunting.[13]

PROVIDING SPECIAL REFUGES AND PRESERVES   In addition to the closed-season regulations, wild animals need areas in which they may be unmolested even during open season, and this is particularly true for migratory forms requiring "rest stations" during travel. Large birds threatened

[13] Wildlife Management in the National Parks, Report of a special advisory board on wildlife management, A. S. Leopold, Chairman, Mar. 4, 1962. (Mimeographed.)

with extinction, such as the American bald eagle, need such refuges for survival and escape from the hunter's gun. In Florida, Audubon Society people have now placed more than 1 million acres under eagle sanctuary status in cooperation with private landowners.[14] A sanctuary for condors, which are dangerously near extinction, is maintained in the Los Padres National Forest in California. The whooping crane, America's tallest bird numbered only forty-two in 1965 (Fig. 9-16). It winters in the Aransas National Wildlife Refuge on the Texas Gulf Coast. Its population shows little increase. The larger refuges provide safe breeding grounds

[14] *Michigan Conservation,* Lansing, Michigan, vol. 33, no. 2, March-April, 1964.

Whooping crane, the tallest of American birds. He winters in the Aransas National Refuge on the Gulf coast of Texas. Only 42 specimens are reported as of 1965, and this population shows little increase. (Photo by W. F. Kubichek, United States Fish and Wildlife Service.)

figure 9-16

figure 9-17

Entrance to a wildlife refuge. This one is in North Carolina. The Fish and Wildlife Service is the Federal bureau concerned with wild-animal resources. (Photo by W. F. Kubichek, United States Fish and Wildlife Service.)

and serve as areas of supply from which the excess numbers of game species "spill over" to territory where they may be hunted. Refuges may be Federal, state, or private as far as ownership and management are concerned and may vary in size from 1 million acres to less than 1 acre. National and state parks serve as animal refuges indirectly, and even a cemetery or a small posted estate may make a real contribution to continuing supplies of wild animals (Fig. 9-17).

Refuges and "sanctuaries," as certain of them are called, should not be confused with game preserves or shooting preserves, which are increasing in number and are operated as paid hunting enterprises. Preserves may consist either of rented land managed by some gun club for its own members or of large areas privately owned by clubs or individuals and closed to all but club members or paid guests. Any efforts to increase the wild-animal population, other than waterfowl, on preserves must be undertaken at private expense and are consequently likely to be neglected. On the other hand the gun pressure inside the preserves is well distributed, even though little contribution to the general hunting situation of the nearby territory results.

Twenty-seven states now have laws authorizing the operation of private shooting preserves. The operator of such a preserve must have a breeder's license. He raises birds or other small game, maintains a hunting area, releases birds into cover ahead of the hunter, furnishes dogs and sometimes clubhouse accommodations, and charges his guests for the game they take. Usually these preserves are located near centers of population, occupy limited area, and obtain modification of the state game laws on seasons and bag limits. The use of such areas may go by such names as put-and-take, fee, or controlled hunting.

To get around the alleged unfairness to the less fortunate hunter of the ever-increasing amount of land posted against hunting, some of the states provide extensive public hunting grounds, largely through the use of Federal grant-in-aid funds.

ARTIFICIAL PROPAGATION AND RESTOCKING   To the layman, one of the most obvious ways to keep up the supply of wild animals seems to be rearing them artificially on game farms and using them to restock areas where they are scarce or absent. Frequently it will be contended that some game animal, plentiful in another country, should be introduced. So strong is the sentiment for introduction and restocking that many of the states operate game farms at great expense. The most common effort of these farms is to increase the numbers of upland game birds, the quail and wild turkey being representative of the native species used and the Hungarian partridge and the ring-necked pheasant of the exotic forms. Perhaps the greatest success has been achieved with pheasant, particularly in farming areas of the Middle West. In 1963 cooperation agreements on foreign-game introduction were in force in forty-five states. Trial liberations of introduced birds were under way in sixteen states. Fourteen of the sixteen forms under study were being reared in appreciable numbers on game farms in twenty-one states.[15] Many local gun clubs are interested in their own hatching and release operations. But we have much to learn if propagation and restocking from game farms are to reach a justifiable stage in this country. Meanwhile, we may be thankful that the introduction of exotic species is sharply regulated by Federal law; such important nuisances as the starling, English sparrow, and European carp have taught us a lesson.

Closely related to, and somewhat more successful than, the game-farm restocking devices are the projects of transferring surplus animals from one locality to another where environmental conditions are promising. The reestablished deer herds of Vermont and Pennsylvania are successful examples, and the moving of beaver and wild turkeys in various localities has given good results. Strangely enough, the National Park Service has made a number of "plantings" of wild animals and appears to consider the procedure entirely within its policy of presenting the plant and animal life in a manner opposed to artificially managed relationships. Thus a small planting of three or four elk about 1925 in the Blue Ridge Parkway

[15] *Annual Report of the Secretary of the Interior, 1963, p. 300.*

of Virginia and North Carolina was reported to have increased to about thirty-five adults and five calves by 1950. Seventy-five of the Yellowstone antelope herd also were removed about 1950 to the Theodore Roosevelt Memorial Park in North Dakota, and twelve bucks were released in Wind Cave National Park, South Dakota. Furthermore, plantings of antelope were made in Big Bend National Park, Texas, in 1947 and 1948. Of forty-four deer removed from Grand Canyon National Park in 1952, thirty-nine were released in good condition at the Santa Rita Mountain "transplant site." Twenty bighorn sheep brought from British Columbia in 1955 and released on the Hart Mountain state game refuge in Oregon had increased to an estimated total of 49 by 1957. One of the most interesting introductions is that of elk in Michigan. Eight animals were released in the upper part of the lower peninsula in 1918 and 1919. The resulting herd in 1964 was estimated to be 3,500 (Fig. 9-18). Given full protection for forty-six years, the herd now poses a dramatic dilemma: on the one hand, they attract tourists; and on the other hand, they are a source of damage to crops and fences and they compete with deer on an over-used food supply. An open season with controlled hunting was conducted in 1964.[16]

CONTROL OF PREDATORS It is quite natural for disappointed sportsmen or for habitual lawbreakers to rationalize a dwindling game-animal supply by blaming the situation on some predator (Fig. 9-19, 9-20). Enthusiasm for bounty laws, crow shoots, coyote drives, and other attacks on suspected predators is well known in almost any locality where hunting is an established sport. The marauding of certain wild animals on

[16] Letter from Department of Conservation, Lansing, Mich., Aug. 21, 1964.

figure 9-18
Hunters checking in at a state station after Michigan's first controlled elk hunt. (Michigan Department of Conservation.)

figure 9-19

*This gray-fox pup is branded as a predator on domestic poultry and
will be hunted for his fur and chased by dogs and horses. He probably
deserves less persecution. (Photo by Don Wooldridge, Missouri Conservation Commission.)*

poultry and young livestock affords further reason to pursue and anni-
hilate all predators, whether or not they are proved guilty. Wolves, mountain lions, coyotes, and bears are definitely a problem to the livestock
ranchers and to hunters of big game, and some evidence piles up against
hawks, owls, foxes, skunks, and turtles for destroying domestic poultry
and the eggs and young of upland game and waterfowl. Where these
sorts of predation get out of hand, there is justification for the employment of paid trappers working for public agencies and for the inclusion of
predators as a part of the sportsman's quarry. But the predators have
their uses, and they are frequently persecuted. While they do kill numbers of desirable animals, it is scientifically established that they perform
useful services in devouring insects and undesirable rodents and reptiles.
What predators actually devour can be determined by examination of
stomach contents after they are killed. It is well established that of the
crow's diet of animal matter, which is about one-fourth of the total,
about two-thirds consists of crop-destroying beetles, grasshoppers, locusts,
crickets, and other insects. Four Michigan crows when killed were found
to have been digesting collectively 85 June bugs (May beetles), 72 wire-
worms, 123 grasshoppers, and 438 small caterpillars.[17] This chalks up a
pretty good service record. Analysis of 2,222 coyote stomachs in California

[17] C. T. Black, Ebony Robin Hood, *Mich. Conserv.*, vol. 22, no. 13, March–April,
1953.

figure 9-20

*This little clown will probably grow up to be a predator
and a target for more than one hunter. He represents
an interesting species deserving more general protection.
(Photo by L. G. Kesteloo, Virginia Commission of Game
and Inland Fisheries.)*

indicated the following food breakdown: rodents, 26.5 per cent; birds, 4.6 per cent; plant material, 4.0 per cent; and miscellaneous items, 10.5 per cent.[18] This is not too damning a disclosure, and even if it were worse it is well to bear in mind that fraud, failure, and even harm to the desirable species frequently characterize bounty-payment systems and that paid professional trappers are more successful and more economical. In using the latter, such results of research as are available can be employed to see that the control methods really effect control. One state,

[18] *Pittman-Robertson Quarterly,* for July–October quarter, 1952, vol. 13, January, 1953, p. 16.

Montana, has discontinued all bounty payments after experience with them since 1883.[19]

RESEARCH IN WILD-ANIMAL MANAGEMENT Knowledge of the life histories of all wild animals, whether they are beneficial or predatory, is indispensable to good management of wild-animal resources (Figs. 9, and 24-25). In addition to such knowledge, managers must understand feeding and breeding habits; cover and water requirements; predator, disease, and disaster relationships; actual populations and their fluctuations; and the long-run effects of laws and regulations covering various species. Such knowledge cannot be picked out of the air. It must be won by patient and skillful research and, what is even more difficult, passed out and "sold" to the hunter, trapper, fisherman, farmer, general public, and even to natural-resource administrators themselves. Fortunately, interest in such research is high in this country, and funds from Federal, state, and private agencies support nearly a score of research units at as many state agricultural colleges. These, in particular, are maintained in cooperation with the Fish and Wildlife Service of the Department of the Interior and the Wildlife Management Institute, a private nonprofit enterprise. In addition, graduate studies at a number of universities, usually where wildlife management is taught as a part of a natural-resource curriculum, attack important problems each year. Numerous important studies have been made over the past 50 years by the Federal bureaus concerned with wild-animal resources, and, fortunately again, these have covered more than just the game and fur-bearing species.

FUR FARMING The actual husbandry and systematic breeding and pelting of fur animals—such as silver foxes, minks, chinchillas, rabbits, and, to a lesser extent and by less intensive methods, muskrat—constitute a considerable industry (Fig. 9-21). The annual yield now amounts to hundreds of thousands of valuable pelts. Such fur-farming procedure is a far cry from usual wild-animal management practices. It can be considered as conserving natural resources only in the sense that it helps to supply fur to a market which must otherwise be served by hard-pressed wild stock.

Federal Agencies and Wild Animals. In addition to the Fish and Wildlife Service in the Department of the Interior (a bureau made up by combining the earlier Bureau of Biological Survey in the Department of Agriculture and the Bureau of Fisheries in the Department of Commerce), some four other bureaus are concerned with wild-animal resources. In the Department of the Interior, the National Park Service is charged with, among other things, the protection of wild-animal forms in the parks for their educational and spectacle values (Fig. 9-22), and the

[19] Michigan Department of Conservation, News Release, June 28, 1962.

figure 9-21

Silver fox in Alaska fur farm near Fairbanks. (Photo by John D. Guthrie, United States Forest Service.)

Bureau of Land Management must deal with the conflicts between live-stock grazing and wild-animal occupancy on the Taylor Grazing Districts. The Forest Service in the Department of Agriculture, in managing the more than 150 national forests, finds wild animals on its domain, both desirable and undesirable, including about one-third of the big-game population of the United States; and this bureau must reconcile other

Mountain goats at mineral lick in Glacier National Park. (Photo by Joseph S. Dixon, National Park Service.)

figure 9-22

land uses with those serving the game and fur species. Also this agency must to some extent service a vast army of hunters every year, totaling considerably more than 2 million, and help to enforce the game laws. In the Department of Agriculture are the Soil Conservation Service, interested in assisting farmers to make the most of wild-animal resources in their soil conservation districts and farm plans, and the Bureau of Animal Industry, concerned with wild-animal diseases and parasites. Besides all these the Department of State is called upon to negotiate treaties covering international aspects of wild-animal-resource administration.

Private Agencies Concerned with Wild-animal Resources. There are probably more than a thousand local rod and gun clubs under various designations which concern themselves with the promotion of better hunting and fishing. A considerable number of them are seriously engaged in conserving the resources which serve them through connection with national organizations. These in turn influence legislation both directly and through their cooperation with state fish and game agencies. But before there were any national organizations, state groups of private citizens constituted the "game commissions" in Delaware, North Carolina, and South Carolina, and these groups were active not only in obtaining legislation but in enforcing it. Among the early groups were the Massachusetts Fish and Game Protective Association, organized in 1874; the Delaware Game Protective Association, incorporated in 1879; the first Audubon Society in New York, 1886; the League of American Sportsmen, 1898; and The American Game Protective Association, 1900. The two latter groups were powerful in the legislative field for many years previous to 1925, and the National Association of Audubon Societies, which in 1902 grew out of the earlier New York group, is still active in the protection of nongame species and in the promotion of popular education.

Among the private national groups active in wild-animal conservation at present, besides the National Association of Audubon Societies, are the following: The Izaak Walton League of America, organized in 1922 and particularly militant on water-pollution control, in opposition to high dams which it feels are unjustified economically, and in promoting acquisition of wildlife refuges and inviolable wilderness areas; the North American Wildlife Conference called first by President Franklin D. Roosevelt in 1935 and combining in an annual meeting all wild-animal interests; the Wildlife Management Institute, which operates somewhat as a foundation, promoting education and research; the National Wildlife Federation, a publishing and educational group; and the International Association of Game, Fish, and Conservation Commissioners. The American Forestry Association should also be mentioned for its publicizing and support of legislation affecting wild-animal conservation.

How Wild-animal Administration Is Financed. One of the great accomplishments of game-conservation agencies is the firm establishment of the license fee as a source of funds for administering game resources. Laws covering this feature have long been in effect in all the states, and additional revenue on a Federal level has come from the Migratory Bird Hunting Stamp Act of 1934. Under this law hunters of migratory waterfowl buy a stamp for $3 which is attached to their state license. The revenue is used for acquiring and administering refuges and for research. Still another Federal source of funds comes from the Pittman-Robertson Act of 1937. Under this act, amounts each fiscal year "equal to the revenue accruing . . . from the tax imposed by the . . . Revenue Act of 1932 on firearms, shells and cartridges" are set aside to constitute "the Federal aid to wildlife-restoration fund." This fund is allotted to the states, by a matching agreement, on the basis of area and the number of paid hunting-license holders. It may be used for acquisition of land, construction of facilities, and research related to wild-animal restoration. A similar act in the fisheries field, known as the Dingell-Johnson law, was passed by the Congress in 1950. This law makes available to the states, on a matching basis, the moneys raised from the excise tax on the sale of fishing tackle. It may be used for such purposes as the purchase of public fishing sites, fisheries research, and the improvement of environmental conditions. Both of these acts specify that matching shall provide 3 Federal dollars to 1 state dollar. Occasionally private funds from individuals or groups are sought to cover such things as emergency winter feeding or the buying of some special area for which public funds are not immediately available. The conservation of wild-animal resources, however, is not entirely self-supporting, and both state and Federal appropriations are required. Examples of special Federal authorizations in this direction include the Upper Mississippi River Wild Life and Fish Refuge Act of 1924, the Bear River (Utah) Migratory Bird Refuge Act of 1928, the General Migratory Bird Refuge Act of 1929 (as amended in 1935), and the Cheyenne Bottoms (Kansas) Migratory Bird Refuge Act of 1930.

Important Legislation Affecting Wild Animals. In addition to a great number of regulatory acts passed by the various states in the past 50 years, attention should be called to the following Federal laws:

The Lacey Act of 1900 extended certain powers of the Secretary of Agriculture and contained regulations on interstate and foreign commerce in wild birds and other animals. The enforcement features of this act were strengthened by amendment in 1935.

The Migratory Bird Treaty with Great Britain (on behalf of Canada) was signed in Washington and, after ratification, was proclaimed December 8, 1916. This treaty or "convention" lists game and insectivorous and other nongame birds, provides for closed seasons which put an end to

figure 9-23

The Migratory Bird Treaty Act of 1918 protects birds such as these Canada geese. (Photo by Paul H. Moore, Tennessee Conservation Department.)

spring shooting, and agrees that legislation for carrying out all terms will be sought by the contracting powers in their own countries (Fig. 9-23).

The Migratory Bird Treaty Act of 1918 gave full effect to the above treaty. A similar act was passed by the Canadian Parliament in 1917. The validity of the latter and the constitutionality of the former have been established by court decisions.[20]

The Migratory Bird Treaty with Mexico was signed in Mexico City and, after ratification, was proclaimed on March 15, 1937. Provisions of this treaty are similar to the one with Canada but also include the interesting prohibition of hunting from aircraft. Appropriate amendment of the Migratory Bird Treaty Act of 1918 was approved in 1936, pending ratification of the treaty with Mexico.

The Wildlife Refuge Exchange Act of 1935 provided for the acquisition of refuge lands privately owned in exchange for Federal lands or products from Federal lands, when the public interest will thus be served.

The National Forest Fish and Game Sanctuary Act of 1934 granted authority to the President to establish refuges by proclamation within the national forests with the approval of state legislatures in the states involved. This act is important because of the vast area of the national forests and their wild-animal populations.

[20] State of Missouri v. Ray P. Holland, 252 U.S. 416; United States v. Lumpkin, 276 Fed. 580; King v. Russell C. Clark, Supreme Court of Prince Edward Island, Michaelmas term, 1920.

The Wildlife Coordination Act of 1934 as amended in 1946 was designed to reconcile objectives of various bureaus in the construction of flood control, power, and irrigation works in any river valley. It recognized that there is plenty of chance in these instances to interfere with the best interests of wild-animal resources. This situation received the attention of the Congress as early as 1934, when the so-called Wildlife Coordination Act was first approved. It provided that consideration should be given to the effects on wild-animal life of the construction of public works and that, before construction, the bureaus concerned with wild-animal resources should be consulted. Unfortunately the law does not require the construction agencies to hold up or to abandon projects. Some progress was achieved in attempting to reconcile the operation (rather than the construction) of the Bonneville and Grand Coulee Dams with the conservation of the salmon resources of the Columbia River; but, in general, the results of the law have been disappointing. Since the amendment of the act in 1946, interdepartmental committees have been set up in the Columbia, Missouri, and other river valleys, but they have power only to advise. The Bureau of Reclamation in the Department of the Interior and the Office of Engineers in the Department of Defense, which are the construction agencies, usually dominate the committees, and the rush of their interests allows little time for study and adjustment of wild-animal resources to the vast changes which occur with the construction of power, irrigation, and flood-control works.

However, among the 2,000 water-use projects examined since 1946, by the Fish and Wildlife Service, a number have received the attention of the Congress and the construction agencies. Among them are the following:[21]

Purchase of flood-water rights of the grasslands on a tract located in the Central Valley Project of California threatens a considerable area of adjacent waterfowl habitat unless water supplies are reserved from project use. Here a joint report by the Fish and Wildlife Service, the Bureau of Reclamation, and the California Department of Fish and Game recommended water development for waterfowl management in the lower San Joaquin Valley. The Congress approved the recommendations of this report and, by an act passed in 1954, authorized appropriation for carrying them out. By 1957, $40,000 had been expended on the Merced National Wildlife Management area for the rehabilitation and development of wells to furnish water to the area for the benefit of the wildlife resource.

Typical of the work on nine of the Bureau of Reclamation reservoirs in the Missouri River Basin Project, the result of studies and reports on the

[21] Letter from D. H. Janzen, Director, U.S. Bureau of Sport Fisheries and Wildlife, Nov. 4, 1957.

replacement of upland-game habitat lost in the impoundments, was the establishment of cover around the Enders Reservoir in Nebraska in 1950 and 1951. Trees, shrubs, and herbaceous cover were planted to serve the needs of pheasant, prairie grouse, and deer. The areas are administered cooperatively by the Nebraska Game, Forestation, and Parks Commission.

Licenses have been issued by the Department of the Army to the Oregon State Game Commission on 100 acres and to the Washington Department of Game on 7,567 acres for the development, conservation, and management of all wildlife resources on the McNary Lock and Dam Project on the Columbia River. A cooperative agreement was entered into in 1955 whereby this important unit of the waterfowl-refuge system of the Pacific Flyway would be administered by these agencies and the Fish and Wildlife Service.

Upon construction of the Nimbus Dam on the Anunciar River in California, the spawning runs of large percentages of the king salmon and steelhead trout population were blocked from spawning areas previously available. To compensate for this loss, a salmon hatchery was built upon recommendation of the Fish and Wildlife Service and the California Department of Fish and Game. This hatchery is operated by the state of California under a 5-year renewable contract, with funds provided by the Federal government.

Illustrating the persistence of private enterprise in cooperating to work out problems similar to those described above, there is the story of the local power company operating the Holyoke Dam in the Connecticut River under a Federal Power Commission license and its attempts to pass shad to the spawning grounds above the dam. After the failure of fishways in 1940 and 1952 to pass these fish, the company devised a mechanical-lift system which put 5,000 shad over the dam in 1955 and almost 9,000 in 1957.

The Wetlands Loan Act of 1961. Because of the need to acquire wetlands and other habitat needed to conserve the waterfowl resource, while such lands were still available, loans from the duck-stamp funds still to be collected were authorized by the Congress for this purpose. The sum of 105 million dollars was authorized for use over a period of 7 years. Lands may be acquired in fee or by easements to assure the wetlands character of the areas. It is planned that about two-thirds of an ultimate goal of 4.5 million acres will be acquired in this 7-year period.

The Wetlands Inspection Act of 1962. To supplement the work under the Wetlands Loan Act and to resolve certain conflicts in Federal land programs, wetlands for which technical assistance in drainage has been requested are examined, under this act, by Fish and Wildlife Service men; and when the land is adapted to waterfowl conservation, offers are made to lease or purchase it.

CERTAIN IMPORTANT MISCELLANEOUS FEDERAL ACTS AFFECTING THE CON-
SERVATION OF WILD-ANIMAL RESOURCES   Penalties are set in special laws
on the following activities: capturing or disturbing wild animals, nests,
eggs, or Federal property on refuges—act of March, 1909, as amended
1924; assaulting Federal officers and resisting arrest—act of 1934, as
amended 1936; importation, unlawfully, of plumage, skins, and game—
Tariff Act of 1930; and setting fires on the public domain—act of 1909.
Certain treaties affecting whales and seals, both sea-going mammals, are
discussed under Fisheries on pages 295 to 297.

Neglected Wild Animals. The conservation, or even the control, of
certain of our wild-animal forms receives relatively little official attention
in this country, and yet a majority of our citizens are not hunters, trappers,
or fishermen and may be much more interested in this miscellaneous
neglected group. The list includes songbirds; reptiles; scavenger species,
such as gulls and buzzards; certain of the harmless insects, some of which
are of great beauty; unusual animals such as armadillos, alligators, porcupines, prairie dogs, field mice, jack rabbits, lizards, ferrets, pack rats, bats,
eagles, and owls (Fig. 9-24); and even horses and burros that have gone
wild over the years. What a motley parade they make! They are here
listed unsystematically with the purpose of calling attention to their
number, variety, and difficulty of classification. (The reader is spared a
separate discussion of fleas, bedbugs, cockroaches, lice, ants, flies, rats,
mice, and other of the accursed "wild animals," but not because they are
not wild.)

Aside from the more common songbirds, snakes, turtles, and very small
mammals, about the only place the general public sees many of the forms
mentioned here is in a museum, a zoo, or a bird store. And yet they are
all a part of the natural scene, and many of them are parts that we should
not lose. Their services cannot be appraised in definite material terms,
their nuisance characteristics are hardly greater than those of their game
and fur-bearing brothers, and they have to depend on their Audubon
Society and other nature-loving friends. But they repay with antics, color,
movement, song, dance, roar, and scream, reminding us that this is a
living world. One of their strongholds is the national parks; another is
the small public and private nature sanctuaries maintained under dozens
of designations. Still another is found in the thousands of back-yard feeding stations for birds. Laws, too, are of some help, but in most states
protective legislation concerns itself with the more commonly known
game species.

THE FUTURE OF WILD-ANIMAL RESOURCES

As far as natural resources are concerned in any culture, their conservation is a matter of conscious or unconscious decision on priorities. In

figure 9-24

A barn owl with his powerful claws has captured one of the rodents least deserving of consideration, the rat. He holds the victim in his beak as if to exhibit his usefulness to mankind. (Photo by Leslie A. Campbell, courtesy of Massachusetts Audubon Society.)

terms of modern technological development, the extension of a city or of an industrial area may appear to be more urgent than maintaining forest, vacant land, or even farming areas which would support wild animals. When the chance arises to raise cash crops by draining a swamp rich in wild-animal resources, the animal life may seem unimportant. And certainly the impoundment of water for the various defensible purposes of providing power, irrigation, flood control, or even municipal water may mean the doom of many animal forms whose favorite habitat will be buried under water. Similar alternative situations could be multiplied almost without limit. A blunt query, "What do you want, payrolls or fish?" was reported a few years ago during a state campaign against industrial stream pollution. That is oversimplification at its worst, but the rejoinder might well be, "What will it cost to have both?" A lot of people in this richest country in the whole world are asking just that, which seems to prophesy a few good breaks for the animals.

The Need for Understanding. Many of our mistakes in managing natural resources can be blamed on ignorance both of facts and of their significance. Some of the well-known exaggerations of fishermen, bear hunters, and even of amateur research men suggest that, after all, the term "true facts," in the vernacular of the advertising people, may have its uses. Surely wider public understanding of the things discussed briefly so far in this chapter is to be hoped for and cannot but be helpful in achieving successful management of wild-animal resources. But how can such knowledge be made common property?

First of all, there is no substitute for public-school education, even if it goes no deeper into wild-animal conservation than elementary courses in nature study or, at most, courses in high-school biology. Where the public-school systems recognize the value of translating such courses into the language and principles of wild-animal conservation, there is a tremendous start on educating the public. Such effort is increasingly widespread as public-school teachers in science, vocational training, and the social studies become equipped and interested themselves. Of all natural resources, too, animals have perhaps the strongest appeal to children. A National Committee on Policies in Conservation Education has operated for several years, promoting teacher training and introducing conservation slants into the fields of secondary education mentioned. More and more courses in conservation of natural resources are becoming available to undergraduate college students. Few of these in other than preprofessional programs are required, but they are popular and widely elected. The material presented on wild animals is usually an important feature. Graduate work in forty or more institutions offers opportunity for the development of professional technicians, teachers, and administrators in the wild-animal-resource field. The total college crop, undergraduate and graduate, is, however, relatively small and serves only to leaven the vast public whose support must be won.

The task of educating the public outside the schools and colleges is by far the most difficult. It requires the use of every device of communication. Here is a list of the facilities now used to do this job and, in some instances, to grind a business ax at the same time: the sportsmen's, and a few of the trade, associations with their magazines, news releases, efforts to influence legislation, public meetings, various cooperative projects with public agencies, and, in rare instances, their codes of outdoor behavior for their members; the considerable group of outdoor writers who have their special pages or columns in all the leading newspapers and who have their own organization; the variously sponsored radio and television programs which vary all the way from bedtime stories to popularized reports on the latest researches; the financial contributions to contests, researches, and general education and the advertising material of the arms, ammunition, and gear manufacturers; the youth organizations and vacation camps; and, not the least effective, the visual and publication materials (Fig. 9-25), programs and tours available from the public agencies and from such organizations as the National Wildlife Federation and the National Audubon Society.

All this sounds like a vast concerted effort at public education, but it is at best scattered, difficult to unify, and only slowly effective against the competition it meets in all channels and against established attitudes such as "my license entitles me to bag and creel limits," or "the violation consists of getting caught," or "I don't hunt or fish, why should I worry?" or "it's wrong to kill animals under any circumstances," or "it's better to throw away the kill than to be called a meat hunter," or "wild-animal life is the most important of all the natural resources," But while desirable action may even lag behind public information and understanding, there will be little wild-animal or any other kind of conservation without the latter. It is our biggest single task in this field, because it makes possible the support of needed research and action programs.

The Need for Flexible Policy. The various states, with their duty to administer the wild-animal resources, have included in actual laws many regulations and decisions which might well be left to the "commissions" entrusted with the task of conserving these resources. Sportsmen frequently find themselves appointed to these commissions, and "politics" seems to figure less and less in their selection and that of other interested, but untrained, citizens. But many commissioners are too busy to give the necessary time and thought to a resource which is continually fluctuating both in quantity and behavior and in the gun pressure it is subject to. On the other hand, wherever policy making is taken seriously and worked at conscientiously, certain discretionary powers may well be delegated to commissions so that seasonal and other emergencies and changes can be dealt with promptly. The fixing of open and closed seasons and of bag limits, the allotment of such earmarked funds as are available for enforcement and research, and the choice of top administrative and technical personnel are all examples of situations where flexibility of policy and discretionary administrative power can be useful.

The Need for Continuing Research. While interest in and financing of research are encouraging in the important hunting states, there is much to be learned about fundamentals, such as life histories and habits of the animals; new problems arising daily in the conflicts of land use and in the influences of weather, disaster, and the use of insecticides and herbi-

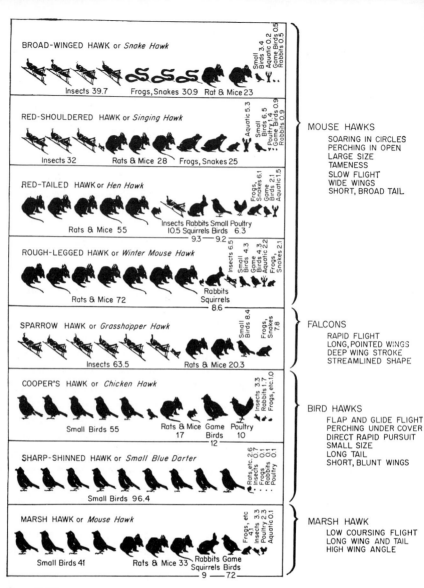

figure 9-25
What hawks eat. Based on U.S. Dept. Agr. Cir. 370, "Food Habits of Common Hawks." (National Association of Audubon Societies.)

cides; and, last but not least, in that thing that might well be called "the life history and hunting habits of the sportsman." Research programs, therefore, must be maintained and strengthened.

The Need for Law Enforcement. Hardly a year goes by in which there is not a report of the killing of some state or Federal game warden or field agent, and it is safe to say that the record of the more common violations of game and fish laws each year fails to cover the actual number which occur. In spite of the advances in conservation education reported by the Fish and Wildlife Service and a growing awareness of the need for protection, game-law violations have risen as hunting pressure has increased. In the fiscal year 1963 Federal forces apprehended 6,609 persons charged with violation of state or Federal game laws. Of these cases, 4,269 involved violation of the various migratory-bird laws and seventy-four involved violation of miscellaneous offenses, including four of assault on game officers. In addition, Federal agents, in cooperation with state conservation officers, assisted in the apprehension and prosecution of 2,275 violators of state laws and regulations involving resident game and fish. Of the latter, 2,215 were found guilty.[22] Even the many states with efficient staffs of enforcement officers have trouble in bringing violators to justice. Law enforcement is considered a useful, if inadequate, tool of game management, and more of it is needed.

Other Needs for the Future of Wild-animal Resources. Overlapping to some extent the needs for understanding and for more flexible policy, research, and law enforcement, the future welfare of wild-animal resources requires increased area of public refuges and hunting grounds, the reconciliation of conflicting departmental objectives (here a case in point is the use of wildlife areas by the Department of Defense), and perhaps an increasing appreciation of the value of wild animals aside from their usefulness as targets. Only as wild-animal resources gain some definite and enduring place in the natural-resource priority list can we be assured of their ultimate survival along with our technological developments and their competing needs.

BIBLIOGRAPHY

ALLEN, DURWARD L.: Our Wildlife Legacy, rev. ed., Funk & Wagnalls Company, New York, 1962.
Annual Reports of the Secretary of the Interior, 1956–1964.
BACHRACH, MAX.: Fur: A Practical Treatise, rev. ed., Prentice-Hall, Inc., Englewood Cliffs, N.J., 1947.
CARSON, RACHEL L.: Silent Spring, Houghton Mifflin Company, Boston, 1962.
Conservation News, National Wildlife Federation, Washington, D.C., March 15, April 1, and May 1, 1964.
DAMBACH, CHARLES A.: Conservation of Wildlife, Chap. 18 in Conservation of Natural Resources, Guy-Harold Smith, ed., John Wiley & Sons, Inc., New York, 1950.
Federal Wildlife Activities, 1950, Report of the Committee on Expenditures in the Executive Departments, S. Rept. 317, 82d Cong., 1st sess., 1951.
GABRIELSON, IRA N.: Wildlife Conservation, The Macmillan Company, New York, 1941.
————: Wildlife Refuges, The Macmillan Company, New York, 1947.

[22] *Annual Report of the Secretary of the Interior,* 1963, p. 287.

GRAHAM, EDWARD H.: The Land and Wildlife, Oxford University Press, Fair Lawn, N.J., 1947.

International Association of Game, Fish and Conservation Commissioners, Proceedings, 1956–1964, St. Paul, Minn.

JAMISON, JAMES K.: This Ontonagon Country, 3d ed., Ontonagon Herald Company, Ontonagon, Mich., 1948.

JANZEN, D. H.: Letter as Director, U.S. Bureau of Sport Fisheries and Wildlife, Nov. 4, 1947.

LEOPOLD, ALDO: The American Game Policy, in *Trans. Seventeenth Amer. Game Conf.*, Wildlife Management Institute, Washington, D.C., 1930.

———: Game Management, Charles Scribner's Sons, New York, 1933.

Los Angeles Times, June 18, 1964.

Michigan Conservation, Lansing, Mich., vol. 22, no. 13, March–April, 1952; and vol. 33, no. 2, March–April, 1964.

Michigan Department of Conservation, News releases, Lansing, Mich., Mar. 19 and June 4 and 25, 1964.

Michigan Out-of-doors, Lansing, Mich., January, 1962.

National Survey of Hunting and Fishing, *U.S. Fish Wildlife Serv. Circ.* 44, 1956.

PALMER, E. LAURENCE: Fieldbook of Natural History, McGraw-Hill Book Company, New York, 1949.

PETERSON, ROGER TORY, AND JAMES FISHER: Wild America, Houghton Mifflin Company, Boston, 1955.

PITTMAN-ROBERTSON QUARTERLY, for July–October quarter, 1952, vol. 13, January, 1953.

Status Report of Wildfowl, 1957, *U.S. Fish Wildlife Serv. Spec. Sci. Rept.: Wildlife*, vol. 37, Aug. 19, 1957.

TRIPPENSEE, REUBEN EDWIN: Wildlife Management, vol. I McGraw-Hill Book Company, New York, 1948.

Wildlife Conservation Activities of the Federal Government, 1949, Hearings before the Sub-Committee to Investigate Wildlife Conservation, Committee on Expenditures in the Executive Departments, U.S. Senate, 81st Cong., 2d sess., 1950.

10 FISHERIES

WITH MORE THAN 19.8 million licensed sports anglers in the land representing more than a 100 per cent increase through the 1960s—and with a commercial fishing industry taking a 5.4 billion-pound catch in 1962—worth almost 400 million dollars to the fishermen—the fisheries of this country represent an important natural resource with plenty of conservation problems (Fig. 10-1). And regardless of the difficulty of giving away any part of the catch which the enthusiastic sport fisherman brings home or which he contributes to an overloaded camp larder, *his* total contribution to the food of the country is probably almost as impressive as it is costly. It is estimated that fishery products are exceeded only by beef, pork, and poultry as leading protein foods in the world, and in many countries they rank first. Consumption in the United States is about 11 pounds per capita, whereas in Finland it is about 50 pounds. Nor should it be forgotten that various animal feeds, valuable oils, fertilizers, and raw materials for plastics and glues make up an imposing list of by-products from commercial fisheries.

The term *fishery* may therefore include not only the business of capturing fishes, the meaning most commonly understood, but the taking of shellfish, whale, kelp, and other resources of the sea and of inland waters.

The Nature of the Fishery Resources. Fishes are less understood than many other natural resources because their aquatic habitat hides them from easy observation. They ignore man-made boundaries between political units. They are particularly vulnerable to modern technology, both with regard to instruments for capturing them and to interference with their environment and migrations by dams, pollution, and drainage. Fishes respond well to husbandry and its many artificial devices, but only as the life histories and needs of the species are understood. Demand for both commercial and sport fishes has increased steadily since the early days of settling the country.

Factors Which Deplete the Fisheries. As with other natural resources, exploitation by man has depleted the supply of many of the important fishes. It has occurred on the assumption if any, that the resource is somehow automatically renewable on a sustained-yield basis, without any help from mankind. Notable examples of reduced annual catch are common. These include cod from North Atlantic waters, which in less than a century decreased from almost a 300-million-pound annual catch to 50 million pounds in 1962; a 50 per cent decrease in the lobster catch from New England waters; the reduced catches of Pacific coast pilchard (sardine species) in recent years compared with the former catches from this area which led others in the United States in size; and the case of the Atlantic salmon, which was once important commercially and is now only a sport species in United States waters.

Barriers in streams have long interfered with the free movement and

the spawning habits of certain fish species, several of them, such as salmon
and shad, being of real commercial importance. Usually these barriers
have been dams of various types, from the early small gristmill-power
dam to the enormous structures for impounding waters for irrigation and
power in the West, which challenge the imagination as engineering
accomplishments. Indeed it is a question whether the increased demand
for power in the Northwest will not force a choice between use of water
in a truly multiple sense, including fish production as an important function, and permanent destruction of the latter resource on the theory that
hydropower is more important and that the public cannot have both.

Fish are sometimes trapped or marooned in pools and other high-
water impoundments which eventually dry up, and in irrigating ditches
and even out on fields which are being watered from ditches where the
intake is not properly screened. Rescue of these stranded fish is sometimes
attempted, but it is difficult and costly.

Pollution of water occurs from many sources and in almost every instance tends to deplete the fisheries of the waters concerned. Perhaps the
most common source is domestic and municipal sewage, insufficiently
treated or not treated at all and entering the public waters to leach

figure 10-2

Pulp waste being emptied into stream from paper mill. (Photo by Rex Gary Schmidt, United States Fish and Wildlife Service.)

from them the life-giving oxygen. Industrial wastes—including so-called pickling liquors from steel plants; sulfite and other refuse from paper mills (Fig. 10-2); poisons from plating works; oil-refinery, coal-mine, and atomic-pile wastes; and a host of others which may be relatively free of bacteria but are full of taints and poisons—all present relatively new problems. Industrial wastes from packing and other food-processing plants may, of course, also carry harmful bacteria, but they are most often of concern because of their oxygen demand. Finally, the silt carried into streams, lakes, and reservoirs from farm and other lands makes the water intolerable to preferred kinds of sport and commercial fish species and may be considered a kind of pollution. (The reader is referred to pages 86–91 for a general discussion of the problem of the inevitable use of water for the transportation of waste.)

Drainage of land for agricultural or occupancy purposes obviously removes water and interferes with the fish populations of ponds, lakes, sluggish streams, and marshes.

Natural enemies, including predators, are probably not so important in the depletion picture as the other factors listed; but, occasionally, the invasion of waters by a new form, such as the entry of parasitic sea lamprey into the Great Lakes, reaches serious proportions and threatens an entire industry (Fig. 10-3).

Closely related to the predator problem is the invasion of fresh waters by so-called "trash fish." A recent example of this is the appearance of the alewife in Lake Michigan. Previous to the opening of the Welland Canal, this species was unknown above Niagara Falls. It is a fish native to North Atlantic waters and important there in the fish-canning and by-products industries. It is relatively worthless at present in the lake and may be a serious competitor of more valuable fish species. However, attempts are now under way to utilize the alewife in canned animal foods. Another aspect of the trash-fish problem is seen in the manner in which carp, suckers, and similar species come to predominate in many inland waters from which predaceous game species are depleted. Furthermore, the dumping of surplus live bait is likely to introduce forms competitive with desirable species of fish, and many states forbid this practice and sometimes even the use of live bait at all in certain waters.

General Devices Used to Conserve Fisheries. As in all efforts to conserve wild-animal resources, legal restrictions of various kinds have been much more common than any positive devices to increase the productivity of the resource. With only limited knowledge of certain fishes, laws and regulations have been established as the easiest and the only immediate means of control available. Enforcement is, however, anything but easy, and ways of "getting around" such regulations are frequently discovered. General restrictions on capture involve catch quotas (sometimes spoken of as "creel limits" in sport fishing) and limits on types of gear, on season, on size of specimens taken, on time of day, on territory over which fishing may be done, and on fishing without purchase of a license. Most of these measures apply both to sport and commercial fishing. Where they are based upon knowledge of life histories and habits of the fish and are really enforced, they have been effective. They are most successful when closely adapted to localized situations. The current move to relax older laws restricting size, season, and creel limits, especially on warm-water fish, serves both to retard overpopulation and stunting and to increase recreational opportunity.

Positive measures of fishery management are undergoing constant

Lamprey on creek chub. Usually this pest attacks lake trout. (Michigan Department of Conservation.)

figure 10-3

figure 10-4

Feeding young trout in a hatchery. Scientifically designed diets are used. (Photo by Michigan Department of Conservation.)

increase in both variety and sophistication. Hatcheries, once regarded as almost a panacea for declining fisheries (Fig. 10-4), still loom large in specialized applications, but in broad practice they have yielded their primacy to manipulation of the native environment (so-called stream and lake improvement) and of the fish populations themselves.

The energy of running water has been widely employed, on trout streams especially, to restore habitat damaged or destroyed by erosion or by changes in water supply and drainage basin (Fig. 10-5). Such practices result in increased food, shelter, and spawning facilities for trout and often greatly enhance the aesthetic qualities of the stream as well.

A better understanding of fish-population dynamics has led to increased use of specific fish toxicants, such as rotenone, to reduce or remove unwanted populations and so to release desirable species from damaging competition. This practice is becoming especially common in creating trout lakes from waters once overrun by stunted yellow perch or other

(a)

(b)

figure 10-5   *Improvement of trout stream by bank stabilization. (a) Bank before treatment being seriously eroded; (b) same site immediately after grading and rock riprapping; (c) same site a few months later. (Photo by Michigan Department of Conservation.)*

(c)

figure 10-6

Farm pond in Barbour County, W.Va. Impounding water in this manner and planting warm-water fish is a positive measure of fishery management. (Photo by Hermann Postlethwaite, United States Soil Conservation Service.)

undesirable forms and in combating the tendency toward overpopulation and consequent stunting in otherwise desirable pan fishes such as the bluegill.

The creation of new fishing waters through excavation of ponds (Fig. 10-6) or impoundment of streams is growing in popularity with both government conservation agencies and private landowners.

Examples of Important Commercial Fishes. SALMON Few Americans are unfamiliar with canned salmon, for the salmon, based on five species —red, king (chinook), coho (silver), pink, and chum (dog)—makes up the largest catch by weight of any of our commercial species used as human food. About one-sixth the catch is packed. The balance is sold fresh, frozen, smoked, or cured. Almost 80 per cent of the domestic production of salmon comes from Alaska, and this comprises close to 50 per cent of the world's production. Only one other commercial species, the masu, is known in the Pacific, and it inhabits Asiatic waters. The Atlantic salmon is important now only as a sport fish except in a few localities in the Maritime Provinces of Canada.

The salmons are so-called *anadromous* fishes. This means that they migrate from the sea, where they spend their growing years, to the spring-fed, gravel spawning grounds of rivers entering the sea (Fig. 10-7). In most instances they seem to find their way to the same stream, and almost the exact spot, where they themselves were spawned. The adult Pacific salmon die after spawning. The eggs incubate in the gravel, and the young, 2 months after hatching, reach the stage called fry and begin the search for food. Within the next 4 years, depending upon species, the young have migrated to the sea, and within 2 to 7 years, survivors of the various kinds have swarmed in season back up their native streams —that is, unless some barrier constructed meanwhile has stopped them. But the salmon's life is a struggle from the start. Some birds, fish, and other animals feed on salmon eggs. Ducks, other water birds, and freshwater fishes devour young salmon if the latter have escaped death by earlier enemies or disease. Sea lions, seals, whales, and certain kinds of large fish prey upon growing salmon in the ocean. At the mouth of streams, on the return migration, the most efficient capturing gear that man can devise awaits them. Finally, on their way upstream, bears, wolves, gulls, eagles, and other natural enemies feed upon them. Only the "escapement" is left to spawn. It cannot take unlimited abuse from the construction of man-made barriers and from unscreened irrigation and power diversions.

However, intelligent management based on scientific knowledge holds great possibilities for dramatic increases in salmon production. In Alaska, where the greatest share of tax revenue comes from the salmon industry, such management should prove a sound public investment (Fig. 10-8). Even in the Columbia River system, the year of 1964 saw improved management practices result in the best runs of silver and fall chinook salmon since 1941. An appraisal of conservation opportunities and devices would indicate that restrictive laws and regulations are usually useful, if not always the best, and that they are moderately well enforced. However, since all the coastal states impose different laws and regulations, the Pacific salmon resource is by no means under unified management.

Barriers present a difficult set of problems in getting the spawning

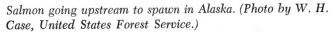

Salmon going upstream to spawn in Alaska. (Photo by W. H. Case, United States Forest Service.)

figure 10-7

Salmon cannery, Tongass National Forest, Alaska. (Photo by Dow V. Baxter, School of Natural Resources, University of Michigan.)

migrants around or over the dams and in getting the young salmon fingerlings safely downstream past the gauntlet of spillways, turbines, and deeply submerged outlets of storage reservoirs. Fishways are used for these purposes and may consist of fish ladders made up of a staircase-like cascade of rectangular pools arranged at rising intervals of 1 to 2 feet so that the fish can make their way upstream (Figs. 10-9 and 10-10). This device sounds simple, but it is expensive and requires that the fish be attracted to the entrance and that the quantity and speed of water flow be carefully regulated. Imagine a self-respecting salmon, however, finding

Looking down fish ladder at Bradford Island on the Columbia River. (Photo by Lawrence E. Griffin, courtesy of American Forests.)

figure 10-10
King salmon ascending falls on spawning run. (Photo by Phil Pister, California Department of Fish and Game.)

himself in a tank truck, a bucket hoist, or a lock similar to those used for navigation! These devices are used occasionally.

Prediction of the salmon crop on a yearly basis is possible within limits and is important if the catch is to represent the advisable degree of population control on spawning grounds (Fig. 10-11). Overcrowding of spawning grounds means lower production and survival. Such prediction therefore contributes to conservation in a positive sense. Upon its accuracy hinges the real management of the resource. This is how it is done: First the number of spawning adults must be estimated or counted as they make their way upstream to spawning grounds (a tough kind of census to take); next the resulting number of young must be determined on their way downstream (and this is not easy); finally these counts must be studied in the light of carefully obtained knowledge of stream and ocean conditions which are actually proved to affect survival. All this must be done for *each* stream population *each* year.

In recent years, the salmon resource has benefited from the considerable expansion of laboratory and research facilities and personnel which has taken place and which has already proved to be a sound investment. The International North Pacific Fisheries Commission, established in 1952, involving Canada, the United States, and Japan, provides for joint action on the problem of maximum sustainable productivity of fisheries of common concern in the North Pacific, including the salmon. Research conducted by the three member countries under coordination of the commission has yielded important information on distribution and origin of salmon on the high seas. Areas in which Asian and North American salmon stocks intermingle are being precisely defined.

HADDOCK   Haddock is another fish well known to American consumers whether in the form of fillets, finnan haddie (smoked), or fish flakes. It

275

figure 10-11

Commercial catch of salmon in barge headed for cannery in Tongass National Forest, Alaska. (Photo by Dow V. Baxter, School of Natural Resources, University of Michigan.)

is the most valuable of all the North Atlantic coast fisheries, and its peak production, which came in 1929, reached 260 million pounds. The 1962 catch of 134.3 million pounds was the greatest since the all-time low reached in 1956.

Haddock do not spawn until 3 or 4 years old. By that time they have come to weigh 2 to 3 pounds, and gathering on the Nova Scotia, Newfoundland, or New England banks, the schools spawn their eggs into relatively deep surrounding waters where they are fertilized and drift while incubating. Early-life periods are spent in drifting until the bottom existence is started. Hazards to young include possible exposure to severe conditions of depth through adverse currents and getting caught. The catch of smaller fish which have not reached the spawning stage is increasing. In 1928 only 9 per cent of the catch was made up of fish weighing less than 2 pounds. By 1941 this had risen to 47 per cent. Studies by the Fish and Wildlife Service indicate that the spawning stock should be nearly doubled if adequate sustained production of young is to be achieved (Fig 10-12). Strangely enough, the simple expedient of taking no fish under 2 pounds would allow many to grow to spawning age, and it is estimated that the catch might, in this manner, be increased eventually by 15 per cent (Too radical methods could presumably increase population too greatly and bring about eventual depletion from lack of food supply.) But so far there are only voluntary agreements by a few fishermen to cooperate on size limits, modification of gear, and sustained effort, in general, to increase spawning stock. No state laws or other regulations require compliance with suggested changes. Whether the increase of convincing evidence that this program is to the interests of the fishing industry will be heeded depends somewhat upon testing out the conclusions of scientists and upon further investigations of young-fish-saving gear and methods of measuring populations. But, as in other natural-resource shortage situations, a tough problem here is to get the support of the public and the industry for a promising program of action. One hopeful development is the 1952 agreement by the Northwest Atlantic Fishery Commission, which had been established in 1951, on the increase of mesh sizes to allow the escape of young. This agreement went into effect in 1953.

PACIFIC SARDINE, OR PILCHARD   This group of herringlike fishes (called sardines when canned) was for a number of years the basic resource for the largest fishing industry in the Western Hemisphere. Pilchard are widely distributed in temperate coastal waters throughout the world, and they are known as pelagic fish, that is, those inhabiting surface offshore

Biologists measuring haddock to obtain information from commercial catch on age and fluctuation in catch from year to year. Many measurements are taken and recorded. (Photo by A. H. Fisher, United States Fish and Wildlife Service.)

figure 10-12

layers of water. Habitually traveling in large schools, or shoals, the range of the group covers the entire Pacific coast of the United States and extends beyond to Mexican and Canadian waters (Fig. 10-13). The catch yielded some 420 million pounds annually of processed food meal, oil, bait, and other materials in prewar years. The years 1946 to 1948, however, showed disastrous reductions in catch, thought to be due to poor production and survival of mature fish from 1943 through 1945 and to possible unexplained changes in migration and availability of the pilchard population. There were sharper drops in production from 1950 through 1953, but an encouraging catch of 137 million pounds was taken in 1954.

The life history and habits of sardines are becoming better understood through cooperative studies of various public agencies, and yet more observations on oceanic conditions affecting spawning, of fluctuations in food supply, and of the effect of weather upon fishing success are needed.

Sardine spawning occurs mostly in March and April in the open sea 50 to 300 miles offshore. A single female may produce as many as 35,000 eggs three times a season. This is a population safeguard, necessary because of the high mortality of the young. Fertilization takes place in open water, the hatch follows in about 3 days, and the young eventually

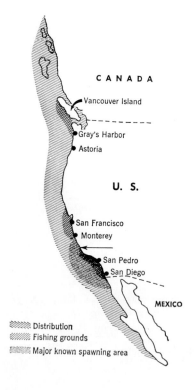

CANADA

Vancouver Island

Gray's Harbor
Astoria

U. S.

San Francisco
Monterey

San Pedro
San Diego

MEXICO

Distribution
Fishing grounds
Major known spawning area

figure 10-13
Map indicating distribution, fishing grounds, and major known spawning area of West coast sardines. Arrow points to relatively small spawning area concerning which knowledge exists. (*United States Fish and Wildlife Service.*)

become free swimming and feed upon minute plant and animal life known collectively as *plankton*. Predation and fluctuations in food supply take a heavy toll of the young.

Two effects of intensive fishing must be considered in maintaining a conservation program for the pilchard: (1) reduction of the total number of fish, with a resulting smaller catch for a given amount of fishing effort and investment; and (2) reduction in the numbers of spawning stock with disastrous results in the annual yield. To meet these situations, much more must be learned of the habits of the fish making up this resource and of oceanic conditions which affect fluctuations in the catch. A program with this in mind is getting under way with Federal, state, and private participation. Legislative control is confined to waters under the jurisdiction of California and is so far confined principally to utilization of the catch. There are closed seasons not on fishing but on the use of sardines for canning and for reduction into industrial products. This affects the management of fishing boats and processing plants but has little effect upon sustaining the resource itself. Only through greater knowledge, sought as mentioned above, may intelligent and effective restriction be drawn up and enforced if needed.

Recent researches supported by California state and private agencies and by the Federal Fish and Wildlife Service indicate that decline of the sardine catch in recent years may be a fluctuation due mainly to reduced spawning stocks caused by intensive fishing, a succession of poor spawning seasons, and poor survival of eggs and young fish.

MACKERELS Both the true Pacific form and the jack mackerel are caught from California ports by certain of the pilchard fishermen and others, and together in 1962 they accounted for 139 million pounds of products sold fresh, salted, canned, and smoked, and worth almost 3 million dollars to the fishermen. Sport fishing for mackerel from pleasure barges is also important, and it is unhampered by legislative restrictions. As with pilchard the only regulations in force concerning mackerel have to do with utilization of the catch, no part being allowed for reduction to industrial products except the trimmings and offal remaining from canning. There are no restrictions on catch, gear, or season. Investigations so far have revealed location of spawning grounds, migration habits (through the capture-tagging-release-capture device), and spawning ages and habits. Use of the resource is, however, increasing, but practically nothing is known of the proportion exploited annually. The same is true of the Atlantic mackerel, the Spanish mackerel, and the king mackerel, all of which are caught off the Atlantic coast. These appear as important fresh-fish products, and the latter, because of speed and fighting power, is a favorite game fish. Atlantic mackerel during World War II appeared increasingly also as a canned product, but violent fluctuations in the runs hamper the industry in sustained catch and use of this valuable food fish. The greatest need for conserving the resource in the sense of use while maintaining productivity is further knowledge upon which to predict each year's potential catch. Total production has fluctuated in recent years from a high of 108 million pounds in 1944 to a low of 13.5 million pounds in 1959. The astonishing changes in abundance from year to year are apparently a reflection of the degree of survival of young of the year.

COD   This fishery should be mentioned, not only because of its historical importance during the past centuries when its catch was our principal salt fish, but because of its present importance in the fresh fish market and its value for liver oils (also taken from pollock, hake, and haddock) as a source of vitamin D. The fish inhabits the same kinds of bottoms as haddock but it runs to greater size and moves about to a greater extent. The skins are a source of high-quality glue.

Understanding of daily variations in catch and maximum utilization of this apparently plentiful resource awaits basic studies not yet undertaken. The cod is represented by two species, one native to the Atlantic, the other to the Pacific. The true Pacific cod, lingcod, and sablefish are all taken in Pacific waters and marketed fresh, frozen and, (except for lingcod) salted. All are under-utilized. In the case of the true Pacific cod this is partly due to the distance of Alaskan waters, where it is taken, from processing centers. The resource offers opportunity for development of marketing techniques which would make it comparable to the Atlantic cod fishery. The quick-freezing method is one of the most promising for better utilization of this resource. Pollock, which has a distribution similar to that of cod, is marketed from Atlantic waters but awaits utilization from the Pacific.

In 1962 United States fishermen landed 50 million pounds of cod valued at 3.5 million dollars. Both catch and value showed a slight increase over the previous year. The Atlantic fishery accounted for about 46 million pounds, Massachusetts ports alone accounting 41 million pounds. Washington produced slightly over 3 million pounds.

GROUND FISHES   Among the "ground fishes," of which cod is one, rosefish, or ocean perch, is now sold regularly on the market as packaged fillets. In New England waters it has become second only to haddock in volume of catch. Intensive fishing appears to indicate decline as stocks of older fish are caught. Ocean perch, another of the ground fishes, is one of few commercial species which give birth to live young. They reach maturity at the eleventh year, and it is important that so-called seed stock be undisturbed and allowed to grow rather than to be taken as a part of the catch. No new vessels have entered the ocean-perch fleet since 1952, and both the size of the fleet and the size of the catch have declined since that year. The downward trend has been attributed to low prices, scarcity of the species in both United States and Canadian waters, and a decrease in the number of vessels capable of reaching distant fishing grounds.

HALIBUT This large form of flounder should be considered here because it is well known in the fish markets and because its exploitation has been turned to conservation through international cooperative means. First taken from the North Atlantic banks, a yearly catch there of more than 14 million pounds has declined to less than half a million pounds, in contrast to a 1962 catch in the North Pacific waters of more than 72 million pounds. On the other hand, heavy and unregulated fishery in the Pacific banks brought about a decline in landings from 69 million pounds in 1915 to 43 million pounds in 1931. These decreases were the more significant because halibut livers and viscera furnish important amounts of vitamin-rich oils.

As early as 1916, signs of depletion indicated that international action would be necessary to regulate halibut fishing, and in 1924 a treaty between Great Britain and the United States set up an International Fishery Commission which undertook a study of halibut resources. This treaty was changed and strengthened in 1930 to prescribe regulatory powers, and it was modified further in 1937. Again in 1953 this agreement, now between Canada and the United States, was amended to broaden further the Commission's powers. One of the provisions had to do with catch quotas for each of four Pacific Coast areas where the seasons were closed when the quotas had been filled. Another prohibited all fishing for halibut in a particular area where the fishes were of small size. Good management under these arrangements has increased the catch to the figure for 1962 given above.

MENHADEN The menhaden is a herringlike fish similar in habit and life history to the Pacific sardines, but used little for human food. Twenty years ago the menhaden fishing industry centered in the Middle Atlantic states. By 1962, however, peak production had shifted to the Gulf of Mexico, which produced 45 per cent of the catch; whereas the Middle Atlantic states rated second with 33 per cent of the total; followed by the Chesapeake area with 14 per cent, the South Atlantic with 7 per cent (Fig. 10-14), and New England with 1 per cent.

Landings of menhaden in 1962 totalled 2.3 billion pounds, representing 44 per cent of the entire United States production of all species and an increase of 33 million pounds over the previous year. When the catch is compared with the 1954 total of 1.7 billion pounds, it is seen that this is one marine-fisheries resource whose limits of exploitation have not been reached.

The three species of menhaden are pelagic and travel in dense schools. At 2 years they have reached a length of 7 to 10 inches, and they are

figure 10-14

Seining for menhaden near Beaufort, N.C. (Photo by Frank Dufresne, United States Fish and Wildlife Service.)

increasingly rich in oil up to maturity, which is believed to be the third or fourth year. They are taken in great quantities for fertilizer, oil and livestock and poultry feeds. Menhaden roe, the unspawned eggs, saved out and frozen, salted, or canned is used for human food. The oil is important in the manufacture of linoleum and rainproof garments. More than 93 per cent of all the marine-animal oils produced in the United States and 77 per cent of all marine-animal scrap and meal used in poultry and livestock feeds are products of the menhaden industry. As with many other fishes, the importance of the catch to national economy indicates need for greater knowledge than is available if conservation of the resource is to be assured. No legal restrictions are imposed upon menhaden fishermen at present. Information is badly needed on migration; location of spawning grounds and of grounds where the young develop; food habits and resulting oil content; parasites said to sterilize the male; and the relation of oceanic climate to fecundity, survival, and welfare of seed stock.

TUNAS   These fishes rank next to salmon in the canning industry, where the waste is worked into industrial products consisting principally of meal and oil. The livers are a source of high-potency vitamin oils. Aside from their commercial values, the tunas are a favorite quarry for sport fishermen. Of the four Pacific tunas—yellowfin, skipjack, bluefin, and albacore—the first two are by far the most valuable. The Atlantic tunas, while having a high value as game fish and reaching large size, have darker, coarser flesh than the Pacific forms and to date are of little commercial importance. Until the late 1950s fishing for Pacific tuna was done principally from clipper vessels, using sardines and other small fish as

282

bait. Barbless hooks and short poles were used, and when among large fish, two or more men might work together with separate rods attached to the same line. Conversion of California Clippers to purse-seine vessels was nearly completed by 1962 (Figs. 10-15 and 10-16). Landings of tuna in 1962 totaled slightly over 312 million pounds, worth 45 million dollars. Compared with 1961, poundage was reduced by 13.6 million pounds but the value was increased by 2.8 million dollars. Another major development in tuna fishing has been the expansion of production on the Atlantic coast. In 1962, for the first time, skipjack were taken by purse seines off the Middle Atlantic coast and landed at New England ports.

Recognition of the scarcity of sound scientific information on these important fishes led to the formation, in 1950, of the Inter-American Tropical Tuna Commission. A permanent scientific staff is based in California, and field stations and laboratories are operated in Ecuador, Peru, and Puerto Rico. By 1961 enough had been learned to conclude that overfishing was depleting the yellowfin stocks. Reduced quotas were recommended to the nations participating in this fishery. With yellowfin production now up to or above the maximum sustainable yield, the commission plans to concentrate next on the much farther-ranging skipjack.

FISHES OF THE GREAT LAKES Not all commercial fishing is confined to ocean species. The Great Lakes, which with their connecting waters from the largest single fresh-water area in the world, have long been famous for their commercial fisheries. Lake trout and whitefish have traditionally been the high-value species, but yellow perch, lake herring, chubs, and the introduced smelt have long been produced in large quantity, with smaller but still appreciable catches of carp, sheepshead, white bass, catfish, and yellow pike being taken.

Overfishing, once eyed as the chief cause of dwindling catches—especially of lake trout and whitefish—was displaced as a limiting factor by the invading sea lamprey (page 285). This parasitic species of marine origin slowly invaded the upper Great Lakes, bypassing the barrier of Niagara Falls by means of the Welland Canal. Although this canal was completed in 1833, it was not until the early 1930s that the sea lamprey was reported from the Detroit River. At first its threat was not apparent: it had done little damage to Lake Erie fishes. However, it encountered optimum spawning facilities in streams tributary to the upper Great Lakes, its numbers increased explosively (as often happens when an exotic species enters an unfilled ecological niche), and its attacks quickly made themselves felt on populations of lake trout and whitefish. By the middle 1950s the sea lamprey was firmly established in Lakes Huron, Michigan, and Superior. Lake-trout production dwindled from a pre–World War II peak of 10 million pounds to 3.7 million pounds in 1954; and by the

(a)

(b)

figure 10-15

Tuna fishing aboard a California clipper operating off Central America. The fish have been excited into a feeding frenzy by chumming them with live bait. Large tuna are caught by attaching two or more poles to one line. (Photo courtesy California Department of Fish and Game.)

figure 10-16

A California tuna clipper leaving the dock at Long Beach. These clippers range the eastern Pacific seeking yellowfin tuna and skipjack as far south as Chile. While fishing, a "chummer" stands atop the bait tanks (situated beneath the canopy near the vessel's stern) and casts live bait into the tuna schools. The fishing racks located along the stern swing down to the water; the crew stands in them while fishing with a bamboo pole and short line. (Photo courtesy California Department of Fish and Game.)

late 1950s the lake-trout population was exterminated, for all practical purposes, except for small remnants in Georgian Bay and western Lake Superior.

In the Great Lakes the sea lamprey runs up tributary streams to spawn in gravel beds and then dies. Larval lamprey occupy the streams as free-living predators for from 4 to 7 or more years; then, undergoing an anatomical transformation which specializes them for a parastic existence, they migrate down to the lakes and attach themselves to any of a variety of fishes (Fig. 10-3) by means of a sucking mouth. They suck blood in quantities which are fatal to smaller fish in a single feeding. Larger fish may survive several attacks, but each time they are weakened and made more vulnerable to subsequent attacks.

Recognizing the crisis to the Great Lakes fisheries, attempts to seek a solution were made, first by the Great Lakes states and Ontario, then by more ponderous but better-supported Federal and international agencies. The Convention on Great Lakes Fisheries, held by the United States and Canada, established a joint Great Lakes Fishery Commission in 1956. This body was charged with (1) eradication or control of the sea lamprey; (2) formulation and coordination of research to improve

figure 10-17
Electric barrier for controlling spawning runs of sea lamprey in Pere Marquette River, Michigan. Alternating current barrier in foreground; behind it (downstream) is a direct current diversionary device leading to a trap. (Photo, Bureau of Commercial Fisheries, United States Fish and Wildlife Service.)

Great Lakes fisheries; and (3) making recommendation to the two governments of appropriate conservation and regulatory measures. Intensive research led to development of a chemical, TFM[1], which exerted a selectively toxic action when released in spawning streams: it would kill larval lampreys with little or no damage to game fishes. Electric barriers to block spawning migrations were installed in streams tributary to the upper Great Lakes (Fig. 10-17). By 1962 combined action of electric barriers and chemical control had reduced sea-lamprey populations in Lake Superior by 80 per cent (Fig. 10-18). Hatchery-produced lake-trout fingerlings are being released to stimulate recovery, and there are grounds for optimism that the sea lamprey in the Great Lakes, like damaging insects and other economic pests, can be kept under control.

Fresh-water Sport Fishing. Fresh-water fishes support the bulk of sport fishing effort in the United States. Many marine forms have devoted followings among sportsmen, but they cannot compete with the more readily available species which inhabit inland waters. Fresh-water fishes may be divided into cold-water and warm-water forms. Of the former, the most commonly sought by sportsmen are various species of trout (Fig. 10-19). The brook trout native to eastern North American has been widely introduced elsewhere but has rather rigid physiological requirements for cold waters rich in dissolved oxygen. Somewhat less demanding is the rainbow trout, which has been widely disseminated from its original range

[1] 3-triflouromethyl-4-nitrophenol.

figure 10-18
One night's catch at a sea-lamprey-barrier trap, Ocqueoc River, Michigan.
(Photo, Bureau of Commercial Fisheries, United States Fish and Wildlife
Service.)

of streams draining into the Pacific Ocean. Least demanding of all is the brown trout (sometimes called "German brown" or "Loch Leven" since it was introduced to our waters from both Germany and Scotland). Because of the brown trout's greater tolerance for adverse ecological factors, it is tending to supplant native forms, especially the brook trout. The group known as cutthroat or black spotted trout includes a native Rocky Mountain form, a sea-run form taken in Pacific Coast waters, and several

figure 10-19
Trout fishing in a mountain stream. (Photo by Bluford W.
Muir, United States Forest Service.)

locally named trout with distinctive appearances. Among these are the famous California golden trout. The lake trout or "Mackinaw," as mentioned earlier, is sought for sport as well as for market.

All trout tend to migrate as their spawning season approaches. Lake trout leave deeper waters to spawn on rocky reefs. Stream species build nests or redds in gravel where the current is fairly strong. Lake trout spawn in fall, brook and brown trout in fall and early winter, and rainbow in early spring. Fall-spawning strains of rainbow have been developed by selective breeding, but the trait is soon lost through backcrossing with the parent strain.

Other cold-water fishes taken for sport include grayling and smelt. The grayling, related to the salmon family, is now extinct in Michigan waters where it was once plentiful, but it still occurs in the headwaters of the Missouri and in Arctic waters, including those of Alaska. The smelt, native to the northeast Atlantic coast and introduced into the Great Lakes, is prized for food and taken both commercially and for sport. Early-spring spawning runs afford exciting opportunity for capturing this small silvery fish. Crowds of anglers converge on spawning streams imparting a carnival air to dipping activities, which are most successful at night.

Five families of fishes comprise the warm-water species of greatest interest to the sports angler. These are (1) the sunfish family, which includes the smallmouth and the largemouth basses, the black and white crappies, and the various sunfishes such as the pumpkinseed, redear, bluegill, warmouth, rock bass, and Sacramento perch; (2) the perch family, represented by the ubiquitous yellow perch and the walleye; (3) the pike family, whose most desirable members, to anglers, are the muskellunge and the northern pike; (4) the catfish family, which includes such diverse forms as the large channel and flathead catfish, the bullheads, and the small madtoms (whose poison-bearing pectoral fin spines can inflict painful wounds); and (5) the minnow family, whose large, introduced representative, the carp, provides sport and food for the angler and a source of trouble for the fishery manager.

Many expert warm-water fishermen prefer the black bass (Fig. 10-20) —either the largemouth found in ponds, warm lakes, and sluggish streams; or the smallmouth which requires clear, cool, gravel-bottom waters. The black bass are good fighters. They are also nest builders, and the male guards the eggs and fry, at which time he is especially pugnacious.

The sunfishes are perhaps the most widely distributed sport fishes. The bluegill is particularly well adapted to stocking in combination with largemouth bass in farm ponds. Here the bluegill serves as forage for the bass, and it is thus kept from becoming overpopulated and stunted.

figure 10-20
Many artificial lakes provide excellent fishing. (Photo by Tennessee Valley Authority.)

The yellow perch is important as a sport fish and also, in the Great Lakes and elsewhere, as a commercial species. Highly prolific, it frequently becomes overpopulated and stunted in smaller lakes if its numbers are not held in check by predatory fish or other means.

The muskellunge and the northern pike, which may surpass weights of 35 and 60 pounds, respectively, are the largest of our warm-water game fish. Highly predaceous on smaller fishes, they help keep prolific panfish populations within desirable bounds and, themselves, constitute a real prize for the trophy-hunting angler.

Both the channel and flathead catfishes are excellent as food and are taken commercially as well as for sport. They attain large size: over 40 pounds for the channel and over 100 pounds for the flathead. The several species of bullheads provide sport and a tasty food in many waters where few other desirable species occur.

The most notorious member of the minnow family is the carp. Native to Asia, the carp has been bred artificially for centuries and distributed all over the world. Introduced into the United States in the early 1870's,

289

it has incurred the dislike of anglers and fishery managers who regard its penchant for roiling waters as injurious to the habitat of more desirable species. It is an important commercial fish for certain specialty markets and provides occasional sport for anglers. However, despite its popularity in Europe and Asia, it continues to be largely unwanted in the United States. It may be noted in passing that many species of minnows are important to the sport fishery both as forage fish and as live bait.

The intelligent management of warm-water sport fisheries is geared to our improved understanding of population dynamics. Creation of new fishing waters and manipulation of habitat and of populations—through such methods as chemical toxicants, nest destruction, and flexible season and bag limits—hold the promise of further increase in the production of such species.

Shellfish Resources. OYSTER   Perhaps the best known shellfish is the oyster. However, owing to a combination of adverse factors—including predators, disease, pollution, and channel dredging—total production dwindled from nearly 82 million pounds of meat in 1956 to 56 million pounds in 1962, the decline taking place in the top producing Chesapeake Bay area. More than half the present yield comes from oyster farming, which is comparable in efficiency and trouble to land farming, but usually far exceeds the income per acre of the latter. The oyster farmer leases barren and unutilized areas of sea floor—usually in protected bays—obtains seed oysters from public reefs, and plants them on the leased bottoms. Depending upon such factors as acreage, quality of bottoms, distance from shore, prevalence and control of pests, costs of transplanting, protection from trespassers, and labor, returns of 100 bushels or more per acre may be expected. Oyster farming is common in the Delaware and Chesapeake Bays, Louisiana waters, and, to a lesser extent, along the northwest Pacific coast. Public oyster grounds are vast in extent, but even under persisting state regulation, they have declined steadily in output.

The life history of the oyster is interesting. An inhabitant of shallow waters, it may be found on muddy grounds but prefers a hard, stable bottom. Oysters vary greatly in size and in the appearance of the shell. On overcrowded grounds they assume a vertical position, and the shells, which are long and thin, form large clusters. On hard bottom the shells are smooth and round. They adapt themselves to wide range of saltiness in the water. Usually there is about a 50-50 ratio of sexes. They breed in summer, and the adult female may spawn as many as 500 million eggs in one season. Mortality is so high, however, that few of the hatching larvae reach a size where they can attach themselves to clean rocks or other hard objects to grow and accumulate a shell. Feeding occurs by straining large quantities of sea water through the gills to obtain the minute organisms which it contains and continues only during the warm months. Oysters feed at a slower rate when even slight pollution of the water occurs and thus fail to reach marketable size. They contain, when mature at 2 to 5 years, about 20 per cent solids by weight and 5 per cent glycogen; the meat is nourishing and digestible.

Among the predators which attack the oyster, the starfish accounts for several million dollars' loss a year (Fig. 10-21). It is able to open even a large oyster shell with the strength of its sucker-equipped feet. It then inserts its own stomach into the shell and digests the oyster. Other enemies include certain predators such as boring snails and conchs, which bore through the hard shell material and devour the meat; and the disease known as MSX.

About two-thirds of the oyster harvest is taken with dredges and slightly over one-fourth with tongs. Hand picking, grabs, and rakes account for the balance. All these devices must be operated with skill, usually acquired only from long experience. Even though self-interest dictates care in method and in design and construction of gear, rapid destruction and decline of production have characterized the exploitation of public reefs and rocks open to those who hold state licenses. Decline is probably due

Young oysters attacked by starfish. Shell is opened by steady pull of sucker-equipped feet, and the starfish then inserts its own stomach into the shell and digests the meat of the oyster. (Photo by J. V. Engle, United States Fish and Wildlife Service.)

figure 10-21

figure 10-22

*Icing down the catch of shrimp near New Orleans, La.
(Photo by United States Fish and Wildlife Service.)*

in a large degree to the rate at which harvesting occurs. Loss from breakage of shells and from forcing the oysters into the mud because of inefficient gear are also contributing factors.

SHRIMP   United States shrimp production for 1962 was 191 million pounds. Of this total, 23 million pounds were taken by Pacific Coast fisheries and 26 million pounds by the South Atlantic states. The Gulf of Mexico area (Fig. 10-22) yielded the largest production, 141.7 million pounds, up 9 per cent over 1961, which saw the lowest Gulf production since 1949. Brown shrimp led in poundage and value followed by pink, white, and sea bobs. Royal red shrimp, located by exploratory fishing operations of the United States Bureau of Commercial Fisheries, were produced in negligible amount. Total shrimp production in 1962 yielded processors a record 161 million dollars. Only tuna products provided a greater return.

Shrimp spawn from early spring until early fall, depositing the eggs in open water. When they hatch, the young find their way to the shallow bottoms and grow rapidly. Many of them are fed upon by various fishes; but enough escape to move eventually into deeper waters, and the larger ones migrate from colder to warmer waters. Here they mature, and by spring they are ready to spawn in open water. Large catches of smaller shrimp in nursery ground waters close to shore during summer months mean a heavy depletion of immature specimens. The same is true of certain winter months in shore waters where the only shrimp present are those still too small to migrate. Conservation of the resource suggests year-round fishing in the outside grounds where the larger specimens are found and a closed season in certain winter and summer months for inside waters where too many immature but fast-growing shrimp make up the population.

LOBSTERS, CRABS, AND CLAMS   The northern lobster supports the full and part-time employment of more fishermen than any other New England fishery and poses the interesting conservation problem of protecting large spawning females (Fig. 10-23). The Atlantic coast and Gulf of Mexico blue-crab fisheries, from which both soft-shelled (captured at one of the many moltings with shell discarded) and hard-shelled (not a separate species) crabs are sold fresh and canned, have been increasing in recent years. Production of Alaskan king crab—an enormous, deep-sea crustacean

This barnacle-encrusted lobster is larger than those usually caught along the Atlantic seaboard. (Photo by United States Fish and Wildlife Service.)

figure 10-23

whose legs may span 11 feet—is also mounting with demand. Production of surf clams is currently more than double that of hard clams and treble that of soft clams, the latter two being taken chiefly from public beds. Clam grounds may suffer from pollution, and much needs to be learned in order to develop improved cultivation methods. Sea and bay scallops, rock crabs, mussels, and spiny lobsters also figure in shellfish production, and all require better knowledge of their life histories and habits if they are to be conserved as resources.

Other Products of the Sea. Although most of the animal products from ocean water are fishes, two interesting mammals figure prominently in the yield—whales and seals.

WHALES Capturing some 8 million dollars' worth of whales annually about 100 years ago, the United States whaling industry employed around 40,000 people, operated more than 700 vessels, and represented an investment of 40 million dollars. In 1962 it operated 6 catcher boats which captured 248 whales, including 124 fin whales, 60 sperm whales, 39 humpbacks, 22 seis, 2 blues, and 1 killer. All but fin-whale captures were down from the previous year. The take—processed to yield 2.9 million pounds of meal, 2.6 million pounds of oil, and 4.3 million pounds of meat (for use, frozen or canned, as animal food—had a value of $706,000 to the producer. Both volume and value decreased by 17 per cent over 1961 (Fig. 10-24). Bad management of the natural resource itself was partly responsible for this decline, but it was hastened by an apparent lack of enterprise in whaling and processing methods. Other countries have developed more efficient methods for whaling and for almost complete utilization of the catch, including products valuable even for human food. In the United States, whale oil is used principally in the manufacture of soap, but in Europe it finds its way into production of edible fats, ointments, leather

Whales off the Southeast coast of Alaska. Tongass National Forest in background. (Photo by Dow V. Baxter, School of Natural Resources, University of Michigan.)

figure 10-24

and fiber dressings, and machine lubricants. Whalebone, once in wide demand, is in decreasing use in Europe for brushes, artificial hair, feathers, and mattress stuffing.

The blue whale is the largest of living animals. One measurement of a "fat nice whale" (of this species) made at Stromness Whaling Station, south Georgia, in 1926, showed a length of about 89 feet and a diameter of 10 feet. This specimen yielded 120 tons of merchantable products, including 56 tons of edible meat.[2]

The whale population was overexploited for many years, with little attempt toward any kind of management of the resource until a committee of experts at the call of the Economic Committee of the League of Nations met early in the 1930s and drafted an agreement which, after being ratified by seventeen countries and acceded to by eight, came into force in 1935. Its provisions covered the protection of whales in general, prohibited the taking of calves or females accompanied by calves, and required full use of captured carcasses in so far as was practicable. These regulations were expanded and strengthened by an International Conference for the Regulation of Whaling, held in London in 1937. The agreement reached here forbade operation of factory ships on calving grounds, strengthened protection of the hard-pressed humpback-whale stocks in the antarctic, and established a whale sanctuary west and northwest of Cape Horn. Under this agreement and the later Whaling Convention of Washington, 1946, whaling vessels must be licensed by their governments and each factory ship must carry an enforcement officer to assure compliance with the international agreement and the particular national license. The International Whaling Commission formed under this Convention, provides a means of modifying international whaling regulations without the necessity of calling a new international conference and concluding a new agreement or establishing a new protocol in each case. The seventeen member countries to the convention are Argentina, Australia, Brazil, Canada, Denmark, France, Iceland, Japan, Mexico, Netherlands, New Zealand, Norway, Panama, Republic of South Africa, United Kingdom, U.S.S.R., and United States.

The future of whales as a natural resource is not yet assured, and repeated restrictive agreements hardly keep pace with the improvements in gear and capture. The last stand of whales is the antarctic, and even stronger international measures will have to limit sizes and numbers taken and seasons and places where operations are permitted. This greatest of all animals must be conserved.

SEALS   Highly valuable for their fur, seals are seagoing mammals which make up an important and well-managed natural resource. The largest

[2] R. B. Robertson, Of Whales and Men, Alfred A. Knopf, Inc., New York, 1954, pp. 136 and 137. By special permission of the publisher.

herd which occupies the Pribilof Islands off the coast of Alaska in the Bering Sea, has been managed under international agreement and has steadily increased in number and value since 1911.

The life history and habits of seals have made their conservation difficult in the past, but these have also served as the key to maintaining and increasing the productivity of the resource. Mating and breeding occurs in late summer following return from migrations which have taken the females as far south as the California coast and the bulls to the Gulf of Alaska. The bulls return in early summer, the most powerful acquiring the best grounds near the shore and establishing harems of forty to sixty females (Fig. 10-25). The mature surplus bulls establish themselves in the immediate rear and await the arrival of the younger females which are left to them by the tired old harem masters who have fought off their rivals, worn themselves out, and also surrendered some of their females. A third colony back on less favorable grounds is occupied by the younger bachelor bulls, of which there are a large number and from which the annual kill is made. Meanwhile the mothers have given birth to their pups—usually single births—and have busied themselves after breeding by swimming far out to sea in search of food. The pups may go along

Bull seal and harem. (Photo by J. C. Ward, University of Michigan Forest Pathology Expedition.)

figure 10-25

or stay at the rookery with the assurance that the mother will return to find and nurse her own pup, if he has not been trampled by the harem master in his battle with rivals. Things get a bit crowded after the young females arrive in August, and within 4 months the arctic weather has driven the whole herd including the pups, which are on their own at 2 months, into the sea for migration. There is a considerable loss of pups at best, but improved herd management involving harvest of predetermined numbers of females as well as males may permit better survival of young pups.

The seals of both sexes and all ages are at sea for a major part of their lives, and this fact, coupled with the habit of feeding and then resting afloat, makes them easily vulnerable to capture while resting at sea. This kind of hunting is known as "pelagic" sealing and has resulted in past years not only in a heavy kill but also in a heavy loss of carcasses with their valuable hides. It was this type of exploitation which reduced the Kuril and Commander Island herds almost to extermination and cut down the Pribilof herd, once estimated to number more than 3 million, to less than 150,000.

Taking their cue from practices of the Washington and British Columbia Indians who learned to creep up on the sleeping seals by canoe, some 100 ships of the Canadian, Japanese, and American sealing fleets were operating in the 1890s and are estimated to have taken almost 1 million skins between 1868 and 1911. Counting the losses, including pregnant females and nursing pups, this figure should perhaps be doubled at least. The Russians had placed some restrictions in earlier years on the numbers which could be taken, but the successful restriction of pelagic sealing under the four-nation treaty of 1911 was the stroke which reestablished the Pribilof herd and kept it at about its former size. The provisions of this agreement were bold and have been well enforced. The old Bureau of Fisheries and later the Fish and Wildlife Service have carried out the systematic harvesting of skins after a prescribed 5-year period during which no seals were to be taken. The first systematic kill was made in 1918 at the rookery from the young bulls, and in accordance with the treaty the revenue from the sale of skins was divided among the four nations, Great Britain (Canada), Japan, the U.S.S.R., and the United States. There is no better example of the rehabilitation, maintenance, and sound management of a natural resource to be found than that of the Pribilof seal herd.

Beginning in 1941 the U.S.S.R. gave its entire attention to the Commander Island herd. The U.S.S.R. is, however, a member of the North Pacific Fur Seal Commission together with Canada, Japan, and the United States. This Commission was established in 1958 under provisions of the Interim Convention for the Conservation of North Pacific Fur

Seals, which not only reaffirms the basic principles of the 1911 *(antea)* but also provides for a joint regulatory and research program to accumulate data needed for a permanent arrangement on conservation of North Pacific seals. The Commission formulates and coordinates the regulatory and research programs and makes recommendations to the four signatory governments. Under terms of the existing treaty Canada and Japan each receive 15 per cent of the Pribilof Island skins. In 1962, sale of the United States share, 48,513 skins, grossed 4.4 million dollars. After payment of costs of handling, dressing, dyeing, and selling the skins, and of administrating the islands—as well as payment of over $700,000 to the state of Alaska—net receipts to the United States government amounted to $32,810.

International Fisheries Commissions and Councils. Development of improved gear and methods for capture, storage, transportation, and processing of fishery resources has opened the world's oceans to fishermen of all nations. In consequence new international problems have arisen as nations seek either to establish and maintain sovereignty over their own offshore waters or to exploit those of others. In an effort to solve such problems through diplomatic channels, a number of international bodies have been formed. Their names, listed in Table 10-1, often imply quite clearly the problems they were created to solve. The obvious success thus far characterizing the achievements of some of these

TABLE 10-1. INTERNATIONAL FISHERIES COMMISSIONS AND COUNCILS

Code	Name
CIESMM	International Commission for the Scientific Exploration of the Mediterranean Sea
CPCERMPS	Permanent Commission for the Conservation and Exploitation of the Maritime Resources of the South Pacific
EIFAC	European Inland Fisheries Advisory Commission
GFCM	General Fisheries Council for the Mediterranean
GLFC*	Great Lakes Fishery Commission
I-ATT*	Inter-American Tropical Tuna Commission
ICES	International Council for the Exploration of the Sea
ICNAF*	International Commission for the Northwest Atlantic Fisheries
INPFC*	International North Pacific Fisheries Commission
IPFC	Indo-Pacific Fisheries Council
IPHC*	International Pacific Halibut Commission
IPSFC*	International Pacific Salmon Fisheries Commission
IWC*	International Whaling Commission
NPFSC*	North Pacific Fur Seal Commission
PCIFC	Permanent Commission of the International Fisheries Convention 1946 (This may be succeeded by a Commission of the new International Northeast Atlantic Fisheries Convention.)
CCSEGM*	Commission for the Conservation of Shrimp in the Eastern Gulf of Mexico

SOURCE: Courtesy Great Lakes Fishery Commission.
* United States participation.

commissions, e.g., the North Pacific Fur Seal Commission just described, lends hope that combined efforts in the fields of biology, diplomacy, economics, and exploitative techniques will provide ever-increasing bounty to man from the treasure chests of the sea.

BIBLIOGRAPHY

Annual Reports of the Secretary of the Interior, 1945–1962.

BACHRACH, MAX.: Fur: A Practical Treatise, rev. ed., Prentice-Hall, Inc., Englewood Cliffs, N.J., 1947.

CARSON, RACHEL L.: Fish and Shellfish of the South Atlantic and Gulf Coasts, *U.S. Fish Wildlife Serv. Conserv. Bull.* 37, 1942.

———: Food from the Sea, *U.S. Fish Wildlife Serv. Conserv. Bull.* 33, 1943.

CLEMENS, HAROLD B.: The Migration, Age, and Growth of Pacific Albacore (*Thunnus germo*), 1951–1958, *Fish Bull.* 115, California Department of Fish and Game, 1961.

Conservation News, Wildlife Management Institute, Washington, D.C., 1960–64.

Fish and Wildlife Report, U.S. Fish and Wildlife Service, Washington, D.C., 1964.

Fishery Resources of the United States, S. Doc. 51, 79th Cong., 1st sess., 1945.

Fishery Statistics of the United States, 1962, *U.S. Fish Wildlife Serv. Statis. Digest* 56, 1964.

HUBBS, CARL L., AND KARL F. LAGLER: Fishes of the Great Lakes Region, *Cranbrook Inst. of Sci. Bull.* 26, 1958.

INTERNATIONAL ASSOCIATION OF GAME, FISH AND CONSERVATION COMMISSIONERS: Proceedings of Forty-sixth Convention at Toronto, St. Paul, Minn., 1956.

LAGLER, KARL F.: Freshwater Fishery Biology, William C. Brown Company, Dubuque, Iowa, 1952.

———, JOHN E. BARDACH, AND ROBERT R. MILLER: Ichthyology, John Wiley & Sons, Inc., New York, 1962.

LEOPOLD, ALDO: The American Game Policy, in *Trans. Seventeenth Amer. Game Conf.*, Wildlife Management Institute, Washington, D.C., 1930.

MCHUGH, J. L., AND ELBERT H. AHLSTROM: Is the Pacific Sardine Disappearing? *Sci. Monthly*, vol. 72, pp. 377–384, June, 1951.

MARTIN, HOWARD H.: Fisheries for the Future, Chap. 19 in Conservation of Natural Resources, Guy Harold Smith, ed., John Wiley & Sons, Inc., New York, 1950.

National Survey of Fishing and Hunting, *U.S. Fish Wildlife Serv. Circ.* 44, 1956.

Report of the U.S. Bureau of Fisheries, in Report of Special Committee on the Conservation of Wildlife Resources, S. Rept. 1203, 76th Cong., 3d sess., 1940.

ROBERTSON, R. B.:Of Whales and Men, Alfred A. Knopf, Inc., New York, 1954.

SHOEMAKER, CARL D.: Report on Federal Conservation Legislation, in Proceedings of the Forty-first Convention, International Association of Game, Fish and Conservation Commissioners, Rochester, N.Y., Sept. 10 and 11, 1951.

The Status of Wildlife in the United States, Report of the Special Committee on the Conservation of Wildlife Resources, S. Rept. 1203, 76th Cong., 3d sess. 1940.

Treaties and Other International Acts Series, U.S. Department of State.

TRESSLER, DONALD K., AND JAMES MCW. LEMON: Marine Products of Commerce, 2d ed., Reinhold Publishing Corporation, New York, 1951.

VAN HISE, CHARLES R., AND LOOMIS HAVEMEYER, Conservation of Our Natural Resources, The Macmillan Company, New York, 1930.

WESTERMAN, FRED A., AND ALBERT S. HAZZARD: For Better Fishing, Department of Conservation, Lansing, Mich., 1045.

Yearbook of Fishery Statistics, 1954–1955, Food and Agriculture Organization of the United Nations, Rome, 1956.

11 MINERALS IN GENERAL AND THE MINERAL FUELS[1]

THE MINERALS SERVED mankind first in the form of crude tools and as means of storing up wealth. In relatively recent times they have become sources of warmth and energy. Today they are used increasingly as the materials of technology in its thousands of applications, from drugs and caustics to space capsules and metal-frame buildings. More than most people have come to realize, too, minerals are the bases of much of our labor-saving and luxury equipment. One could go on almost indefinitely listing uses in which minerals are today indispensable, beginning with surgery and winding up with national defense.

In the economy of the country the mineral resources play a big part. Almost two-thirds of a million men are employed in mining alone, and this figure expands to well over 3 million with the addition of the number required by the mineral manufacturing industries. The figure for annual value of mineral production in the United States runs to nearly 19 billion dollars.

In the face of such facts, it is amazing that mineral resources are taken as a matter of course so far as demand is concerned and dropped like a hot potato when it comes to thinking and acting on questions of their conservation. The brilliant inventor and the unselfish public-spirited conservationist alike frequently ignore the fact of irreplaceability in their mad rush for new uses of mineral resources. New discovery, use of substitutes, and general human ingenuity have, so far, taken care of threatened shortages, but one may well question whether they can continue to do so.

The least that can be asked of a thoughtful citizen of a democracy is that he keep himself informed, that he challenge indefensible waste of mineral resources, and that he support conservation measures in their management. This is true even though he should fail within his lifetime to achieve the ultimate in comfort and convenience.

In order to understand mineral resources it is well to consider some of the accepted classifications. Perhaps the simplest of these are metals, mineral fuels, and other nonmetallics. These general classes are subject to various breakdowns, which is also true of the whole resource group. For example, coal, iron, and copper are sometimes spoken of as *basic* and all others as *contributory* in terms of industrial economy; or certain minerals are called *strategic* because they are necessary for national defense and are likely to be in lean supply, while others are *nonstrategic;* again, the minerals known to world trade may be *primary* as products of

[1]Most of the factual material for this and the succeeding chapter was obtained from five sources: The *Minerals Yearbook*, 1962; *Annual Reports of the Secretary of the Interior*, 1958 through 1963; Resources for Freedom, vols. 1 and 3, the Report of the President's Materials Policy Commission; Landsberg, Fischman, and Fisher, Resources in America's Future, 1962; and the National Coal Association. These works are more fully listed in the footnotes and the bibliography at the end of the chapter.

first capture from nature, or *secondary*, as products of recovered scrap or by-products.

Some idea of the variety of mineral resources may be obtained from study of a generalized classification according to physical and chemical characteristics and use, as shown in Table 11-1.

National Mineral Policy. Whatever the United States may have in the way of mineral policy is made up of unrelated laws dealing with: (1) disposition of mineral lands and of mineral rights on public lands; (2) placement of tariffs on imports to protect domestic producers from foreign competition in the sale of those minerals which are ample in supply or those whose production needs to be stimulated; (3) authorization of surveys to locate, test, and, rarely, to develop new deposits of those minerals which are scarce and needed; (4) purchasing of output at artificially high prices to relieve mining distress; (5) maintaining government monopoly on certain materials or on federally owned property, but providing procedures for their development by private enterprise and thereby obtaining public revenue; (6) allocating strategic minerals in wartime; (7) regulating certain mineral industries, often aimed at production control to maintain prices; (8) stockpiling strategic minerals in time of war or in preparation for war; and (9) negotiating agreements for importation of strategic minerals from foreign sources. Of these items the only ones which put any particular emphasis on conservation of mineral resources are (3), (5), and (6). Theoretically, item 1, which has to do with mineral-land disposal, should operate to conserve these resources, but weak enforcement of patent requirements and superficial appraisal of mineral values under these laws have led sometimes to fraud and to wasteful exploitation and inequitable distribution of public resources.

Recommendations of policies for the various mineral resources were made in 1933 by a special "mineral inquiry" under the leadership of C. K. Lieth; but little legislation has resulted, and a new set of recommendations is contained in the President's Materials Policy Commission Report of 1952. The latter are comprehensive, and among other things they urge: (1) the speeding up of fact gathering and analysis by the Bureau of Mines and the Geological Survey (This would include provision of funds for a complete census already authorized but not financed, of the mineral industries in 1954 and every 5 years thereafter); (2) acceleration of topographic and geologic mapping of the United States and Alaska by the Geological Survey (authorized but weakly supported by appropriation) and intensive study of procedure and instruments of mineral exploration; (3) revamping of the entire mining-claim and lease systems to eliminate opportunities for fraud, without discouraging

TABLE 11-1. GENERALIZED CLASSIFICATION OF MINERALS ACCORDING TO PHYSICAL AND CHEMICAL CHARACTERISTICS AND USE

					Examples
Minerals...	Metals...	Ferrous...	Iron.................		Iron ore
			Ferroalloying..........		Manganese ore / Metallurgical chromite / Molybdenum
		Non-ferrous....	Base.................		Copper / Tin / Mercury
			Light.................		Aluminum / Magnesium / Titanium
			Precious		Gold / Silver / Platinum
			Rare.................		Uranium / Radium / Beryllium
	Non-metals...	Mineral fuels......	Fluid....	Liquid......	Petroleum
				Gaseous.....	Natural gas
			Solid....	Hard coal...	Anthracite / Semi-anthracite
				Soft coal....	Bituminous / Lignite
		Other non-metals....	Building materials.............		Sand and gravel / Stone / Cement materials
			Chemical materials.............		Sulfur / Salt / Chemical chromite
			Fertilizer materials.............		Phosphate rock / Potash / Nitrates
			Ceramic materials.............		Clay / Silica / Feldspar
			Refractories...........		Silica / Fire clay / Refractory chromite
			Abrasives.............		Sandstone / Corundum / Industrial diamonds
			Insulating materials.............		Magnesia / Asbestos / Mica
			Pigments and fillers................		Ocher / Clay / Diatomite / Barite
			Precious and semi-precious stones........		Gem diamond / Amethyst / Amber

SOURCE: William Van Royen, Oliver Bowles, Elmer. W. Pehrson, The Mineral Resources of the World. (Copyright 1952 by Prentice-Hall, Inc., Englewood Cliffs, N.J.) Reproduced by permission of Department of Geography, University of Maryland, and the publisher.

legitimate prospecting and mining. An act passed by the Congress in 1955 is a good start on this task. (This act was discussed on page 17.)

A considerable program of piecemeal legislation is continually before the Congress, without too much attention being paid so far to the commission's statesmanlike recommendations. In 1954, however, President Eisenhower approved the report of the Cabinet Committee on Minerals Policy. This led to the drafting of a "Long-range Minerals Program" quite similar to the recommendations of the earlier President's Materials Policy Commission. Hearings in the Congress on this program were held in 1958. Some legislation resulted but no comprehensive policy.

State Mineral Policies. All the important mineral-producing states have their own laws which comprise their particular mining policies. Some of them attempt to regulate mining, and many have to do with tax provisions and other incentives to production. Safety laws vary widely, and those which are pointed toward conservation of minerals are principally in the fields of petroleum and natural-gas production.

The treatment of minerals which follows will be necessarily confined to three groups—the mineral fuels, the metals, and the nonmetallics other than fuels.

THE MINERAL FUELS

Sometimes spoken of as the "fossil fuels," coal, petroleum, and natural gas appear to have been furnished to the human race with all of Nature's talent for variety and storage. They are solid, liquid, or gaseous in form, and—along with sunlight, falling water, and animal strength—they have been our sources of energy. In spite of all the potentialities of atomic energy, we shall probably be demanding the mineral fuels in increasing amounts as long as they last. Their conservation is most difficult, not only because of their irreplaceability and of human habits of wasteful use, but because their discovery and capture is expensive and even dangerous to human life. Their capture and use is also accompanied frequently by necessarily brutal wrecking of landscapes and by pollution of air and water. Yet their conservation is necessary not only for energy purposes but because human health and convenience are tied in to the use of hundreds of their products and services, which range all the way from aspirin to the treatment of wooden railroad ties for durability (Fig. 11-1).

COAL

It is fortunate that coal, which in many ways may be thought of as the most important mineral, is relatively plentiful, for it has been mined in this country in recent years at the rate of more than 900 tons a minute

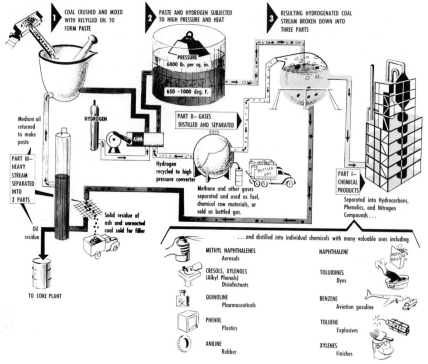

COAL INTO CHEMICALS— Carbide and Carbon Chemicals' Coal Hydrogenation Process

figure 11-1
Heating is not the only use of coal. Such products as these could become its highest use should nuclear energy ever compete with conventional fuels. (Diagram by Carbide and Carbon Chemicals Company. Courtesy of Bituminous Coal Institute.)

and used or exported at about the same rate. It has been said, however, that if our coal reserve were represented by a solid cube 15 miles on each edge, only one corner of it would be used up. But it so happens that this is the most valuable corner.

Coal has been known in what is now the United States since 1679 when the French missionary Father Hennepin recorded its presence along the Illinois River. News traveled slowly in those days, however, and the coal-mining industry has been in operation only since 1814. The first instance of large-scale mining was reported in Virginia in 1822, although shipments from small Virginia mines had been sent to New York as early as 1758 and some coal had been used in Pennsylvania in 1769.

Second in dollar value only to petroleum on the basis of annual mineral production, coal constitutes the greatest tonnage of any mined product. It is burned to generate more than one-half the electric power used in the United States. It contributes to the manufacture of steel in the form of coke, a solid residue of the coal left after it has been heated and certain by-products have been removed. The sulfa drugs, nylon, and plastics used for the manufacture of thousands of useful articles are all products of coal (Fig. 11-1). The list may be continued to include fertilizers, insecticides, and food preservatives. In modern life, coal is indispensable.

Origin and Occurrence. Coal is of organic origin and differs in this way from the metals. It is the result of centuries of accumulation of plant material which grew luxuriantly in past ages in the periods of generally mild, moist climate. Layer after layer of dying vegetation built up in the form of leaves, branches, and trunks which gradually changed to peat (such as is cut, dried, and burned in European countries and used in the United States for soil conditioning, packing material, and other purposes). Ordinarily the accumulations of such material would decay rapidly, but only in contact with oxygen. This was cut off as the peat became deeply buried and subjected to pressure from the weight of upper layers and of water and silt as it sank below swamp and ocean levels. Gradually the vegetation and its residues were buried deeper until seas overflowed the ancient swamps, from whose waters and floods still greater layers of silt and mud increased the heat and pressure. All this compressing with its accompanying heat turned the accumulations slowly into coal which is now mined after millions of years. Limited deposits were subject to movements of the earth's crust in mountain-range upheavals. This brought about increased pressures and greater heat and produced the "high-rank" coals such as anthracite.

Rank is a term applied to coal which signifies the relative proportions of fixed carbon, moisture, and volatile (easily vaporized) material. In general, rank increases as moisture and volatile material decrease, with an accompanying increase in fixed carbon. For purposes of general understanding it is sufficient to list the ranks from high to low as follows:

1. Anthracite (three groups)
2. Bituminous (five groups)
3. Subbituminous (three groups)
4. Lignitic (lignite and brown coal, the latter unconsolidated)

It is well to bear in mind that both composition and heating power are used in classifying coal into "ranks." The term *British thermal unit* (Btu), frequently encountered means the amount of heat required to raise the temperature of 1 pound of water 1 degree Fahrenheit.

Knowledge of the ranks of coal is important to the coal industry because of the variations in usefulness and the consequent differences in profit when the product is marketed. Such knowledge is also important in conserving coal since the higher ranks are likely to be used up first and because actual waste, rationalized as economically unavoidable, varies with the exploitation of the different ranks.

If lignite were to become anthracite, the following approximate changes would have to occur over a million years or so:[2]

	Lignite	Anthracite	Change
Fixed carbon, per cent	33	92	59 (increase)
Volatile matter, per cent	26	5	21 (decrease)
Moisture, per cent	41	3	38 (decrease)
Total (ash-free basis)	100	100	

Lignite, of which there are vast deposits in eastern Montana, the Dakotas, and Texas, is a relatively soft coal which may vary from light brown to almost black but which always leaves a brown mark when rubbed over a white surface. It contains as much as 40 per cent moisture when first mined, slakes easily (becomes powder-like), and is difficult to store.

Industrial use of lignite has been slow to develop, but it is now being utilized widely for electric power generation. One cooperative power company in North Dakota, for example, has recently contracted for a supply of 1.2 million tons of lignite annually for 10 years. Another group of cooperative companies in Minnesota has begun construction of a 240-mile transmission line to bring power from a plant near a North Dakota lignite mine which will supply the plant with fuel.[3]

The use of lignite is also possible in the production of pipeline-quality gas (usable generally for domestic and industrial purposes). In June, 1964, the Secretary of the Interior announced that a contract to develop such a process had been made between the Department's Office of Coal Research and a Pittsburgh company.[4]

Subbituminous coal is black and resembles the well-known bituminous or "soft" coal. Its moisture content of 15 to 30 per cent is lower than that of the best-quality lignite, but it slakes easily in contact with air and is

[2] Sherman, Allan, and Allen B. Macmurphy, *Facts About Coal,* U.S. Bureau of Mines, 1950, p. 2.

[3] *Coal News,* National Coal Association, Washington, D.C., Jan. 22, 1965 and Nov. 30, 1962, p. 7.

[4] News Release from Office of Coal Research, U.S. Department of the Interior, June 16, 1964.

subject to the same difficulties of storage. The potential of Western sub-bituminous coal for generation of power for West Coast markets is also under scrutiny. It is widely distributed in the Rocky Mountain region and in western Washington. Coal would be delivered to West Coast power plants via pipeline, or electricity would be generated at mine-mouth plants and transmitted via extra-high-voltage lines.

Bituminous coals, with which most people are familiar and which are most widely used industrially and for transportation power, vary sharply in their make-up and in the way they burn. In appearance they may be either dull or lustrous black. Industrially and from the standpoint of efficient use for the many heating purposes, it is important to know which bituminous coals will "coke," that is, leave a porous gray residue when heated in ovens with little air and relieved of certain volatile and liquid components. Coke is a clean efficient household fuel and is used in the smelting of iron ore and the manufacture of steel. The recovered by-products from its production are the source of many useful materials, and their use represents good conservation. Some of the otherwise efficient bituminous coals burn to an ash or powder instead of coking. *Ash* consists of the mineral impurities incapable of becoming gaseous and devoid of fixed carbon. With modern methods of preparation and with increasing demand for pulverized coal by electric power plants, however, such non-coking coals can be utilized very efficiently (Fig. 11-2). The various bituminous coals are widely distributed.

Anthracite, or "hard" coal, is the least abundant coal and the most adaptable one for domestic use. It is slow burning, has a somewhat lower heating value than the highest grade bituminous coals, and produces little soot.[5] It is black and lustrous in appearance and leaves a considerable volume of very light-weight ash. The smaller sizes of anthracite are used to some extent industrially.

Distribution of Coal Resources. There are six coal "provinces" in the United States, all but one of which (the Gulf province) extend into Canada. Forty-seven per cent of the reserves are of bituminous rank, and the greatest volume of all coal reserves is in the Rocky Mountain province, wholly within the United States. Then comes the Northern Great Plains province, then the Interior province, and the Eastern province, with the Pacific and Gulf provinces constituting poor fifth and sixth places, respectively. Subbituminous coal makes up 25.5 per cent of the reserves; lignite, 26 per cent; and anthracite, only 1.5 per cent. The Eastern province in terms of *volume, concentration of area, and quality combined* is the most important and supports the greatest single volume of production. Of the nation's total estimated reserves, about 40 per cent is located east of the Mississippi River.

[5] Facts about Coal, 1955, p. 4.

figure 11-2
*Coal stockpile at an Eastern power plant. Large quantities of this
important mineral are required to make industry productive and
life convenient for the everyday citizen. This is the Burlington Generating Station of the Public Service Electric and Gas Company, at
Delaware River, Burlington County, south of Camden, N.J. (National
Coal Association.)*

The wide and general distribution of coal resources in the United
States is fortunate for the people and the industries using coal in terms
of the prices they pay since rail transportation is an important item
of expense. Also the occurrence of both coking coal deposits and gas
coals in connection with iron deposits has been an important factor in the
location of steel-production centers. Birmingham, Alabama, is a good
example. In like manner Detroit and Cleveland, both important steel
and industrial centers, are located almost midway between the Lake

310

Superior iron-ore deposits and the Appalachian region of the Eastern coal province.

Distribution of coal resources in the United States is no indication of rates of production. Thus West Virginia, the leader in production, ranks fifth in estimated tonnage of deposits; Kentucky, second in tons produced, is tenth in estimated deposits.

Loss and Waste in Managing Coal Resources. Prior to 1950, loss and waste of coal in mining, preparation for market, and utilization may be said to have been more common and more significant than that of many of the other natural resources. The forms or arrangements of deposits and the depths at which they occur still present handicaps to full recovery. In the past decade, however, the development of more efficient mining equipment has increased the percentage of recovery tremendously. At the utilization stage former waste has been reduced by the use of industrial, and even household, automatic stokers which feed the fuel in such a manner as to obtain greater combustion efficiency. Increasing use of pulverized coal by industrial plants has also been particularly significant.

Coal is mined by sinking vertical shafts to underground deposits; reaching them by openings in side hills which make removal possible horizontally; using "slope" openings; and stripping of the overburden of rock, soil and vegetation from shallow deposits. The latter method makes possible almost full recovery of the coal and thus amounts to good coal conservation, but what it does to the landscape requires reclamation of soil and space resources for good conservation.

Where the coal seam continues horizontally under too thick an overburden to justify economic stripping, auger mining is practiced. Huge bits 16 to 84 inches in diameter, similar to those a carpenter uses in a brace to bore holes in wood, bore into the coal seam horizontally, having been put in position against the hill by self-powered frames. As the coal is loosened, it is pushed back to the auger opening (just as borings come out of a hole bored into wood) and falls onto a conveyor which dumps it into trucks. Although not in wide use, this method is an efficient coal producer per man, exceeding both underground and surface productivity. About 2.7 per cent of the coal output of the United States is auger mined.[6]

A lower rate of recovery may result from shaft mining. Sometimes thinner deposits are bypassed in reaching the thicker ones which may lie deeper. The mining industry uses the expression "technologically unfeasible" in referring to failure to recover these thinner deposits.

Depth of deposits and occurrence of impurities are also factors limiting full recovery of coal deposits in the United States. The deepest active coal mine in the country is less than 1,500 feet underground, and 88 per

---

[6] *Bituminous Coal Facts*, 1904, National Coal Association, 1964, p. 15.

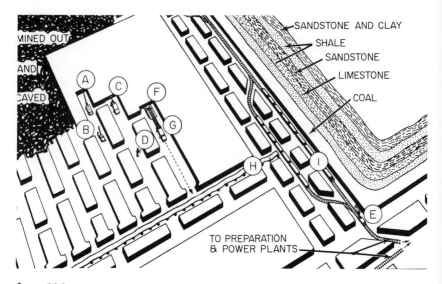

figure 11-3
Diagram of coal mine as operated about 1950. (A) Cutting machine; (B) roof-bolting machine; (C) drilling machine; (D) safety inspector; (E) rock duster [dilutes coal dust to prevent explosion and should more correctly be working near (D)]; (F) mechanical loader; (G) mine shuttle car; (H) conveyor belt; (I) underground railroad. Surface works, including a giant ventilating fan, are not shown. (Adapted from 1952 Bituminous Coal Annual, courtesy of Bituminous Coal Institute.)

cent of the total estimated reserves lie less than 1,000 feet underground. Should it become necessary, deeper seams undoubtedly could be opened economically. European countries are less fortunate: some of their coal mines are more than ¾ mile deep.

Loss also occurs in pillars of coal left to support the mine roof in the "room-and-pillar" method of removing the coal (see Fig. 11-3). These pillars may be 50 to 80 feet thick or thicker and as long as the rooms between them, usually 14 to 30 feet. The rooms are made by removing the coal loosened by cutting and blasting (Fig. 11-4 and 11-5). In the more efficient mines the pillars are largely removed from the rear of the deposit forward to the foot of the shaft after the rooms are exhausted. This causes the roof to cave as the work retreats. In some instances the pillars are left as mining ceases. In general the first method is the better conservation practice but somewhat more dangerous to human life. Timber supports are used along with coal pillars in both methods, and both apply to shaft mines and to those with horizontal entryways. Roof bolting is used in place of and along with timber supports. Continuous mining with powerful machines avoids waste and is increasingly used.

figure 11-4

A cutting machine with a 9-foot blade like a giant chain saw moves up to the face of the coal seam in the Franklin No. 25 mine of Consolidated Coal Company near New Athens, Ohio. The machine will cut a 6-inch slot along the base of the seam so that the coal will break more easily when blasted. (Photo, National Coal Association, May, 1964.)

figure 11-5

A miner inserts a compressed-air cartridge into a hole drilled in the face of the coal seam. Air compressed to 10,000 pounds per square inch will be valved into the cartridge through the flexible tubing at its rear and will build up pressure until it ruptures a plastic seal and bursts out with explosive force, breaking up the coal for loading. Cartridge is used instead of blasting powder. (Photo, National Coal Association, May, 1964.)

figure 11-6

Surface-mining shovel, for strip mining, as tall as a twenty-story building, takes a 140-cubic-yard bite of earth and rock—about 210 tons—in a coal mine near Marissa, Ill. It can turn, dump this load more than a city block away, and return for another bite in less than a minute. The machine digs no coal—it exposes the seam, shown here beneath its 8-foot-high crawler treads, so that smaller shovels can load the coal into trucks. Automobile near the treads shows size of machine. (Photo, Bucyrus-Erie Company, November, 1964.)

In strip mining there is no need of timber or coal-pillar support because there is no "roof" to the mine (Fig. 11-6). The overburden, as noted above, is removed and piled directly into areas from which coal has already been removed. Coal is then loosened and removed with little loss. The problem here is to leave the mined area in shape for some sort of use rather than in shambles of upside-down material. Leveling for pasture development, reforestation without leveling, and development of fishing, boating, and other recreations where water has accumulated furnish opportunities for conserving the areas. Sometimes the soil is leveled, cultivated, and put into grass for pasture or into orchard. An interesting example of the utilization of mined-out land is a race track in Du Quoin, Illinois, where the Hambletonian, the Kentucky Derby of harness racing, is held each year. Of the 80,000 acres mined in Indiana, 67,000 have been reclaimed by tree planting and conversion to lakes or other productive and recreational uses (Fig. 11-7), and half of the record catch of fresh-water fish in Illinois in 1963 came from lakes that were once coal mines.[7]

Waste and loss in the preparation of coal for market, once important, is now almost a thing of the past. The record of the industry in this situation is good. The 19 per cent of the material treated that is discarded represents, principally, such impurities as rock and iron sulfide. Valuable associated materials which would otherwise be considered waste are occasionally recovered in coal mining. These include germanium, a minor metal used in the manufacture of transistors and as a color modifier in fluorescent lights; high-alumina clays; and other clays potentially useful for ceramic purposes. One of the projects of the Office of Coal Research in the Department of the Interior is an exploration of the quantity, quality, and manner of economic recovery of these secondary products.[8]

In final utilization, for whatever purpose, incomplete combustion is a problem which must be met by the thoughtful and careful operation of modern heating equipment.

From the business-management standpoint it should be noted that the coal-producing industry is highly competitive and has certain inherent

[7] *Ibid.*, pp. 15–16.
[8] *Annual Report of the Office of Coal Research,* U.S. Department of the Interior, 1964, p. 7.

figure 11-7
A residence on one of the many lakes created on strip-mined land in Indiana. More than 2,800 acres of such land have been reclaimed for residence purposes, and more than one-tenth of all land affected by strip mining in the state, exclusive of the lakes, is devoted to recreational use. (Indiana Coal Producers Association.)

hazards to human life. It was long subject to labor troubles, but both management and labor have worked hard to achieve measures of co-operation with the result that a decade and a half, as of 1965, have passed without an interruption of coal production.[9]

It is well to remember also that the very nature of the industry brings it into conflict with the conservation of certain replaceable natural resources in terms of air and water pollution, blighting of surface space resources, and the disarranging of otherwise productive soil.

Ownership of Coal Resources. Before 1873, when the first coal-land law was enacted by the Congress, public lands underlain with coal were sold as agricultural lands and any coal involved became the property of the purchaser. Enormous areas of coal-bearing land thereby passed into private ownership in Ohio, Kentucky, Illinois, Missouri, and Kansas. Coal lands farther east had been disposed of similarly by the states which owned them. The coal statute of 1873 provided for the sale of known coal lands at prices "not less than ten dollars per acre" for lands farther than 15 miles from a railroad and "not less than twenty dollars per acre" for lands within 15 miles from a completed railroad. Only 160 acres were to be sold to any individual, but associations could purchase 160 acres for each member. No attempt was made to classify or evaluate the lands, and the Department of the Interior read "not more than" for "not less than" so that $10 and $20 became the standard prices up to 1906. During this period in spite of the provisions of the law, vast areas of coal lands were still sold as agricultural land. The total of all lands so disposed of approaches 100 million acres.

A new interpretation of the plain language of the law was put into force by the Department of the Interior in 1906 so that rates of $75 to $100 per acre were charged, and in 1909, $100 to $300 were the prevailing rates. Even at these prices the actual coal cost the producer only a few cents a ton, which was but a fraction of its value in terms of royalties per ton paid in the West by operators to private proprietors of coal lands.

Thus the disposal of much of the coal-bearing area in the United States is the old story, perhaps not of actual fraud, but of neglect so common with respect to timber and agricultural lands. And although it may be argued that private enterprise has not done so badly in making coal available to the people of the country, it is fortunate that President Theodore Roosevelt, prompted by the report of the short-lived National Conservation Commission appointed upon the recommendation of the 1908 White House conference of governors, withdrew from settlement and entry 80 million acres of public lands thought to be coal bearing. This was in 1909, and out of these and additional withdrawals since that time some 35 million acres have been classified definitely by the Geological Survey as coal

[9] *Bituminous Coal Facts*, p. 37.

lands, with about 24 million acres still to be classified. Previous to these withdrawals President Roosevelt had withdrawn in 1906 almost 9 million acres of coal-bearing lands.

The buying rush on Western lands was halted by the enactment of the Mineral Leasing Law of 1920 covering nonmetallics on the public lands. Under this law the Federal government assumed obligations of proprietorship and specified a lease procedure whereby operators could recover coal, petroleum, potash, phosphate, and other nonmetallics and would be required to use certain conservation measures and to pay the Federal government on a royalty basis, either in money or in kind. Some of the Indian lands bearing coal are managed under a similar arrangement by the Federal government in behalf of the tribes.

The Mineral Leasing Law of 1920 is the only important step taken by the Federal government which challenges wasteful exploitation of the country's coal resources. The industry, however, is gradually achieving a management record in which waste is much reduced.

Conserving Coal Resources. Since coal is the first one of the truly irreplaceable natural resources so far considered in this text, it is well to remember that coal, like other fuels, is destroyed when used. Only in a limited sense it is "capitalized" or put into form for continuing use. It differs here from the metals, clays, and building stones which may go on serving mankind in one or another form for centuries after being mined. Coal does get into the form of plastics, textiles, and in small quantities it becomes a part of steel; but it is used mainly as fuel (Fig. 11-1). How then can coal be conserved? Certainly mankind cannot "grow" any more coal. People can, however, avoid some of the inexcusable waste and be fair enough to future generations to leave them some of the deposits, particularly of the higher ranks which are in relatively short supply. Much along this line can be done if the public wants it done. Here are some of the ways to conserve coal:

1. Promoting the avoidance of waste in mining. The room-and-pillar method has been mentioned (Fig. 11-2). Removal of pillars will be done by operators only if it pays and if reasonable safety for workers can be assured. Continuous mining provides for recovery of some of this pillar material.
2. Promoting avoidance of waste in preparation. Here the dredging of streams to recover washing wastes for briquetting offers some opportunity for profit; and, indeed, when the market is good, as many as 1 million tons a year have been recovered. Mechanical cleaning, washing, and sizing were used on only 5 per cent of the bituminous coal produced in 1925 as against almost 40 per cent in 1950. This figure had risen in 1963 to 64 per cent, and it will have to continue to rise to

keep pace with the increasing demand for pulverized coal to be burned in suspension in power-plant furnaces. Research by the Bureau of Mines in this general direction deserves full and continuing support.

3. Increasing the use of lignite as fuel for power production in remote localities. Experiments by the Bureau of Mines are progressing in this direction in Texas. (It has been suggested by those who are disturbed over the increasing number of high dams for power, with their many problems of conflict with conserving wild-animal life, that the vast lignite resources can compete with water in the production of power if water for steam plants is available.)

4. Allocating coking coals as far as possible to coke production in modern by-product ovens (Fig. 11-8). It will be claimed that this is done wherever it is economically possible and convenient. Action of this kind with regard to many natural resources has not been uncommon in time of war and might well be invoked in the event of sharply shrinking supply of these high-grade coals.

5. Exploring courageously and fairly various regulatory practices of coal exploitation and production as an alternative to more drastic action by the Federal government. One experiment along this line has been made. The industry was given its chance in the Guffey Coal Act (Bituminous Coal Act of 1937), which said in effect: "Let us try regulation through a commission, as a means of getting some order into a wastefully competitve business which seems always to be in trouble. Take a look too at your management-labor situation in behalf of the public interest." The act was to be in effect for 4 years, and in 1941 it was extended for 2 years and then for 90 days more. It was allowed to lapse in 1943. The industry and the Federal officials concerned felt that the administration of the provisions was helpful but the former blames "certain political factors outside the industry with conflicting interests" for being "opposed to continuation of this measure."[10] This was the Federal-industry approach. Perhaps regulation on a state basis may be worked on as a more promising approach, but lack of uniformity in state laws has proven a stumbling block.

6. Continuing the Mineral Leasing Law of 1920 in force as a fair and successfully tested procedure by which the Federal government can discharge its obligation as a proprietor of vast coal and other deposits. There is considerable talk of weakening this law by amendment or of repealing it in favor of passing Federal mineral lands into private possession. The stipulations contained in these leases covering conservation practices by holders is the only really effective means now

---

[10] Comment by National Coal Association, Washington, D.C., accompanying letter of Feb. 12, 1965.

figure 11-8

Coke for steel production. The incandescent mass being pushed from an oven into a quenching car is the first produced in a battery of eighty-five new by-product ovens built at United States Steel's Coke Works at Clairton, Pa. (Photo from United States Steel Corporation, courtesy of National Coal Association.)

in force to conserve as well as to develop the coal resources which belong to all the people. Coal leases continue to be a small but steady and important proportion of all mineral leases issued under the law.

7. Requiring by Federal or local law certain equipment and/or practices designed to curtail waste in the heating of buildings. Such regulations might apply to all buildings above certain minimum space-heating requirements and might even, through local building codes, require adequate insulation. Centralized heating could be used to a greater extent also, with real fuel saving.

8. Pushing research into various improvements in coal exploitation and use. Completed and current research projects include export-market studies and analysis of feasibility of converting coal into gasoline and of a new use for coal in treating sewage and industrial waste.[11]

9. Requiring or promoting cooperation in accomplishing rehabilitation of the surface in strip mining (Fig. 11-7). Certain states now require the posting of a bond by operators on an area basis in order to assure

[11] *Annual Report of the Office of Coal Research*, pp. 4, 7, and 9.

such action. Others promote voluntary action through advice and other forms of mild subsidy. In general, however, the problem is not solved. State regulation appears to be most promising.

10. Working for and obtaining the enactment of uniform coal-mine safety laws to conserve human lives and powers as well as coal. Before 1952, over and over, responsibility for shocking disasters was dodged because regulations were neither adequate nor uniform. What was defined as a gassy mine situation in one state, for example, was not so agreed upon in another. Until 1952, the fine work of the Bureau of Mines could lead only to recommendations, not to adoption and enforcement of practices. However, the use of "permissible" (tested) blasting devices and explosives recommended by the Bureau must be adopted by the industry. Some real progress has been made under the new Federal Coal Mine Safety Act of 1952. This strengthens the earlier law of 1941 by authorizing Federal enforcement of safety recommendations in mines employing fifteen or more men underground. It is only fair to say that considerable improvement did occur after 1941. Up to the end of 1956, 1,876,000 persons had completed the first-aid course offered by the Bureau of Mines, and 107,000, its mine-rescue course. In recent years an encouraging reduction in fatalities per million man-hours has been achieved as follows: from 1.25 in 1961 to 1.15 in 1962 and 1.07 in 1963.

Present Status and Future Outlook for Coal Resources. While competition from petroleum and gas has reduced the general demand for coal in the past 25 years, the demand for electric power and for coke is increasing; and in the latter instance, coke for metallurgical uses can be produced in sufficient quantity only from coal. This and other special uses in which coal is free from competition account for approximately 20 per cent of the total coal consumption. Thoughtful investigators believe generally that coal will figure more and more importantly in the increasing energy demands of the country. More economical production of coal and increasing cost of producing competing fuels bid fair to overcome, eventually, any shrinkage in the traditional demands for this useful fuel.

With estimated total reserves of around 1,660 billion tons[12] (2,000-pound tons), one-half of which is subject by present standards to economical recovery, the 1963 production of 476 million tons (anthracite, bituminous coal, and lignite) would appear to indicate that more than 1,900 years will be required to exhaust the resource. It should be borne in mind, however, that coking coals account for almost 20 per cent of

[12] The actual figure for the total reserves as of January 1, 1960, was 1,660,290,-000,000 short tons of which 50 per cent, or approximately 830 billion tons, is assumed to be recoverable. Paul Averitt, Coal Reserves of the United States: A Progress Report, Jan. 1, 1960, *Geol. Surv. Bull.* 1136, 1961, pp. 10–11.

the *production* and only 2 per cent of the *reserves;* that the steel, electric-power, and chemical industries will have increasing coal demands; and that, eventually, diminishing reserves of oil and natural gas will put new burdens on the coal resources.

Mechanization in mining—marked by such devices as coal-cutting and continuous-mining machines (Fig. 11-3) and mechanical loaders and belt conveyors to move more rapidly the products of continuous mining—and strip and auger mining have all increased productivity per man-day and have made considerable contributions to the reduction of waste. Improvements in transportation also have helped to control the cost of coal. The railroads, which hauled 72.8 per cent of all bituminous coal in 1963, have developed unit trains that are loaded in a few hours with 7,500 to 10,000 tons or more and are dumped with equal speed at the receiving end. Plans in progress call for even bigger single-haul capacities, from 15,000 to 25,000 tons and up. Twenty barges lashed in a solid unit ahead of a 400-horsepower towboat can carry 20,000 to 30,000 tons of coal on inland waterways. Barges carried 11 per cent of the bituminous coal traffic in 1963. Short-haul trucking moved 13 per cent of the coal output to market in 1963. Mine-mouth generation of coal-powered electricity has increased with development of extra-high-voltage transmission lines making possible delivery of coal "by wire." A 108-mile coal pipeline carrying a slurry made up of finely ground coal and water to be burned as a fluid or dried at destination operated successfully for 5 years and was only shut down when railroad rates were greatly reduced (Fig. 11-9). Pipelines, however, are still in the picture.[13]

It should be noted that all of this increased efficiency and reasonable-price maintenance by the industry has necessarily taken full advantage of automation and that the workers who made their living in the bituminous and lignite industries were reduced from 415,582 in 1950 to 141,646 in 1963.[14] Also, many of these displaced workers have been uable to locate other opportunities for making a livelihood. This poses the question as to whether the necessity to introduce automation in order to compete in our economy is at odds with conserving human powers. This question is touched upon in the final chapter of this book.

In the series of searching studies recently published on the future energy needs of the United States and the world, there is remarkable unanimity of opinion that higher production of coal will be necessary to meet the needs of the next quarter century to say nothing of the years beyond.[15] Undaunted by the future, however, the coal-mining industry takes an optimistic view and submits this analysis:

[13] *Ibid.,* pp. 31–35.
[14] *Minerals Yearbook,* 1963, U.S. Bureau of Mines, (Preprint).
[15] *Bituminous Coal Trends,* National Coal Association, Washington, D.C., 1950, p. 6.

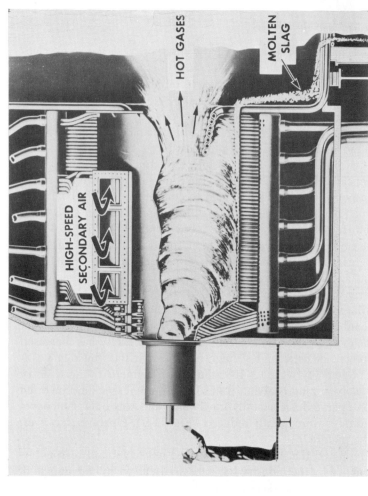

figure 11-9

Liquid coal (left) composed of water and finely ground coal. It can be moved long distances by pipeline and burned as a liquid. Side view of cyclone furnace where "slurry," as the liquid is called, is burned. It enters through pipe at left and is sprayed out of nozzle in a whirl of high-temperature air. (Courtesy of Bituminous Coal Institute.)

Of the 830 billion tons of economically recoverable reserves, it is estimated that one-fourth can be produced by present mining methods—enough for more than 500 years. Another 30 per cent is available at 25 to 50 per cent increase in production costs, with the remainder available at one and one half to four times the current price. These cost estimates, as well as the theory that only half of the U.S. coal reserves are recoverable, may well be revised as new mining techniques increase the percentage of recovery. These, plus new utilization techniques to increase coal's efficiency, could extend the life of recoverable coal reserves well beyond current estimates.

Thus abundant coal is available to replace oil and natural gas as the supply of those fuels dwindles. Coal will be available to generate more and more electricity for light, power, heat and air conditioning, and otherwise to supply the vital energy required to turn the wheels of industry. Coal will be more than equal to these tasks for centuries to come.[16]

In war or peace, coal is indispensable, and its conservation merits the attention not only of industry and government but of every citizen.

PETROLEUM

If for no other reason than the development and well-nigh-universal ownership of the automobile and its variations in this country, petroleum is an indispensable natural resource. Our present economy would be paralyzed without it. Transportation, space heating, agriculture, mining, power production, and the chemical industries all draw heavily on the petroleum reserves. Representing less than one-tenth the nation's energy supply in 1900, petroleum and natural gas have become the source of more than one-half the present energy supply. In 1950 the people of this country used 2⅓ billion barrels of petroleum. This amounts to 6½ million barrels a day, and this is three times the amount used in 1925. By 1962, total domestic consumption of petroleum had reached 3,070 million barrels, or 8.4 million a day. Comparative consumption of gasoline alone by motor transportation equipment for 1940 and 1960 with projections for 1980 and 2000 is indicated in Table 11-2.

The petroleum industry, starting in 1859 with the bringing in of the first paying well by a certain Colonel Drake in Pennsylvania, chalked up a production of half a million barrels in 1860 (Fig. 11-10). Ninety years later, in 1950, production had increased 4,000-fold and demand for particular products had changed radically. Originally kerosene for lighting had been principally in demand, and not until after the First World War did gasoline take the lead. By 1951, demand for distillate, a heavier product, and residual fuel oil combined exceeded slightly the demand for gasoline, as it had done for a short time about 1929. A slowly rising price

[19] *Bituminous Coal Facts*, p. 43.

TABLE 11-2. USE OF MOTOR FUELS, 1940 AND 1960, AND
PROJECTIONS FOR 1980 AND 2000
(In billions of gallons)

Fuel user	1940	1960		1980	2000
Automobiles	16	41	L	77	135
			M	81	165
			H	97	252
Trucks	5	16	L	28	48
			M	36	77
			H	48	128
Buses	*	1	L	1	1
			M	1	1
			H	1	2
Total	22	58	L	106	184
			M	118	243
			H	146	382

SOURCE: Hans H. Landsberg, Leonard L. Fischman, and Joseph L. Fisher, Resources
in America's Future, The Johns Hopkins Press (for Resources for the Future, Inc.),
Baltimore, 1962, p. 147. Used by special permission of the publisher.
L = low projection; M = medium; H = high.
* Less than half a billion.

*The world's first oil boom. Edwin L. Drake's achievement
in bringing in the world's first commercial oil well in 1859
launched an oil boom in western Pennsylvania comparable
to the California gold rush of 1849. In modern conservation
practice, which is relatively recent, wider spacing of wells
is practiced. (Photo from the Texas Company, courtesy of
National Coal Association.)*

figure 11-10

for crude oil has been overcome by improvements in the refining of motor fuels and lubricants. Much is made today in the news of discovery exceeding production, and this is a fact. It is far from a fact, however, that discovery trends indicate adequate reserves indefinitely, in the face of rapidly increasing demand.

Origin and Occurrence of Petroleum and Natural Gas. The notion that oil is likely to be found "anywhere" might well have been held by early settlers in the United States. Petroleum skimmed from the surface of springs is known to have been a part of the Indians' medical stores, and petroleum seeps and water pollutions are reported to have plagued the colonists. Guesses as to how oil occurred underground were as common as they were inaccurate, and only in relatively recent years have the petroleum geologists and other scientists put discovery on a basis of scientific knowledge.

Petroleum is a product of buried marine sediments and as such is distributed more widely than present production centers would indicate. This is because accumulations are found only where a combination of source beds, formations adapted to storing accumulations, and underground traps that can hold them are found. This combination is somewhat rare, but here and there vast quantities of organic materials, probably of both plant and animal character, have been subject to millions of years of change through heat and pressure. The resulting compounds of hydrogen and carbon together with varying impurities, colorless to black in appearance, flow from the ancient muds to domes or traps formed by tilting, faulting, or folding of the earth's crust (Fig. 11-11). It is at such points that petroleum can be obtained by drilling. Along with the oil, natural gas occurs and serves, when pools are reached by drilling, to force the oil to the surface. The gas itself is valuable as a fuel of high efficiency and for the manufacture of certain derivatives, one of which is carbon black used in printer's ink, in the manufacture of rubber articles, and elsewhere, in the arts.

Petroleum occurs commercially in twenty-six of the fifty states, and natural gas is produced in most of the fields.

Ownership of Oil Resources. In the United States the commercial development of oil resources is relatively young, and this has meant that much of the land under which oil lies has passed, by one procedure or another, into private ownership. Furthermore, under our system of government, the owner of the land is usually the owner of its subsurface resources. This situation preceded the discovery and development of many state and federally owned oil lands and, combined with certain misconceptions about the occurrence and behavior of oil deposits, led to wasteful exploitation. Both oil operators and owners of oil land were inclined to believe that petroleum was "galloping around underground like

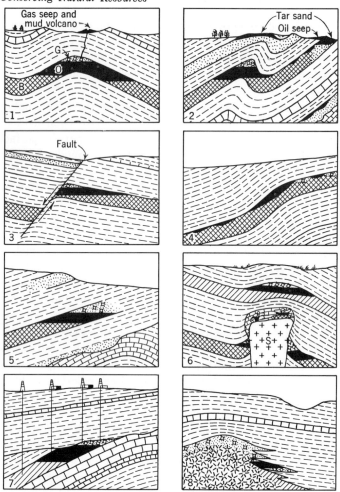

figure 11-11

Common types of oil traps. (1) Symmetrical anticline, (G) sand saturated with gas, (O) sand saturated with oil, (B) sand saturated with brine; (2) asymmetrical anticline; (3) sand sealed by fault; (4) monoclinical fold, or structural terrace; (5) lensing sand (e.g., sandstone grading into shale); (6) salt dome, oil accumulations in upturned sands at side, in cap rock, and in gently flexing overlying sand; (7) oil accumulating at an angular unconformity; (8) buried granite hill. [T. S. Lovering, Minerals in World Affairs, p. 150. (Copyright 1943 by Prentice-Hall, Inc., Englewood Cliffs, N.J.) Reproduced by permission of the publisher.]

a wild animal" and that it should be pounced upon while it was under certain ownerships and leases. It thus became customary to drill wells on each one and to seek a quick "flush" yield, with resulting rapid decline in the amount of oil obtained. Of course this system, or lack of system, exhausted the gas which had served to force out the oil. Pumping could be resorted to in some of the wells, but the general effect was to abandon wells from which production had shown a sharp drop. During the 1920s geologists and engineers became increasingly well informed on the "reservoir-energy" function of natural gas, and such knowledge as existed earlier was made use of in drafting the Mineral Leasing Act of 1920. Stipulations written into oil leases under this law were aimed at better drilling practices on Federal lands, and in recent years many of the states have taken account of the need for requiring that state-owned oil properties be operated under similar leases. Ownership, then, has been an important consideration both in the depletion and conservation of petroleum resources.

Factors Which Deplete Oil Resources. As with coal, it must be remembered that petroleum is an irreplaceable natural resource and that it does not get its share of attention concerning conservation needs.

Ownership and expense of drilling set the stage for wasteful exploitation, and certainly the fact that there are too many wells badly spaced, has reduced the production life of the older fields. Certain of the fields showed a decrease from peak production of as much as 90 per cent in 3 years, owing mainly to the dissipation of the gas drive, as it is frequently called.

Competition and resulting overproduction, particularly in the early days of discovery, have been common, with inevitable waste in marketing and consumption.

Two world wars have stepped up demand in turn, and strangely enough, both have stimulated the domestic demand. Oil operators and merchants will point out that one cannot produce without a market and will emphasize the benefits which production volume and resulting lower prices have brought to society. But they can hardly contend that waste has not characterized the industry and its marketing procedure.

The design of the internal-combustion engine in its myriad uses has, of course, improved tremendously since the turn of the century, and more powerful engines are appearing continually. However, failure to achieve lower consumption of gasoline in the development of the automobile engine, so that lesser amounts of petroleum would be required, is characteristic of the automobile industry in this country, and change would probably greatly depress the petroleum industry. The recent popularity of the smaller European automobiles in the United States indicates a mild rebellion against the cost of operating the conventional type of automobile and may affect slightly the demand for gasoline. At any rate the opinion may be risked that automobile transportation today consumes much more gasoline than could be made to do the job if some attention were given to more economical engines and, particularly, to lighter-weight cars.

The growing use of fuel oil for household heating and for power production brings convenience but, along with it, wasteful consumption of petroleum. The product required is not just a refinery residue but contains valuable constituents subject to recovery. It is known that the rapid development of oil-burning heating equipment was stimulated by the need to find a market for fuel oil when inventories of the latter began to show a surplus. Industrially, the use of petroleum has competed strongly in this area with coal, which is much more plentiful.

The very nature of the petroleum industry with its high costs of discovery, drilling, and refining and its competitive character have made waste difficult to avoid. High rate of consumption has been a corollary of constant productive capacity. All this means that any effort to curtail consumption as a conservation measure is doomed to failure. That is why conservation stops at the field or, at the latest, in the refinery.

Possibilities of Conserving Petroleum Resources. With the "known economic reserves inadequate" according to the President's Materials Policy Commission and the two phrases "discoveries geologically likely— though not necessarily adequate" and "synthesis progress expected" as the only optimistic comments, the people of the United States may well be concerned with the possibilities of reducing waste and making one barrel of oil do the work of two. The following are some of the directions in which effort can be speeded up:

1. Improve recovery from present producing oil fields through operation of pools cooperatively or, by legal requirement, as units (Fig. 11-12). Agreements of this sort provide for efficient well spacing and best use of "reservoir energy" or "gas drive." Other provisions include "repressuring," or returning gas or water to the underground oil formations; "acidizing," or using acid to open up the less porous "sands" and increase oil flow; and "fracturing." All these bring otherwise irrecoverable oil to the drilled well. State regulatory laws have been successful in bringing about these practices. So-called secondary recovery has been greatly stimulated by the Interstate Compact to Conserve Oil and Gas. This compact and its commission are further discussed on pages 334–335.

2. Process natural gas at the well for the production of gasoline and other liquids, generally used by the industry. This measure has real possibilities.

3. Attack transportation losses by better inspection and maintenance of

figure 11-12

Modern well spacing. Contrast with Fig. 11-10. Agricultural crops are frequently undisturbed between wells. (Standard Oil Company of New Jersey, courtesy of American Petroleum Institute.)

pipeline equipment and by land shipment instead of water shipment wherever possible during war periods.

4. Prorate production on a voluntary basis by the industry so long as it works to prevent flooding the market and the consequent encouraging of waste. This may be accomplished by law if necessary (see Connally Hot Oil Act, page 334).

5. Perfect and keep available the methods of obtaining oil from coal and from oil shale, both of which are vastly more abundant than petroleum. Research and development work by the U.S. Bureau of Mines on the hydrogenation of coal for the production of oil (Bergius process, used extensively in Germany) and in gas synthesis (Fischer-Tropsch process) have led to an estimate that gasoline and other products can be made from Wyoming coals at prices competitive with petroleum products. And while these findings are challenged by the National Petroleum Council,[17] they indicate progress and promise a generous chance for supplying petroleum substitutes. Likewise the Bureau of Mines has had experiments under way on the production of oil from oil shale on a demonstration basis at Rifle, Colorado. The mining of oil shale at this location was shut down in June, 1956, because the Congress failed to appropriate funds for its continuation. But reactivation of the government works here, through agreements with private industry, were predicted by the Secretary of the Interior in 1964. The bureau has estimated that oil-shale deposits located principally in Colorado, Utah, and Wyoming represent a possible oil content of some 500 billion barrels which might be recovered at several times the cost of producing natural petroleum and that 80 billion bar-

---

[17] Official industry advisory group to the Secretary of the Interior.

rels of this could be produced at cost only slightly higher than the present costs of finding and producing petroleum. In this estimate the study of the National Petroleum Council agrees that a daily production of 200,000 barrels could be marketed at about 2 cents a gallon higher than comparable grades of natural petroleum products on the Los Angeles market. The council does not appear too enthusiastic, but several oil companies have oil-shale holdings and are said to be planning future operations.

An oil-shale industry runs into another natural-resource problem, however. The deposits are located in dry country. Water even to supply the necessary labor-force community is none too plentiful. Oil from shale therefore may be a question of water supply. Location of plants in sparsely populated territory also introduces difficulty in marketing until natural-petroleum production shrinks and lessens present competition.

6. Develop and manage publicly owned reserves. Under the Mineral Leasing Law of 1920, oil-prospecting permits and oil leases must be used in accordance with good conservation practice. As mentioned on page 317 this is one of the few regulatory devices in the hands of the public. This system should be continued and, in modified form perhaps, applied to the *outlying* submerged lands of the continental shelf over which the Federal government still has control. Those submerged lands which passed to the states by the law of 1953, within their historic boundaries, will need appropriate legislation for their exploitation. Some of these states have already had experience along this line within their land boundaries, notably California, Texas, and Louisiana. These various submerged lands, state and Federal, are estimated to be underlain with oil resources running into the billions of barrels; their development is beset with unusual expense and difficulty (Fig. 11-13), and drilling works would be vulnerable in time of war. Low royalty rates and other incentives will probably be necessary to encourage private enterprise to develop them.[18]

7. Encourage discovery. It is highly questionable as to whether discovery can be called conservation. Certainly, however, it serves to replenish the steady draft on reserves, and it should be considered. Discovery efforts have increased tremendously in the past few years. In 1939 fewer than 3,000 exploratory "holes" were drilled, and for every one that became a producer, 8.5 proved dry. Thirteen years later, in 1952, some 12,425 exploratory holes were drilled with one producer for

[18] The question of Federal as against state jurisdiction of the nearby submerged lands has been settled by law but not in the minds of many citizens who believe that the resources belong to all the people rather than to the particular states. The controversy is a good example of the difficulty of determining what amounts to equitable distribution in managing natural resources in a democracy.

figure 11-13

Drilling barge at sea. Helicopter on the flight deck shuttles
workers back and forth between shore and their jobs. (Photo
from Standard Oil Company of New Jersey, courtesy of American Petroleum Institute, N.Y.)

every 4.8 dry ones (Fig. 11-14). The average depth of drilling was
4,476 feet, although extreme depths of more than 3½ miles have been
reported. One well has been drilled to a depth of 25,340 feet. This one
is in Texas and was completed in 1958.

In the past much was heard of the so-called "doodle bug," by which
is meant any sort of gadget alleged to be useful in indicating the
presence of oil and belonging to the same family as the sticks used in
"dowsing" for good water-well location. In recent years, scientific
geophysical methods have been developed and used widely in exploration for oil. The information obtained by these methods has to do with
promising rock formations beneath the surface, rather than with the
actual presence of oil itself; their usefulness, however, has been proved.
They include, among others, the "artificial earthquake," or seismographic, method in which successive charges are exploded a short distance below the surface, and the time of the rebounding shocks is
recorded by delicate instruments. Thus the occurrence of a dome in a
hard underground stratum, for example, may be plotted (see Figs.
11-15, 11-16). An instrument known as a *magnetometer* and another
known as a *gravity meter* are also useful in obtaining information
about the character of underground rock formations. The former is
towed behind an airplane or carried otherwise in a definite pattern of
paths over the surface, and the recordings are plotted for underground

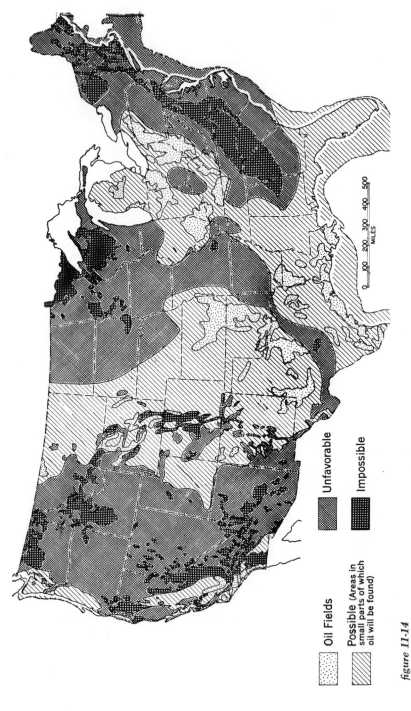

Oil Fields

Possible (Areas in small parts of which oil will be found)

Unfavorable

Impossible

figure 11-14
Map of United States oil possibilities. [William Van Royen, Oliver Bowles, and Elmer W. Peterson, The Mineral Resources of the World. (Copyright 1952 by Prentice-Hall, Inc., Englewood Cliffs, N.J.) Reproduced by permission of Department of Geography, University of Maryland, and the publisher.]

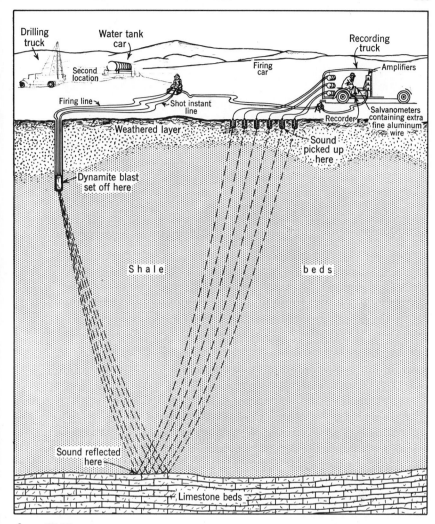

figure 11-15
Diagram of seismographic method of exploration for promising oil structure. Artificial earthquakes are set off by a blast at surface, and the reverberations are recorded for interpretation. (Askania Corporation of America.)

mapping. But most of the exploration for petroleum, as well as for other minerals, is the slow, careful, and systematic work of the geologist with his hammer; and there is much left to be done. Oil is not obtained without drilling, and although this involves less guesswork than formerly, it can hardly be done with less expense. The reserves that lie deeper than present producing zones and the possible horizontal re-

figure 11-16
Setting up apparatus to touch off an explosive charge in Louisiana bayou country. Shock waves will be checked on a seismograph (see Fig. 13-18) to obtain clue to earth formations that may be oil-bearing. (Standard Oil Company of New Jersey, courtesy of American Petroleum Institute.)

serves between producing fields offer chances for further production of both oil and gas.

8. Import oil from other countries. This, too, is hardly conservation if, as we must, we think only of those natural resources available within the United States. Ships are lost, international agreements are broken, and, eventually, dependence on importation of so essential a product carries the seeds of war.

Connally Hot Oil Act. This law was enacted by the Congress in 1935 and prohibited the interstate transportation of petroleum produced, transported, or withdrawn from storage in excess of the amounts permitted in the state of origin. The act, which was to have expired in 1942, was made permanent that year.[19] Its enforcement has had a halting effect upon overproduction and, in consequence, upon the conservation of petroleum.

The Interstate Compact to Conserve Oil and Gas. In 1935, six states— Colorado, Illinois, Kansas, New Mexico, Oklahoma, and Texas—approved an Interstate Compact to Conserve Oil and Gas, and the Congress granted consent to its organization for a 2-year period. Since then its life has been extended, the latest action by the Congress being for a period ending in 1967. Since 1935, twenty-four other producing states have approved the compact and three states have acquired associate memberships. Its pur-

[19] 49 Stat. 30, (1935); 56 Stat. 381 (1942).

pose was declared to be "to conserve oil and gas by the prevention of physical waste thereof"; and to effect that purpose each member state was required to enact within a reasonable time, or to continue to keep in force, effective petroleum conservation laws and to provide stringent penalties for violations. The executive body of this compact is the Interstate Oil Compact Commission composed of the governor or his designated representative of each participating state. The commission was authorized "to recommend . . . measures for the maximum ultimate recovery of oil and gas . . ." and was declared not to be a price-fixing agency. This compact, with its commission, is perhaps the most thoroughly organized of the many interstate compacts which have come into being for conserving natural resources—including those concerned with forest-fire control, water conservation and distribution, and pollution control. It has only the power of persuasion, holds meetings frequently, maintains headquarters at Oklahoma City, and in the years of its existence has made notable progress in obtaining increasing recovery in oil and gas operations. However, it studiously avoids efforts to prevent waste at the marketing and utilization stages, assuming that demand may always be interpreted as "reasonable market demand" and that a healthy drilling industry is only possible if demand is high.

Trends and Prospects for a Continuing Oil Supply. Landes points out that the petroleum industry operates upon a small inventory and gambles, as does its consuming public, on ability to continue discovery. But he calls attention to the three directions in which we must look—present reserves; undiscovered deposits; and "technological reserves," which include dormant supplies at great depth and the manufacture of synthetics.[20]

Items 7 and 8 above indicate our main chances to avoid a trend toward failure to meet the 1975 demand *if we depend on crude oil only.*

Recoverable reserves in 1951 (exclusive of 4.7 billion barrels of natural-gas liquids) were estimated at 27.5 billion barrels. Against the sum of these two (27.5 + 4.7 = 32.2) the 1950 consumption by the United States was 2.375 billion barrels. In 1962 demand was 3,794,462,000 barrels.[21] This was supplied from domestic crude-oil and natural-gas-liquids production of 3,020,296,000 barrels plus imports of 836,869,000 barrels, or from a total of 3,857,165,000 barrels. Domestic proved reserves of crude oil and natural-gas liquids as of December 31, 1962, were estimated at 38,700,740,000 barrels[22] (enough with moderate imports, to last for only 12.7 years at present rates of consumption). Something will need to happen fast on this basis if discovery is to win the 13-year race from 1962 to

[20] Kenneth K. Landes, Petroleum Geology, John Wiley & Sons, Inc., New York, 1951, pp. 601–602.
[21] Preliminary data from U.S. Bureau of Mines, quoted by American Petroleum Institute, Petroleum Facts and Figures, New York, 1963, p. 129.
[22] American Petroleum Institute and American Gas Association, in *ibid.,* p. 47.

1975. History of discovery and drilling so far would indicate that it may *just* be won.

Meanwhile, the American people have the opportunity to understand their petroleum resources more fully, to discard the idea that waste of gasoline and fuel oil is unimportant, and to insist that an efficient liquid-fuel industry can be reconciled with increasingly intensive conservation practices.

NATURAL GAS

Because it is largely free of inert nitrogen, is clean, produces no residual waste products, and requires no storage space on the premises of the consumer, natural gas is the most efficient of the natural fuels. It is also used to blend with gas manufactured from coal and petroleum; and where available direct from the field, it is relatively inexpensive.

Moreover, it is an important raw material for the chemical industry. But it has not always been easy to capture or to handle and distribute. For these reasons and because of the early attitudes toward waste of natural resources, natural-gas waste represents to date one of the most dramatic pictures in the entire natural-resource field. Dr. Charles R. Van Hise, whose book *The Conversation of Natural Resources in the United States*[23] was the first one published exclusively on this subject, pointed out in 1910 the five ways in which natural gas was being wasted at that time.[24] (1) Losses from high-pressure gas wells before drillers knew how to cap them. If lighted and allowed to burn, as many of the gas wells were, there would be a caving in of rock around the casing, a sinking of the surface, and the development of a veritable flaming lake. For a considerable time, 70 million cubic feet of gas a day was estimated to be thus wasted in one Louisiana field. (2) Losses in connection with oil wells which were frequently also gas wells. Here the lack of easy markets and difficulty of capture had resulted in the practice of allowing the gas to escape or to be "flared" (lighted and burned as it escaped through pipes a safe distance from the derrick). Van Hise comments that all attempts to halt this practice by law had been defeated by 1910, save in Indiana. (3) Loss in pipeline transmission to market. In the early days of the industry, construction and inspection of pipelines were indefensibly careless when one considers that as far back as 1907 the country was utilizing 400 million cubic feet of natural gas a year. (Transmission losses in 1950

[23] Charles R. Van Hise, The Conservation of Natural Resources in the United States. The Macmillan Company, New York, 1910, pp. 56–60.

[24] Those who feel that we need not worry about conservation of minerals will lick their chops over Van Hise's prediction that the natural-gas supply would be short by 1930, but at the rates it was being wasted in his day he might have been uncomfortably correct. Curtailing waste has proved to be good conservation.

still amounted to 171 billion cubic feet.) (4) Loss related to allocating gas to uses for which more plentiful fuels such as coal were readily available. Here the use of gas for generating steam power is challenged. This particular loss is significant today and is receiving some attention where there is sharp competition for gas by industry, as against the demands of the householder. (5) Loss in the disproportionate amount of natural gas used inefficiently to produce carbon black. Crude methods of recovering the sootlike deposit from deliberate burning of gas and the slightly improved "channel" process produce considerably less than the modern furnace plant process, but the former are still widely used. This loss of natural gas is both dramatic and important, since the 1962 consumption of natural gas for carbon-black manufacture was about 134 billion cubic feet from a total production of about 13,877 billion cubic feet. Use of carbon black in the United States ranks highest in rubber manufacture followed in order by that of ink and paint and miscellaneous products, among which are plastics, chemicals, paper, metals, fertilizers, cement, and shoes.[25]

From the years of heavy surplus of natural gas at the fields and corresponding unsatisfied demand at distant localities, this excellent fuel had come in 1962 to supply 34.2 per cent of our total energy needs as against 4.1 per cent of lesser need in 1920. Greater supply from increased discovery of both oil and gas, improved gathering and transporting facilities, reduction in price, and better performance have all figured in this remarkable increase in the use of natural gas and may have also brought about increasing conservation. One remarkable development is the fact that the disposal of natural gas has become subject to regulation, not only by state public-utility commissions but also by the Federal Power Commission. The latter has been roundly challenged in recent efforts at legislation, but most of the objections have been against interference with prices and volume of business. In general, regulation has helped to conserve the resource.

It is probable that there is a market ahead for all the natural gas that the country can produce, whether it continues to be less expensive than other energy sources or not. Its very efficiency and convenience can cause it to compete successfully. This resource is produced in more than twenty-five of the states. Production for 1962 saw Texas leading with 43 per cent, Louisiana next with 25 per cent, and Oklahoma at 7 per cent. The Appalachian field—including Pennsylvania, West Virginia, Ohio, Kentucky, and New York—accounts for less than 5 per cent.[26]

The actual future of the natural-gas business appears to rest upon four courses of action which may require increased public regulation.

[25] *Minerals Yearbook*, 1962.
[26] Rounded off from data in *ibid.*, vol. 2, p. 329.

The President's Materials Policy Commission lists these as follows *without emphasizing need for increased regulation:*[27]

1. Stimulate maximum discovery of natural-gas resources.
2. Avoid waste in the production of natural gas and ensure that full advantage is taken of the driving force of natural gas in lifting oil in order to get maximum economic recovery of the oil and gas.
3. Improve the pattern of use so that relatively more gas goes to those uses in which it has a special advantage and relatively less to those which could be served just as well by other fuels.
4. Lay the basis for an orderly transition to other fuels at that distant but inevitable date when natural-gas production falls off.

Because these "challenges to our natural-gas economy" are so clearly stated by the Commission, the means by which they may be achieved should be discussed here.

Present incentives for discovery are powerful and are reflected in exploring activity for gas as well as for oil. Prices, demand, and tax provisions are all favorable.

Except for the Federal Mineral Leasing Law of 1920, which governs exploitation of oil and gas as well as other nonmetallic minerals on the public domain, regulation of the natural-gas industry is in the hands of the states so far as waste reduction is concerned. While such regulation is anything but uniform and needs to be improved, it augurs well for higher standards and better operating practices.

Allocating natural gas to its highest use is subject to more than market forces and improved distribution and processing facilities. Unusual profit incentives will be necessary to obtain action in this direction by the industry, and Federal and state policy will have to give a hand.

The following uses were reported for 1962:

Use	Billion cubic feet
Residential	3,478,563
Commercial	1,206,668
Oil and gas fields	1,993,128
Carbon black	133,302
Petroleum refineries	789,877
Pipeline fuel	382,496
Electric public-utility power plants and other industrial	5,906,095
Total 1962 consumption	13,890,129

SOURCE: *Minerals Yearbook,* 1963, U.S. Bureau of Mines, vol. 2, pp. 336–337.

[27] Resources for Freedom, vol. 3, The Outlook for Energy Sources, Report of the President's Materials Policy Commission, 1952, p. 16.

Adjustment to an eventual shrinkage in supply will result in grasping at imports from Canada and Mexico; at a much cheaper substitute gas from coal than is now available (if it can be developed); and, eventually, at the harnessing of solar energy. Of course, the promise of atomic energy is ahead, but this is also a natural-resource problem, with a far vaster research and development frontier to be conquered.

Proved, economically recoverable reserves of natural gas at the end of 1962 were 273.8[28] trillion cubic feet, or about seventeen times the 1962 withdrawal of 16 trillion cubic feet (withdrawal includes marketed production + waste + gas repressured and vented). One estimate of future discoverable and recoverable reserves is 510 trillion cubic feet,[29] but nobody has estimated future annual consumption.

Consideration of natural gas and its equitable distribution brings up the interesting question as to why its distribution and marketing fall in the public-utility field along with hydroelectric energy, whereas other indispensable mineral resources, and even some of the replaceable resources, are not so considered. Certainly the experience of this democracy in regulating trade and transportation of the two natural resources—one a service, water power, and the other a fuel, natural gas—will be useful in developing future policy.

NUCLEAR ENERGY AS A COMPETITIVE POWER SOURCE

There is a great deal of speculation on the displacement of other sources of power by nuclear or atomic energy. The question arises, "When will competition from nuclear energy definitely affect our power economy?" This is why the subject is taken up here under fuels, instead of in the discussion of uranium and thorium in the next chapter.

In seeking an answer to this question, it should be understood first of all that electric power is not at present a *direct* usable product, even experimentally, of the release of nuclear energy. Power *is* produced by substituting for heat energy from conventional fuels, the heat energy released by the fission of nuclear-energy materials. Furthermore, the fossil fuels—coal, oil, and natural gas—represent only from 10 to 17 per cent of the cost of producing power, and except for impounding and control of falling water, "fuel" cost is nothing in the process of hydroelectric power production.

The terrible coincidence of the culminating of years of research and thinking on the potentialities of power from the atom and the occurrence of the greatest war in history brought us nuclear energy as a destructive

[28] *Minerals Yearbook,* 1963, vol. 2, pp. 322–323. (Quoting American Gas Association.)
[29] L. F. Terry, The Future Supply of Natural Gas Will Exceed 500 Trillion Cubic Feet, *Gas Age,* New York, Oct. 26, 1950, p. 58.

agent first, and only by turning this discovery to constructive uses can we realize the hope of preventing future wars. Power production ranks high among such uses, and under authority of the Atomic Energy Act of 1954, the Atomic Energy Commission is licensing various power companies, cooperatives, and municipalities to build plants or to market the power produced by the operation of plants for which the Commission furnishes the atomic fuel and a share of the cost in terms of research service or money. The world's first *full-scale* atomic electric-power plant devoted exclusively to peacetime uses is now in operation at Shippingport, Pennsylvania, on the Ohio River (Fig. 11-17). It is being operated by Duquesne Light Company under a contract with the Atomic Energy Commission. Westinghouse Electric Corporation built the nuclear reactor under contract with the AEC, at a cost of about 55 million dollars, with Duquesne Light Company contributing 5 million dollars toward the cost of the reactor and providing the site, turbogenerator, and other parts of the conventional plant. This uses the *pressurized-water* type of reactor (PWR), which is cooled and moderated by ordinary water, under pressure so that it will not boil. The water is then passed through a heat exchanger or steam generator. The steam turns conventional turbines to produce power, and this is delivered to company customers over its lines. The fuel consists of natural uranium and slightly enriched uranium. Fabrication of the uranium adds a great deal to its cost; for instance, the uranium itself costs 2 million dollars, but the entire cost of the fuel prepared for use in the reactor is over 10 million dollars. The initial rated capacity was 60,000 kilowatts; it is recognized, however, that the reactor may produce more than this, and the plant was built on a larger scale, with a possible ultimate generating capacity of 100,000 kilowatts. There is considerable difference of opinion as to when electricity produced from nuclear fuel will be competitive with electricity produced from conventional fuels. The problem is largely one of reducing costs for capital investment and fuel. The knowledge which this operation furnishes will be invaluable.

Another major project in the Atomic Energy Commission's experimental power-reactor program is the sodium-graphite-reactor experiment.

Sodium-Graphite Reactor. The first of this type reactor has been placed in operation on the Santa Susana Mountains, 35 miles northwest of Los Angeles, generating sufficient heat to produce 6,500 kilowatts of electric power. The reactor was constructed by Atomics International, a division of North American Aviation, Inc., for the Atomic Energy Commission. The 7,500-kilowatt-capacity generating plant adjacent to the reactor was constructed by Southern California Edison Company and, on July 12, 1957, became the first plant built by a private utility to generate and distribute electricity from a nonmilitary atomic reactor. In connection

figure 11-17

Tubes of power. Inside these tubes, or shrouds, will move control rods of hafnium metal, which can absorb neutrons and thus retard the atom-splitting, heat-producing process. Inserting the rods into the reactor reduces the number of atoms being split. Withdrawing them increases the number. At the top of this interior photograph of the full-size mock-up of the reactor for the Shippingport, Pa., atomic power station are two refueling ports. Through these will be passed remote-handling equipment for removal of nuclear fuel elements for examination or replacement. Westinghouse Electric Corporation, under contract to the Atomic Energy Commission, designed the nuclear portion of the plant, the first full-scale atomic plant designed exclusively to serve civilian needs in the United States. The power plant is a joint venture of the AEC and the Duquesne Light Company. Duquesne Light has financed and built the electric generating portion of the plant and operates the entire station. (Westinghouse Electric Corporation.)

with the dedication of the reactor in November, 1957, the town of Moorpark, California, with a population of 1,500, was lighted for a brief period exclusively with electricity produced by heat from this reactor. The coolant in this instance is liquid sodium, and the moderator is graphite. The fuel is slightly enriched uranium.

In addition to the pressurized-water and sodium reactors, the Commission is concerned with the following other types: fast breeder, boiling water, aqueous homogeneous, organic moderated, liquid metal fueled, and molten plutonium.

On January 10, 1955, the Atomic Energy Commission announced its Power Reactor Demonstration Program to encourage private industry's efforts to develop atomic power. This resulted in a number of proposals by industry to build reactors, four of which are described below.

Fast-breeder Reactor. The most promising of all the developmental plants is the fast-breeder type, one of which, with a capacity of 100,000 kilowatts, is under construction near Monroe, Michigan, by the Detroit Edison Company and a group of associates known as the Power Reactor Development Company. Here the "coolant" is molten sodium, which carries heat to intermediate heat exchangers. From here the heat is transferred to a secondary liquid-sodium system and then to a boiler where steam is generated to drive a conventional turbine (Fig. 11-18). The fuel used in the core is a uranium alloy that is partially enriched with U^{235}. Surrounding the core is a blanket of nonfissionable U^{238} which, through exposure to the fissioning process in the core, is changed to plutonium (P^{239}), a fissionable material. In fact while 200 pounds of U^{235} are used up, there is produced its weight equivalent plus about 40 extra pounds of the new fuel.

Boiling-water Reactor. The Commonwealth Edison Company and Nuclear Power Group, Inc., have built the Dresden Nuclear Power Station in Grundy, Illinois, under a fixed-price contract with General Electric Company, which is responsible for the design, construction, and placing in operation of the station. In the reactor core, ordinary water, which is used as the moderator and coolant, boils and provides about 53 per cent of the primary steam. The balance of the steam required to produce a full load of 180,000 kilowatts comes from secondary steam generators, which produce steam at 500 pounds per square inch. The fuel is uranium dioxide enriched to 1½ per cent of the isotope, uranium 235.

Pressurized-water Thorium-Uranium Converter. The Consolidated Edison Company of New York, Inc., has built a unit at Indian Point, Buchanan, New York, which is near Peekskill. Heat from the reactor core changes water into steam to produce power in a 275,000-kilowatt-capacity plant—163,000 kilowatts nuclear and 112,000 oil-fired.

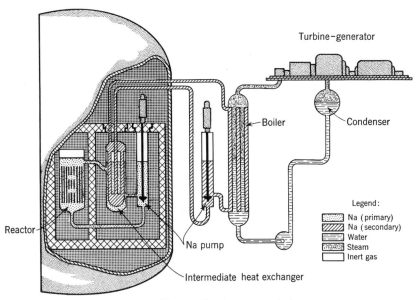

Turbine–generator

Boiler

Condenser

Legend:
- Na (primary)
- Na (secondary)
- Water
- Steam
- Inert gas

Reactor

Na pump

Intermediate heat exchanger

Diagram of nuclear power plant

figure 11-18
Simplified diagram of nuclear power plant showing major steps in producing electric power from atomic fuels. Heat energy from the atom is released in the reactor and carried by liquid sodium to heat exchanger. Here the heat is transferred to secondary sodium systems and piped to the boiler where it changes water into steam. Steam drives conventional turbines and generates electric power. (Atomic Power Development Associates.)

Aqueous-homogeneous Reactor. The Pennsylvania Power and Light Company and Westinghouse Electric Corporation jointly carried out a research and development program on a single slurry (a watery mixture) type of reactor system to operate on the thorium-uranium system. A slurry of uranium oxide and thorium oxide in heavy water constitutes the fuel, the moderator, and the coolant. The steam to operate a 150-kilowatt turbine generator is produced in four steam generators, each handling 4.5 million pounds of steam per hour. Results of research during 1958 and 1959 were satisfactory, and a power plant was thereupon constructed and put into operation late in 1963.

How Nuclear Energy Is Released. It would be impossible to explain the process of atom splitting—known as *fission* and by which heat energy is released—in a few words. But some of the details should be considered. Perhaps the most important one is the fact, now recognized, that the atom is not the smallest thing in the world. Every animal, vegetable, or mineral substance is made up of one or a combination of elements, and all elements from uranium to carbon are made up of atoms. These are so small that as little as a single ounce of uranium contains 70 thousand billion billion (70,000,000,000,000,000,000,000) atoms. The nucleus, or heart, of the atom is 10,000 times smaller. Two particles held together by a binding force make up this nucleus, except in the hydrogen atom. In this tiny "universe" of the atom, electrons— particles carrying a negative charge of electricity—whirl about the nucleus in a manner similar to the movements of the planets around the sun. The protons carry a positive charge of electricity; the neutrons carry no charge. Thus the normal, or unsplit, atom is electrically neutral, since the negative charge of the electron cancels out the positive charge of the proton.

Uranium 238 (the figure represents the sum of 146 neutrons and 92 protons, or its atomic weight) though nonfissionable itself, contains 0.7 per cent of U^{235}, which *is* fissionable. The remaining 99.3 per cent, al- though nonfissionable, *is* fertile, or capable of being changed into a new man-made element that will fission, namely plutonium (Pu^{239}). When more fuel is produced than is used, the process is known as breeding. Thorium is also a fertile material and may be used in the same manner or in combination with U^{238} to produce fissionable material.

In the core of the reactor (formerly called an atomic pile), the atoms of U^{235} are forced to fission (split), and in the chain reaction that follows, enormous amounts of heat energy are released. A lesser amount of heat is produced in the blanket of fertile material surrounding the core. The intense heat from the core and blanket is transferred to a "coolant" and then to ordinary water to produce steam. This steam drives conventional turbines to produce electric power.

The fusion process, such as is produced in the hydrogen bomb, is another promising source of heat to produce usable power. It occurs when, instead of undergoing fission hydrogen atoms combine, or fuse, under tremendous heat and thus produce energy. So great is the heat required that problems of confining it or controlling the energy produced will probably not be worked out for many years, although in 1958 the British were said to be making excellent progress. One interesting fact is that the "fuel" used is "heavy water," or deuterium, which occurs in sea water and is practically inexhaustible.

Advertisements of power companies are beginning to appear in magazines, indicating the construction or completion of "nuclear-energy power plants." In most instances the company and associates build the power plant and contribute a part of the cost of the reactor setup. The Atomic Energy Commission assumes the balance of the cost. The Big Rock Point Plant, shown in Fig. 11-19, was built by the Consumers Power Company at its own expense.

figure 11-19

Big Rock Point Nuclear Plant. Located near the City of Charlevoix, Mich., on Lake Michigan, this plant uses a boiling-water reactor and has produced electrical power since March 21, 1963. It was built by the Consumers Power Company at its own expense, the fifth of the large nuclear plants built in the United States. At maximum expected gross capacity, it will be able to produce enough electricity to supply the needs—residential, commercial, and industrial—of an average city of 100,000 persons. (Photo by courtesy of Consumers Power Company.)

Three big problems and many smaller ones are yet to be worked out before the atom becomes an *economic* source of power: (1) guarantee of safety to the human race from injury by radiation; (2) disposal of atomic wastes; and (3) clearing the economic hurdles to make nuclear fuel competitive with the fossil fuels. With all the tremendous containing walls of metal and all the reassurance that radiation can be controlled, there are still the factors of human and material failure to be reckoned with. This problem of safety has not been worked out satisfactorily. The second problem is related to the first, namely, safe disposal of waste from nuclear plants. Just now it is said that the geologists believe the place to put it is in the sea and the oceanographers say it should be buried deeply in the earth. The effects in either case may be disastrous, and little progress so far has been made in solving the problem. But

345

the economic problem is even more difficult. Brave pronouncements have been made by thoughtful men concerning economic uses from time to time since 1942 when man first set off and controlled a self-sustaining nuclear chain reaction.

The public has been led to believe that, along with military use to which nuclear energy was first put, this great discovery would be employed in peacetime use for the benefit of mankind with relative promptness. And yet 12 years after President Eisenhower's famous address to the United Nations on "Atoms for Peace" and the expenditure of billions of dollars, economically competitive atomic power is still in the distance —a "dream of the future."[30]

But what did the United States Atomic Energy Commission have to say in 1962? The following is a quotation from its report requested by President Kennedy: "Nuclear power is believed to be on or near the threshold of competitiveness with conventional power for large plants, in areas of the country where fossil fuel costs are high."[31] Even this optimistic statement is, in itself, qualified, and elsewhere in the report it is explained that it assumes approval of the Commission's costly program of technical research and development. It goes on to say that with such approval, atomic power will become competitive with conventional power throughout most of the country in the 1970s. By the year 2000, it is further claimed by the Commission's report, all new power plants then being constructed will be atomic power plants and nuclear energy will be source of half of all electricity generated in all new and old plants taken together.[32]

Although this report appears to many as realistic, there is reason to believe that the increased efficiency and ingenuity of the coal industry (see page 321) will continue, keeping costs and supply in the picture much longer than the year 2000. This makes conservation of the fossil fuels of real importance on a basis of cost alone, even though nuclear fuel may be looked to in the distant future. Various authorities estimate that between the years 1990 and 2000, atomic energy may begin to displace conventional fuels for the production of power. Thus the necessity for conservation of coal, oil, natural gas, and falling water for power are still with us. Conservation in the mining of uranium and thorium deposits has hardly been thought of.

[30] Sam H. Schurr, Some Observations on the Economics of Atomic Power, *Reprint* 41, Resources for the Future, Inc., Washington, D.C., 1963.
[31] Civilian Nuclear Power: A Report to the President, U.S. Atomic Energy Commission, 1962, pp. 4–5.
[32] *Ibid.*, pp. 11 and 43 (noted by Schurr, *op cit.*, pp. 9–10).

BIBLIOGRAPHY

Annual Report of the Office of Coal Research, 1963, U.S. Department of the Interior, 1964.

Annual Reports of the Secretary of the Interior, 1950–1964.

AVERITT, PAUL: Coal Reserves of the United States: A Progress Report, (as of) Jan. 1, 1960, *U.S. Geol. Surv. Bull.* 1136, 1961, pp. 10–11.

Bituminous Coal Trends, National Coal Association, Washington, D.C., 1956.

BROWN, HARRISON, JAMES BONNER, AND JOHN WEIR: The Next Hundred Years, The Viking Press, Inc., New York, 1957.

Civilian Nuclear Power: A Report to the President, U.S. Atomic Energy Commission, 1962.

DONELLY, J. LOUIS: The Future Sources of Power, *The Exchange,* vol. 25, pp. 1–6, New York Stock Exchange, New York, June, 1964.

$E = MC^2$, Detroit Edison Company, Detroit, Mich., 1957.

LANDES, KENNETH K.: Petroleum Geology, John Wiley & Sons, Inc., New York, 1956.

LANDSBERG, HANS H., LEONARD FISCHMAN, AND JOSEPH L. FISHER: Resources in America's Future, Published for Resources for the Future, Inc., by The Johns Hopkins Press, Baltimore, 1962.

LOVERING, T. S.: Minerals in World Affairs, Prentice-Hall, Inc., Englewood Cliffs, N.J., 1943.

LYONS, BARROW: Tomorrow's Birthright, Funk and Wagnalls Company, New York, 1955.

Minerals Yearbook, U.S. Bureau of Mines, 1949, 1953, 1954, and 1962.

Petroleum Facts and Figures, American Petroleum Institute, New York, 1963.

Resources for Freedom, vols. 1 and 3, Report of President's Materials Policy Commission, 1952.

SCHURR, SAM H.: Some Observations on the Economics of Atomic Power, *Reprint* 41, Resources for the Future, Inc., Washington, D.C., 1963.

SHERMAN, ALLAN, AND ALLEN B. MACMURPHY: Facts About Coal, U.S. Bureau of Mines, 1950.

Statistical Abstract of the United States, 1963, U.S. Bureau of the Census, 1964.

TERRY, L. F.: The Future Supply of Natural Gas Will Exceed 500 Trillion Cubic Feet, *Gas Age,* New York, Oct. 26, 1950.

VAN HISE, CHARLES R.: The Conservation of Natural Resources in the United States, The Macmillan Company, New York, 1910.

VAN ROYEN, WILLIAM, OLIVER BOWLES, AND ELMER W. PEHRSON: The Mineral Resources of the World, Prentice-Hall, Inc., Englewood Cliffs, N.J., 1952.

What About Strip Mining? Mined Land Conservation Conference, Washington, D.C., 1964.

12 METALS AND MISCELLANEOUS NONMETALLICS

METALS

MANKIND, ALMOST LITERALLY, could not turn a wheel today without metals. Tools, transportation, communication, laborsaving devices of many forms, and thousands of taken-for-granted luxuries involve the use of metals more than any other natural resource. Men were sharply limited in helping themselves when the tools they used were of stone, wood, or bone. Likewise communication and transportation were slow and uncertain before steam and mineral fuels were harnessed in metal trappings. Thousands of slaves did the relatively small volume of physical work, and very few people enjoyed any measure of luxury before metals came into the laborsaving picture.

Metals are usually combinations of elements, lustrous in native form, opaque, often heavy, ductile or malleable—so that they can be melted by heat, drawn, or hammered into various shapes—and capable of conducting heat and electrical current.

Human imagination can hardly picture the origins of metals, and indeed a human being would hardly have lasted in a ringside seat while the processes were going on. Great outpourings of molten volcanic rock were pushing and bubbling out over the surface of this planet. Other masses trying to get out of the interior were forcing the rock crust apart and filling up the cracks. Volcanic waters and vapors were released. Saturated with metallic elements in solution, these waters in contact with other waters, air, and material masses set up violent chemical reactions from which the metals were assembled and deposited to cool over the ages. Through countless millions of years the metals which now serve humanity, from fountain pens all the way to diesel locomotives, were formed without the help or cooperation of men, and men cannot add to the total supply.

Metals as a natural resource are irreplaceable. (Plastics, fiber glass, concrete, and wood can be substituted for them, but only in limited uses.) They cannot be managed for sustained yield in the manner applicable to forests or wild animals. Many cannot even be captured for human use at reasonable expense and effort. In use they are frequently destroyed and consumed in prodigal quantities. It is important to remember, however, that the greatest opportunity for conserving metals is at the stage of use, for in the uses of greatest volume some of the metals are recoverable for "secondary" use. Indeed scrap recovery is depended upon to a considerable extent to keep the steel mills of the country operating. Table 12-1 indicates examples of uses from which metals may or may not be recovered. Table 12-2 shows the domestic supply position for selected minerals.

Usually a metal, whether it is an alloy or not, is named for the principal element in its make-up, and the same is true of the natural-resource form or the ore in which it occurs. One of the old and commonly

TABLE 12-1. SELECTED USES OF METALS—
RECOVERABLE AND IRRECOVERABLE

Recoverable	Irrecoverable—relatively or wholly
Iron:	
Construction	Paints
Transportation	War
Tools	Chemicals
Copper:	
Electrical equipment	Paints and sprays
Automobiles	War
Miscellaneous alloys and utensils	Chemicals
Lead:	
Construction	Paints and sprays
Miscellaneous alloys and utensils	Ammunition
Electrical equipment	Chemicals
	Gasoline mixtures
Zinc:	
Miscellaneous alloys and utensils	Paints
	Galvanizing
	Chemicals
Gold:	
Coinage	Paints and leaf
Jewelry	Drugs
Objects of art	Stained glass
	Dentistry
Silver:	
Photography	Plating and leaf
Coinage	Dentistry
Objects of art	Surgery

used classifications is "major" and "minor," based on volume of use, indispensability, and value, or some combination of these characteristics. The major metals, thus, are listed as iron, copper, lead, zinc, gold, and silver. The minor metals are all the others, of which aluminum, manganese, and platium are examples. Recently, however, two writers have listed as major metals iron, manganese, aluminum, copper, lead, and zinc, on the basis of tonnage. Of course, in such a listing, gold and silver are omitted.[1] Still another way of classifying emphasizes the "light" metals, although "heavy" is not so frequently applied to those such as iron, gold, and lead. The light metals include aluminum and magnesium as examples. The metals also appear in the total mineral classification as "basic," which includes only coal, iron, and copper, and "contributory," covering all other minerals.

[1] Bruce C. Netschert, and Hans H. Landsberg, The Future Supply of the Major Metals, Resources for the Future, Inc., Washington, D.C., 1961.

In Table 12-1, only the major metals are included, and these will be discussed one by one adding manganese and aluminum. Occurrence and use will be taken up under each.

IRON

Because of its strength, hardness, malleability, availability, and numerous other distinctive qualities, iron is considered the most useful of all metals. Certainly it represents the greatest volume of use in cruder forms and in its highly processed form as steel. Ore production totals more than 100 times that of copper, the next metal in terms of tonnage produced. Total domestic reserves of "commercial" iron ore, which means material considered usable under present economic and technologic conditions, as of 1955, were estimated by the United States Geological Survey at about 6 billion short tons. Production in 1962 amounted to around 79 million tons, and it is likely that by 1975, at which time the President's Materials Policy Commission believes consumption will be more than doubled, this reserve will be reduced at least a fourth. On the basis of this kind of arithmetic, the reserves within the United States would keep industry supplied for about 40 years. Imports, however, from Venezuela, Liberia, and the Quebec-Labrador area will no doubt increase significantly. Also, to the extent that lower-grade domestic ores can be "beneficiated," or raised in quality, by concentration and other procedures, imported ores will have to compete with them as additions to the domestic reserve. Finally, there is the chance that increased scrap recovery and reuse will affect the rate at which reserves are exhausted.

Occurrence and Ownership of Iron Resources. Iron ore occurs in five great districts in the United States: (1) Lake Superior with 47+ per cent of ore of better than 50 per cent iron content;[2] (2) Northeastern, with 17+ per cent of ore of 60 per cent iron content; (3) Southeastern, with 25 per cent of 35 per cent ore; (4) Southern, with 1+ per cent of 45 per cent ore; (5) and Western, with 9+ per cent of 50 per cent ore.

Iron is mined in all these districts at present, some thirty-six mines each producing more than 1 million tons of crude ore annually. More than three-quarters of the production comes from open-pit mines, where the overburden is removed and the ore taken out by shovel.

In general, iron deposits are privately owned in the United States, and the important deposits are practically all controlled by large corporations. This fact is significant so far as any public regulation of iron mining is concerned. Various state and Federal tax laws are generally favorable to the industry and constitute the only means at present by which conserva-

[2] Does not include low-grade taconite ore which at present is considered of commercial quality when concentrated.

tion practices may be required by the public. (The Mineral Leasing Law of 1920 does not cover the removal of metallic ore deposits from the public domain.)

Conserving Iron Resources. Relatively few people are in the iron business, but practically everyone uses iron. Large-scale conservation efforts will have to be made by the industry and the industrial manufacturers of iron products. This will occur only, however, with the demand and the cooperation of the public. The following list of ways in which iron may be conserved as a resource may seem to involve only the industries, but the attitude of the ultimate user is important in every one.

IMPROVED MINING Although there is need in underground mining to leave pillars of ore for safety, as in coal mining, the losses in recovery from this angle are less important than might be supposed. Recovery in general is good, and open-pit mining represents real conservation at the mining stage (Fig. 12-1). It is also the method by which most of the mining is done. Mechanization as a means of reducing the cost of mining will make possible better total ore recovery as well, including lower grades.

BENEFICIATION Improving the grade of ore by crushing, washing, and sizing; mechanical removal of rocks of varying sizes; magnetic separation of ore from impurities; mixing low- and high-grade ores; and sintering, or pelletizing, to suitable physical character for blast furnaces are known as beneficiation practices. In the sintering process, fine material is pressed into larger sizes (Fig. 12-2). The effect of these procedures is to increase the iron content of the ore and adapt it otherwise to form and concentra-

figure 12-1
Railroad approach to an open-pit iron mine on the Mesabi Iron Range near Hibbing, Minnesota. (Photo by U.S. Bureau of Mines.)

figure 12-2
Mill for beneficiating iron ore. The "jasper" iron ore, mined by
open-pit method at the Republic Mine, Marquette County, Mich.,
is finely ground to liberate the hematite (iron ore) from the silica
impurity. It is then concentrated by flotation to produce a high-
grade iron-ore concentrate. (Michigan Department of Conservation.)

tions which will permit economic shipment and use. Thirteen plants
existing or under construction in the United States have a pelletizing
capacity of 28 million tons annually (Fig. 12-3). Investigations of the
flotation process have recently been reported in the experimental treatment of low-grade taconite ore. In this process, finely ground ore is
treated with water and chemicals to produce a froth in which the metal
is captured and by which much of the inert material may be discarded.
Thus another beneficiation process promises successful treatment of iron
ore, just as it is now used to treat copper and zinc ores.

SCRAP RECOVERY AND USE   Unlike the mineral fuels, iron can be used
as secondary material or scrap. So important has this practice become in
steel manufacture that in 1954 and in several previous years more scrap
than pig iron (the crude product of smelting iron ore) was used. Price
has much to do with collection, since the small dealer who collects farm
and household scrap can operate only when demand is high and the
price good. The so-called "home scrap" is that which accumulates at the
plants using scrap as opposed to that which is purchased, and is, of
course, an important part of the total used. Industrial scrap from chemical
and other industries is also important. Wartime interest in scrap collection not only helped the industry and the defense effort but cleaned up

a lot of local dumps and eyesores. Consumption of iron and steel scrap in the United States in 1962 amounted to almost 18 million short tons.

The individual can make some contribution here to the conservation of iron by seeing to it that worn-out articles are routed to junk dealers. Even the community scrap drive is a conservation stroke.

MAINTAINING THE LIFE OF MANUFACTURED ARTICLES   Again unlike the mineral fuels, iron can be "capitalized" in the sense of being manufactured into useful form and, with good care, made to serve longer and more efficiently. Of course in an expanding economy, styling and improvement (real and claimed) keep people continually buying replacements and scrapping good equipment. This makes "business" and is one

Pellets of beneficiated iron ore. The concentrate produced at the mill shown in Fig. 12-2 is too fine to be used in the furnaces; so it is agglomerated into pellets at another plant. The fine concentrate, mixed with coal, is rolled into small balls, fired on a traveling grate, and formed into hard pellets which will stand shipment without breakage. These pellets have a desirable structure for furnace feed and an iron content of more than 60 per cent. (Michigan Department of Conservation.)

figure 12-3

of the wasteful practices which Americans, above all people, justify in the names of progress. But good care of steel articles, from the kitchen knife to the farm tractor, is still good iron conservation. Various coatings to prevent rust include paints, tarlike coatings, gun-metal finish applied by superheated-steam processes, greasing of tools in storage, and finally galvanizing. (The latter process, by which iron is coated with zinc, is questionable as a conservation practice, since zinc is relatively scarce.)

IMPROVING USEFULNESS BY ALLOYS Hardening, toughening, and otherwise improving the serviceability of iron manufactured into steel has long been practiced and results frequently in making one ton of steel do the work of two. Manganese, tungsten, molybdenum, nickel, and vanadium are examples of metals added to iron for these purposes, manganese being required in greatest volume. Conservation of iron by these practices also makes imperative the conserving of the alloy materials themselves (Fig. 12-4).

SUBSTITUTION OF REPLACEABLE AND MORE ABUNDANT MATERIALS FOR IRON IN USE Wood, stone, concrete, clay production, and plastics all serve well in many uses to which iron and steel are now put. Poles, bridge and derrick timbers treated for durability, roof trusses, industrial-office and home furniture, laminated and plywood structural members are often available and serviceable as substitutes for iron and steel, and the materials used in their manufacture can be grown in continuous supply on the soil. Stone and concrete with iron reinforcement are practically indestructible and relatively plentiful as original or fabricated natural-resource materials. Their use in bridge and building construction in place of steel is good engineering and good conservation. Brick, tile, and pipe as clay products are frequently as useful if not so convenient as steel. Glass during World War II was used in place of tin-plated steel for food containers. Plastics, many of which are made from fiber or very plentiful natural materials, are common in utensils, automobile accessories, and even construction. All these substitutions can extend our reserves of iron but probably will not if the salesman of iron and steel products can help it. Conservation by substitution therefore conflicts directly with our competitive system. In emergency periods, substitution can be brought about by rationing.

FURTHER DISCOVERY AND IMPORTATION These two lines of action are mentioned together because they amount to alternatives to conserving our present known national iron resources and are not conservation procedures in themselves. While little is heard of exploration for new iron deposits in the United States, such explorations are under way. Rich deposits have attracted American capital for both exploration and development in Liberia, Venezuela, and the Quebec-Labrador area particularly. Iron ore from these localities will be water-borne to this coun-

figure 12-4

White-hot steel pours like water from a 35-ton electric furnace at the plant of the Allegheny Ludlum Steel Corporation, Brackenridge, Pa. The finest-quality steels and alloys are produced in these furnaces which allow much greater control of temperature than other conversion furnaces. Although this process is the most expensive, the proportion of electric-furnace steel is rising steadily. The furnace is tilted for the pouring. (Photo by U.S. Bureau of Mines.)

try, and the Quebec-Labrador development has influenced the completion of the St. Lawrence Seaway. Principal imports of iron ore, up to the present, have come from Canada, to which neighbor exports have also been generous.[3] Thus the United States in terms of its iron industry

[3] It would seem that the 1939 export of more than 3½ million tons of scrap iron, at least half of which went to Japan, was good *business* but not good conservation or good national-defense policy

has found global self-sufficiency the answer to impending national scarcity of iron resources. It should be remembered that the President's Materials Policy Commission sees a 73 per cent increase in demand for iron ore over 1950 consumption by the time 1970–1990 is reached.

COPPER

One of the earliest metals captured for the use of mankind, copper has become an indispensable industrial material if, indeed, only in terms of the electrical and automobile industries. But copper finds outlet in thousands of articles and conveniences, from tea kettles to poison sprays. It is used in both the "capitalized" and wasting senses, as indicated by examples in Table 12-1. Scrap recovery is high, use as an alloy metal is important, and its place in the chemical industry is well established. Copper also is a national-defense necessity. Although it occurs as almost pure metal in occasional deposits, its recovery from ores is expensive, and such economic perplexities as depression in the mining industry occasioned by the recovery of too much competing scrap are not unknown. In the late 1930s the United States became a net copper-importing nation, and since that time, consumption has not been met by production of domestic ores. Consumption for the year 1950 was estimated in this country as 3.6 per cent of its known reserves. In terms of world production, the United States dropped from 54 per cent in 1910 to 25 per cent in 1954.

Occurrence and Ownership of Copper Resources. Copper deposits occur in twenty-nine states. Mine production in 1962 found Arizona in the lead, with 52 per cent of the total for the country. Utah ranked second with 18 per cent; Montana, New Mexico, Nevada, and Michigan came next in the order given and accounted collectively for 25 per cent. Thus these six states produced 95 per cent of the 1962 total. Alaska, California, Colorado, Washington, and Idaho are also steady, if relatively small, producers. The fact that more than 80 per cent of the copper ore produced in 1962 came from open-pit mines gives some indication of its occurrence with respect to depth. The ores frequently yield other metals such as silver, zinc, and lead. The treatment of the ores for concentration is common near the mines, and the richer ores are often smelted directly. Copper occurs widely throughout the world, and imports come from a dozen or more countries, of which Canada, Chile, Cyprus, Northern Rhodesia, and the Republic of South Africa are among the most important.

Conserving Copper Resources. The growing deficit in consumption over production of copper in the United States presents a need for conservation which is at present somewhat clouded by a generous world production, and yet there are plenty of opportunities to extend our domestic reserves through conservation practices. The industry is alive to most of these. They may be listed as follows:

IMPROVED RECOVERY IN MINING The efficiency and thoroughness of copper mining is a credit to the industry so far as recovery is concerned. The very fact, previously noted, that most of the ore comes from open-pit mines would indicate that loss is thus avoided. Underground recovery also has generally been high, and increased mechanization offers the principal chance for improvement in cost of recovery.

TREATMENT AND USE OF PROGRESSIVELY LEANER ORES Because the percentage of copper in many ores is very low (from 0.55 in some Michigan deposits to 2.04 in certain of those in California), the treatment of ores to produce concentrates is common at the mines. Flotation (described on page 354) is one of the important concentration methods (Fig. 12-5). In 1954 the amazing figure of 95.7 per cent of the material smelted was made up of concentrates. Less than 5 per cent was considered rich enough ore for direct smelting. A small amount was recovered by leaching, a process whereby water is run through the ore and copper obtained from the drip. Ore with as small a copper content as 0.8 per cent is mined economically at present, whereas in 1880 only a content of 3.0 per cent was considered usable.[4] Smelting also frequently takes place at the mining centers and by various methods has become very efficient. It should be mentioned here that copper mining and treatment of the ores constitute anything but conservation of space and landscape. Smelter fumes which kill vegetation, and which may be treated to some extent

[4] O. C. Herfindahl, Copper Costs and Prices, 1870–1957, The Johns Hopkins Press, Baltimore, 1960.

Flotation cells in a copper concentrator in the Western United States. (Photo by U.S. Bureau of Mines.)

figure 12-5

for by-products, are still an air-pollution problem. Slag and other waste products are ugly, disorderly, and space-requiring. Open mining pits are useless when abandoned—ugly and unavoidable.

RECOVERY FROM MINING WASTES Two forms of mining waste offer opportunities for reworking and thus recovering additional copper. The terms "tailings" and "stamp sands" are encountered in local and statistical jargon. The former are rock dumps in which some copper-bearing waste occurs, and the latter consist of finer wastes from the mills where ore is crushed for concentration. When price incentives are sufficient, these materials can be made to yield significant amounts of copper.

SCRAP RECOVERY In many uses the manufactured copper either in relatively pure or alloy form is easy to recover, and the scrap business is of real importance as a conservation measure. Sometimes the recovered material is used in the alloyed form, but in terms of copper content slightly more than one-half of the total copper produced in 1962 was "secondary" from scrap. Here is an opportunity, as with all metals, for the individual to help by seeing that discarded copper articles reach the scrap dealers. Strangely enough, however, our copper economy is so delicately rigged that the appearance of too much scrap in any one year has had the effect of depressing the mining industry.

ALLOCATING COPPER TO ITS HIGHEST USES In time of war the citizens and the industries accept a measure of rationing applied to scarce and strategic materials. In peacetime such rationing or allocation would be considered something of a persecution, and yet copper in an insect spray is conceivably a more important use than copper in an object of art. The first destroys the copper in use, the second "capitalizes" it. On the other hand a copper paint or coating is a less essential use than copper in bombs and shells stockpiled for future national defense. Both are wasting uses. Finally, copper for wiring and for equipping diesel locomotives and ships could easily be proved more important than copper for roofing. Both of these are "capitalizing" uses. Theoretically, public action to ration or allocate copper equitably to various uses is good conservation. If this kind of rationing became practiced in the future, it could lead to the development of substitutes. Steel shell cases for military use are examples of such substitutes.

NEW DISCOVERIES AND IMPORTS As observed in the instance of other mineral needs, filling them by new discovery and, more particularly, by imports will extend total domestic reserves but can hardly be termed conservation, save in the sense of equitable distribution both among the present nations of the globe and between the present and future generations. Both discovery and imports, however, are important, and although discovery in this country has been mainly contiguous to present workings, American capital has figured significantly in foreign discoveries.

Imports have been necessary from the time of World War II and will probably be unavoidable in the future. These imports are, of course, *net*, exports being considered in reporting them.

The Outlook for Copper Supply. In spite of the prediction of an increased demand of 43 per cent by 1970–1980 over the 1950 consumption of copper exclusive of scrap in this country and with importation, new discovery, or the more drastic moves of rationing and special allocation as the assumed remedies for shortage, copper-supply policy amounts to no definite policy at present. These and other findings of the President's Materials Policy Commission need to be made known to the people of this country and by them to the policy makers.[5]

LEAD

From the lead-plate cushion under a great skyscraper to give it certain qualities of stability in spite of motion, to the hundreds of tons of lead blown wastefully into the air from the tetraethyl motor fuel, lead appears to be indispensable in the modern world. It has served mankind as metal in ammunition, bearings, alloys in brass and bronze, storage batteries, pipe, cable covering, and type. In pigments it is well known in white and red lead and as a base in blended colors. In chemicals it appears in drugs, sprays, and tetraethyl fluid for gasoline. Miscellaneous uses include galvanizing, lead plating, and ballast. Because of its versatility, reduction of use in one direction—plumbing, for example—is replaced by increase of use in a new field such as sprays, batteries, and gasoline.

The bottom of the barrel seems to be in sight with regard to domestic reserves of lead. The 1950 domestic production amounted to 6 per cent of the known reserves. Net imports have always been large and in 1962 amounted to more than one-half of the total consumption.

Occurrence and Ownership of Lead Resources. Lead is mined in eighteen states, the highest production occurring in ten Western states. The West Central states come next, with Missouri leading, and those east of the Mississippi constitute a poor third (Fig. 12-6). By individual states Missouri, Idaho, Utah, and Colorado are in the lead and account for 85 per cent of the 1962 mine production, 237,000 short tons. Lead is often found in ores containing zinc, copper, gold, or silver in various combinations. On a world basis the United States, Canada, Mexico, and Australia have accounted for nearly three-fourths of the world output in recent years. Lead is mined, however, in thirty-one countries. Deposits in this country are practically all in private ownership, and should an important deposit be discovered on public lands, no policy except passing it into private hands exists.

[5] The fact that production exceeded demand in 1962 would not have occurred except for considerable imports.

figure 12-6
Lead-zinc mine in Missouri. A mechanical shovel loads ore from one level, a locomotive works at a higher level, and drillers sink blast holes from a catwalk up near the roof. (Photo by U.S. Bureau of Mines.)

Conserving Lead Resources. Perhaps the greatest difficulty in conserving lead resources lies in the irrecoverable uses to which it is put. Mining and separation from other metals and rock wastes are highly developed. In our economy, price affects mining and smelting procedures considerably, and only as imports may become more difficult and prices higher will the more radical conservation practices be adopted. Hopeful signs, however, are the reworking of chert rock dumps for lead-bearing materials; the general use of flotation for better recovery of lead in ores more valuable for copper, zinc, and silver; and the recovery of secondary lead from storage batteries, metal articles, and gun-club areas. Substitution of titanium and barium for lead in pigments is increasing.

The Future of Lead Resources. Lead is classified under the heading of Known Economic Reserves Inadequate by the President's Materials Policy Commission, and it is noted that although geological discoveries are likely, they are not necessarily predicted to be adequate. As in the case of copper, our alternative appears to lie in heavy importation which may or may not be good global conservation. Certainly any economic procedure that will extend our domestic reserves should be a definite part of a so-far-lacking national mineral policy.

ZINC

Galvanizing, which is a process for coating iron electrolytically or by dipping it into molten zinc to protect it from rust, has long been the principal use of zinc and has made it almost indispensable. Brass, which is an alloy of copper and zinc, and the so-called zinc-base alloys used in dies and die castings constitute the second use in volume. Other uses include rolled zinc for fabrication of many articles; zinc oxide, used in paints and as a drug; wet batteries; removing silver from lead; light-metal alloys; and many miscellaneous small uses such as fertilizer, and zinc chloride for the preservative treatment of timber. In most of these uses the zinc is irrecoverable, and domestic reserves are being reduced at the rate of about 8 per cent a year. Discovery of new deposits is likely but not sure, and reserves are inadequate for technological needs for the remainder of this century. Deposits of economic importance occur in some twenty-four states of the union, the heaviest production coming from twelve Western states, with Idaho and Montana in the lead. New York, Oklahoma, New Jersey, Colorado, and Utah also figure prominently in the zinc-production picture. Among the other countries of the world Mexico, Canada, and Peru are leading zinc producers.

New zinc deposits are being developed in Nevada and New Mexico which may add appreciably to reserves, and from March, 1954 to July 1, 1962 the Defense Minerals Exploration Administration had subsidized the search for lead and zinc through exploration contracts. About the

TABLE 12-2. DOMESTIC SUPPLY POSITION OF
SELECTED MINERAL MATERIALS

Known economic reserves adequate for well over 25 years.

Magnesium	Lime	Gypsum
Molybdenum	Salt	Borax
Coal	Sand	Barite
Phosphate	Clay	Feldspar
Potash		

Known economic reserves inadequate

Discoveries geologically likely—though not necessarily adequate:

Copper	Vanadium	Petroleum
Lead	Tungsten	Natural gas
Zinc	Antimony	Sulfur
Uranium		

Beneficiation progress expected:

Iron	Beryllium	Fluorine
Aluminum	Thorium	Graphite
Titanium	Oil from shale	

Synthesis progress expected:

Oil from coal	Gas from coal

Little or no known economic reserves, significant discoveries not expected

Beneficiation progress expected:
    Manganese

Synthesis progress expected:

Industrial diamonds	Quartz crystals
Sheet mica	Asbestos

Significant beneficiation or synthesis not expected:

Chromium	Tin	Platinum
Nickel	Cobalt	Mercury

Source: Resources for Freedom, vol. I, Report of the President's Materials Policy Commission, 1952.

only other means of extending domestic reserves would be the more general use of substitutes for zinc now employed in galvanizing. More plentiful paints, tarlike compounds, and "gun-metal" finishes offer possibilities, but because they would hurt an established business and are less serviceable, their increasing use is unlikely.

Some zinc scrap is recovered, and reuse of this material is of course good conservation. Only a little less than half as much secondary zinc was produced from scrap and chemical compounds in 1962 as the amount produced from mines in the United States.

Importation seems to be the only sure course ahead to provide adequate supplies of zinc.

GOLD

Because of its scarcity, beauty, resistance to corrosion, and other distinctive characteristics, gold has served throughout the ages as a standard of value and, until recent years, was not only minted into coin but widely used for that purpose. Compared with other major metals in terms of total resources, usefulness, and indispensability, the world would perhaps miss it less than any. On the other hand, industrial consumption has recently assumed considerable importance, and use in the arts increased rapidly during World War II. Also, while much of the supply has been allocated to monetary use, this portion of the supply is in the form of government stockpiles from which it may be released to industry and the arts without smelter or refinery preparation. New applications of gold in the electronic industry and in various components of missiles and space vehicles, such as Mariner and Telstar, continue to increase. Here the high electric conductivity, superior resistance to corrosion, and high reflectivity of heat and light are the qualities sought in the use of gold. In 1962 the net consumption by industry and the arts totaled almost twice as much as the new gold produced from domestic mines. The actual net industrial consumption amounted to about 3.6 million ounces. The use of gold in the arts goes far back in history. In modern times, high marriage rate and generally high wages have created a heavy demand for gold articles along with other luxuries. Gold has long been used in dentistry, and recently its compounds have come to be used in medicine, notably in the treatment of arthritis. Gold leaf on the domes of public buildings and in the window signs of prosperous business and professional firms seems to do a lot for morale, but these uses are neither essential nor large in volume. The outflow of gold, resulting from the continued balance-of-payments deficit and conversion-of-dollar credits by foreign central banks, reduced the United States gold stock in 1962 about 900 million dollars to 16.1 billion dollars, the lowest level since 1939. This interesting metal, however, is not only a symbol but an economic good and should be conserved.

Gold occurs in nineteen of the states. In order of production the rank is South Dakota, Utah, Alaska, and California. Among the Eastern states, Pennsylvania, Tennessee, North Carolina, and Georgia produce small amounts.

Gold occurs in gravel deposits and in underground ore deposits usually with quartz, both alone or with copper, silver, lead, or zinc. It is mined as "placer" when free gold is washed from the gravel using hydraulic methods, or dredge which also treats the gravels (Fig. 12-7), and as ore which must be crushed for various separation procedures. The Utah production comes largely as a by-product from the mining of copper ore in the West Mountain (Bingham) district. Recovery is generally high.

figure 12-7

Bucket-line gold dredge in the Fairbanks district in Alaska.
(Photo by U.S. Bureau of Mines.)

Gold resources may be conserved principally in the utilization stage. Mining requires little improvement, and if there is more gold to be found, the age-old incentive to quick wealth will keep the prospectors hunting. Scrap recovery is well organized, and gold in "capitalized" form, particularly in the arts and in coinage, is subject to little wear. "Seniorage," which is loss from wear of coinage in use, has been taken care of by the Federal withdrawal of gold coin from circulation. Losses from ship sinking, hoarding, and the death and burial of people will generally have to be written off.

The release of stockpiled gold by Federal authorities for use in industry and the arts gives a measure of control and represents good conservation.

SILVER

Although used and valued to some extent in the same manner as gold, silver has a much wider industrial use and is actually generally in circulation as coinage. Its bid for a place among the major metals calls to attention its indispensability in the photographic industry. It is also indispensable as surgical material and finds considerable use in dentistry. An increase in United States industrial consumption in 1962 came from the metal joining, electrical, and electronic industries, as a result of uses for both defense and civilian products. Consumption of silver for United States coinage rose sharply, reflecting continued growth in the use of coin-operated vending machines. Like gold, silver has been used in objects of art since before written history.

Silver is produced in twenty-four of the states, including Alaska. The principal producers rank as follows in order of volume: Idaho, Utah, Montana, Arizona, and Colorado. Among the Eastern states Tennessee, Vermont, Michigan, and Pennsylvania are interesting producers but of little importance. Silver occurs in various ores and is a by-product at many mines from the recovery of copper, zinc, and lead. Output of recoverable silver from domestic mines in 1962 showed an increase of 6 per cent to 36.8 million ounces and was exceeded only by that of Mexico. The United States accounted for about half the total silver consumed in the industries and coinage of the free world. Neither silver nor gold were included in the studies of the President's Materials Policy Commission of 1952.

The most promising conservation measure for silver is recovery from industrial and other uses. Significant amounts are now salvaged from motion-picture and other photographic film, and silver scrap is important in the scrap-metal market. Mining and treating methods are generally efficient. Seniorage, or wear, is high on silver coins, and in the event of severe shortage some saving could be made here by larger issue of paper currency. This, however, would hardly be necessary unless some rationing to the luxury industries had first been explored. Silver is an important material and should not be wasted.[6]

ALUMINUM

Following the six major metals, aluminum assumes importance in terms of volume used and growing acceptance. Much of this importance arises from its use in building and in the transportation industries because of its high strength-weight ratio and convenience in handling. Power cable, foil for insulation and packaging, and even experimental gas pipeline represent other rapidly developing uses. Consumption by the automobile industry is reported to have risen to around 70 pounds per vehicle in 1962. More than 50 per cent of United States automobiles in 1962 were finished with paints that contained aluminum pigments, and aluminum-coated steel sheets were utilized in the exhaust systems of around 90 per cent of all cars. Bridge rail, barges for water transportation of chemicals, beverage cans, and small appliances accounted for a considerable amount of the use of the 1962 production. Also, in November, 1949, aluminum was added to the list of strategic materials for stockpiling. In many of these uses, excluding foil and paints, the material is recoverable, and strangely enough aluminum scrap is an important item of export. In total consumption the United States is a net importing nation.

[6] As this book goes to the printer, laminated quarter-dollars with copper cores have come into circulation in response to suggestions by President Lyndon B. Johnson.

While aluminum is widely distributed in the clays of the United States, it occurs commercially as bauxite in the form of ore principally in Arkansas, Alabama, Georgia, and Virginia; 1962 production in terms of dried ore was 2,184,876 short tons. Reserves of economically recoverable ore on the same basis were estimated in 1958 by the Bureau of Mines and the Geological Survey at 50 million long tons. Other abundant world sources are Hungary, the Gold Coast, and British Guiana. Certain deposits in Haiti and in Jamaica are promising, with three companies producing. Little is heard about further domestic discovery or the use of lower-grade ores.

Conservation of domestic aluminum resources includes reduction of waste in beneficiation plants and general improvement of beneficiation methods to make possible the use of leaner ores. Cheaper and more abundant power will also make possible the reduction of leaner ones. Scrap recovery is a possibility for increased conservation, although war losses are high and will again be high if there are great wars in the future. Eventually the United States will probably depend even more fully on imports.

THE MINOR METALS

Manganese. Because of its service in steel manufacture, i.e., counteracting the sulfur and oxygen in iron ores and producing changes as an alloy which improves steel quality, manganese is a most important strategic material. It might well be considered one of the major metals. More than 96 per cent of the domestic consumption goes into the metal-manufacturing industries. On the other hand only 10 per cent of the total amount consumed in 1949 was produced by domestic mines, and this proportion had not improved up to 1962. Other important uses of manganese include manufacture of dry battery cells and use in chemicals. Domestic ores vary widely in manganese content, and of the meager production hardly any contain the 48 per cent of metallic manganese desirable as a major proportion of furnace charges of ore. Blending the domestic low grades with high-grade imported ores to manufacture ferromanganese alloys or progress in beneficiation of domestic ores before shipment appear to be the only ways that their quality can be made sufficient for use in steel manufacture. As long as foreign ores are readily available, the United States will depend upon them. Brazil, Mexico, the Gold Coast of Africa, and India are the main sources of imports. The U.S.S.R. also has generous deposits. Montana, Minnesota, and Arkansas are the largest domestic producers. There is considerable speculation concerning generous amounts of high-manganese-content nodules obtainable from ocean floors when recovery methods can be worked out.

Conservation of manganese resources cannot gain from use of substitutes because, so far, none have been developed as steel processing materials. Mining recovery and by-product recovery from slags and from treatment of zinc ores is good. Even better recovery from slags is possible if costs can be lowered. This leaves beneficiation of low-grade domestic ores as the most promising future conservation measure. Severe emergency might be expected to force such practice and also to promote "ocean mining."

Tin. Domestic production, including that of Alaska, is less than 1 per cent of domestic consumption. Solder, automobiles, tin-plated food packages, and various alloys depend upon an adequate supply. In the years 1940 to 1944, almost one-eighteenth of the amount of tin consumed in this country came from secondary material recovered from saved scrap which was handled by detinning plants. The average consumption of tin per year for the period 1953–1957 in the United States was about 86,000 long tons, while production from domestic mines was less than 9 per cent of this figure. Production figures since that time are unavailable. For this scarce and versatile metal, it is not easy to find satisfactory substitutes, and while Alaska offers promise of future discovery and profitable development, the tiny production in the other states appears principally as a by-product of the mining of molybdenum in Colorado, copper in Nevada, and as one of the products of a rock known as pegmatite in South Dakota. Probably because cassiterite, the most common mineral of tin, is heavy and frequently occurs in pebble form, much of the tin mining is of the placer type, in which the pebbles are washed out of gravel deposits and shipped to smelters. The distinctive weight of this mineral may also account for the fact that it was easily separated and used by ancient peoples.

Specifically the uses of tin are confined almost entirely to six items: (1) tin plate, which is the material most people know as tin, and terneplate, a similar product plated with a tin-lead alloy; (2) solder for sealing tin-plate joints and used in other metalwork; (3) bronze, an alloy of copper and tin; (4) babbitt, a soft metal alloy used in plumbing and bearings; (5) tinning and type metal. These five accounted for 95 per cent of the consumption, and the remainder goes mostly into (6) tin chemicals. Manufactured tin imports come to the United States from fifteen countries, Malaya, Belgium-Luxembourg, Portugal, the Congo, China, and the United Kingdom ranking in order of volume. Three other countries supply tin concentrates for smelting in this country. These in order of volume are Bolivia, Indonesia, and Thailand. The low-content concentrates from Bolivia increased from the time of the opening of a federally owned smelter at Texas City in 1942, but the United States, always the heaviest consumer, smelts only 23 per cent of the world production of ore as against more than 50 per cent smelted by the British Empire and lesser amounts by the Netherlands, Belgium, and China. The Congress authorized the sale of the Texas City smelter in June, 1956.

Since tin is so essential and is, next to gold and silver, the most costly of the commonly used metals, its conservation is of first importance. So far little progress has been made in this direction. Three of the chances which need further research and study are the following: (1) Finding substitutes, in which aluminum for foil and collapsible tubes and glass for food packaging have already figured importantly, offers possibilities. Ironically enough the use of tin plate for beer cans and soft-drink cans has increased sharply over the traditional bottle long used and made of less essential materials. Just how the merchandising of lubricating oil in small tin-can units can be rationalized may well be considered also. Solders with less tin content than usual have been developed. (2) Improvement in concentrating low-grade ores has not kept pace with the treatment of such ores as copper and lead, and recovery from lode mines particularly can be greatly improved. (3) Wider adoption of the electrolytic plating process which uses less tin, for the product of equal serviceability, than the hot-dip method has good possibilities.

As far as new discovery is concerned, only Alaska appears to offer promise for the United States. Elsewhere, explorations in Malaya, Belgian Congo, and Bolivia are rumored to be encouraging.

Mercury. As the source of a detonating agent for explosives and as a material used in control instruments, mercury (quicksilver) was one of the seven minerals mentioned as "strategic" and listed for study by the Bureau of Mines in the Strategic Minerals Act of 1939.[7] Encouraging results have been obtained by these studies in terms of domestic occurrence and recovery possibilities. A slump in prices following World War II, however, put the United States back into the position of a heavy net importer, and this situation persisted through 1962 in spite of some recovery in price after 1950. Besides the two mentioned, mercury finds a number of other uses of which electrical apparatus, pharmaceuticals, agriculture (insecticides and disinfectants), paints, chemicals, and dental preparations are the leading ones.

Mercury occurs in a large number of minerals but is obtained only from cinnabar, a sulfide ore, worked early in some Western mines for the sulfur rather than the mercury. Domestic production comes from California, Oregon, Arizona, Arkansas, Idaho, and Alaska. Italy and Spain lead the world in production, and, with Mexico, they furnish the United States with the bulk of imports. Possibilities of conservation lie in making profitable the mining and treatment of low-grade domestic ores and

---

[7] The others were antimony, chromium, manganese, nickel, tin, and tungsten. The list now includes more than fifty.

promoting the use of substitutes for dental and antiseptic uses and for paints. Porcelain, sulfa drugs, and base paints using other metals are respective examples of such substitutes now finding considerable favor.

Nickel. Resistance to corrosion and usefulness in hardening, toughening, and strengthening steel make nickel indispensable even though almost the entire amount used in the United States must be imported. The steels containing nickel are especially adapted to use under high-temperature conditions such as are obtained in jet engines. Such nickel as is domestically produced comes as a by-product of smelting copper ores. Formerly, also, small amounts of nickel ore were obtained as a by-product of talc production. A considerable amount of nickel is also recovered from scrap, but the total domestic production is hardly a tenth of what is required. That from primary sources is considerably less than 1 per cent. Fortunately a friendly neighbor to the north, Canada, is the world's heaviest producer, and the United States is its top customer, taking about one-half the 237,044 short tons total production. At the rate of consumption in 1962, these Canadian deposits are estimated to last for about 40 to 50 years. Another source of imports is New Caledonia.

Conserving nickel is largely confined to the ways in which it is used and reused. Technology is well advanced, but satisfactory substitutes are so far not available except in some plating procedures and in the limited use of molybdenum.

Molybdenum. Abundant in the United States, indispensable in the manufacture of molybdenum steel and gray iron, and serving as a substitute for certain scarce alloy metals, molybdenum has been used increasingly since World War I. It is particularly valuable in producing high-speed and stainless steels. In the latter it is used with chromium and nickel and may replace the scarcer tungsten. It is also used in steels subject to high temperatures in performance and so has become important in jet aircraft engines. Steel manufacture employs about five-sevenths of the 35 million pounds total consumption, the remainder finding outlet in the manufacture of gray iron, malleable castings, ceramics, and pigments; in chemical and electrical industries; and in a small but effective use as fertilizer.

Molybdenum occurs with other metals—notably tungsten, copper, gold, and silver—principally as molybdenite, of which there are large deposits in Colorado and New Mexico. Copper mines in Utah, Arizona, New Mexico, and Nevada yield molybdenum as a by-product, and the same is true of tungsten operations in California. Even at wartime rates of consumption, the reserves in the United States, which are the largest in the world, are estimated to last for several hundred years. Possible further discoveries are likely, and improvements in concentration methods of handling the ores offer good conservation opportunities. It is interesting to observe that this metal, which is abundant, is helping to replace tungsten and nickel, which are less plentiful, and is becoming a conserving agent in making iron more serviceable and durable in the form of high-speed alloy steels.

Tungsten. Because of its important but small-volume use in electric-lamp and radio-tube filaments and in fluorescent lamps, tungsten is somewhat better known popularly than other alloy materials. By far its greatest use, however, is in steel for cutting tools, automotive-valve steels, and special heat-resisting alloys employed in jet-propulsion devices, gun-barrel liners, and armor-piercing projectiles. Tungsten salts are used in tanning leather and, to some extent, in pigments. Tungsten occurs as *wolfram*, its crude mineral form, in various ores containing 0.5 to 2.5 per cent wolfram and is usually beneficiated to a 60 per cent shipping concentrate. Nevada is the leading domestic producer, followed by California, North Carolina and Colorado. Eleven other states produce smaller amounts. Reserves are considered inadequate. At the height of World War II in 1945, consumption reached more than 14 million pounds, but it had shrunk to about 5 million in 1949. By 1954 consumption stood at about 4 million pounds, domestic production at 13 million pounds, and imports at 23 million. This furnished generous amounts for government purchase and stockpiling. China, Burma, Portugal, Bolivia, and Korea are the principal foreign sources. Bringing the situation up to 1962, domestic production had increased for the third consecutive year and totaled 8.3 million pounds. Imports also increased but amounted to only 29 per cent of the tungsten consumed in the United States. As noted earlier, molybdenum, which is more plentiful than tungsten, serves to some extent as a substitute for it in steel manufacture. And although further discovery of deposits is predicted, importation and substitution will probably have to be resorted to in the future. It is encouraging, however, that nineteen certifications of discovery had resulted from the program of the Defense Minerals Exploration Administration by 1954.

Vanadium. Versatile and recoverable from numerous ores, flue dusts, asphalt-using industries, and also occurring as an ore, vanadium is so important strategically that information concerning it has been withheld in recent years for security reasons. It is a hard metal with a high melting point, and about 90 per cent of the domestic consumption goes into high-speed and other tool steels, other alloy steels, and into metal purification. The remainder is used principally in other metal alloys. Production is developed chiefly in Peru, the United States, South-West Africa, and Northern Rhodesia. Domestic ores are mined in Utah, Colorado, Nevada, and New Mexico. Small quantities of vanadium are recovered from the mining and treatment of phosphate rock, iron, uranium, and chrome ores and from processing bauxite for recovery of aluminum. As a result of greatly increased output of uranium ore on the Colorado Plateau in recent years, the production of by-product vanadium has exceeded industry requirements, and much of the surplus after treatment has been placed in the National Strategic Stockpile. Economic reserves, however, are inadequate, and conservation will probably take the direction of more thorough by-product recovery from known and potentially promising methods of metal processing.

Titanium. About 25 per cent of the 1962 production of metal mill products of titanium went into missiles and spacecraft. This metal is remarkable in its resistance to high temperatures, and in one Navy attack plane, it saved 300 pounds of weight when used in place of stainless steel (Fig. 12-8). Titanium alloys on a strength-to-weight basis are superior to steel or glass as potential materials for the construction of rocket motor cases. Titanium is also used widely as a pigment. Recovery of titanium metal scrap had increased measureably in the 1962 production of 10,000 tons of ingots.

Cobalt and beryllium are other alloy metals of which domestic resources are insufficient.

Platinum-group Metals. In spite of the fact that the jewelry trade has long been the principal outlet for platinum, a group of metals made up of palladium, osmium, osmiridium, rhodium, ruthenium, and iridium are

figure 12-8
Titanium metal, produced with techniques pioneered by the Bureau of Mines, was used in the framework and "skin" of the Mercury capsule's cabin, helping to shield astronauts from the high temperatures encountered in the frontiers of outer space. (Used by special permission of McDonnell Aircraft Corporation, courtesy of U.S. Bureau of Mines.)

also in demand for dental, medical, electrical, and chemical use. Most of them are recovered from other metallic ores, notably those of gold and copper. Alaska and California are the leading producers. (Gold, which has been heretofore discussed as a major metal, is sometimes included in this group.)

Uranium, Radium, and Thorium. Because it can be used for the manufacture of atomic bombs and has possibilities of extensive use for industrial power production, uranium is an important key to ruin or to the good life. At first its use for other than military purposes was largely confined to medicine, but by 1958 a number of power plants were being constructed to generate power from the heat produced by the release of atomic energy involving the use of uranium. One of the ores from which it is obtained is pitchblende, in which it is associated with other metals such as copper, bismuth, lead, cobalt, and silver. Carnotite, the domestic ore from which uranium is produced in the Colorado plateau, is associated with sandstone and low-grade material which has been identified in oil shales. Carnotite yields around 1 per cent uranium compounds, a similar percentage of vanadium, and much smaller amounts of radium. Data on reserves and rates of military use are, of course, for security reasons, unavailable. It is probable, however, that progressively leaner domestic ores will be tapped in the near future. Production and marketing throughout the world are generally in public control. In the United States the official body in control is the Atomic Energy Commission. More than 1,000 mines were producing uranium ores in 1962. Production for that year totaled more than 7 million short tons of ore. The leading state in production by far was New Mexico followed by thirteen other Western states and Texas. There were 190 nuclear reactors operable in the United States at the end of 1962.

Radium is used in the treatment of tumors and cancer, in the manufacture of luminous paint, and for exploring metal articles for defects. It is obtained from pitchblende and other uranium ores, and its production and conservation are linked with uranium.

Thorium, unlike uranium and radium, is obtained from a mineral known as monazite, occurring in certain sand and gravel deposits. Domestic deposits occur in gold-bearing gravels in Idaho and in sands of northeastern Florida. Thorium was formerly used principally in the manufacture of gas mantles and in ceramics. Its present value is its radioactivity, which makes possible its use with uranium to extend the supply of the latter. Throughout the world it is, of course, subject to the same public control as uranium. Whatever is done to exploit or to conserve these fissionable (multipliable in terms of energy) metals is a matter for which the public, in the form of its governments, cannot escape responsibility. So far little conservation activity or policy is evident.

NONFUEL NONMETALLIC MINERALS

Although most of the serious conservation problems in the mineral-resource field have to do with fuels and metals, other products, many of which are accepted as inexhaustible, pose problems of their own in conservation and in the interferences which their exploitation present to conserving other resources. Water pollution, scarred and disorderly landscape, and space requirements for waste materials are examples of these interferences. Use as substitutes for less plentiful materials, indispensability in the building trades and in the recovery and treating of natural fuels and metals, replacements for nutrient materials removed by crops, and medical and food-seasoning use are example of values demanding that the resources themselves be conserved.

In the following discussion only a few examples will be covered, and these will be chosen on the basis of the conservation problems which they raise. Uses will, of course, overlap in such broad groups as building materials, salts, abrasives, and refractories (heat- and corrosion-resisting materials).

BUILDING MATERIALS

Mineral building materials include sand and gravel; clays; special cement materials, such as limestone, shales, and marl; materials from which lime is prepared, including oystershell; gypsum; and the various special building stones, such as slate, granite, marble, sandstone, and limestone. Even in this breakdown there are several overlaps.

Sand and Gravel. Of all the earth's natural resources, sand and gravel would seem to be the least exhaustible and perhaps, with the exception of air, the most widely distributed. But there are actual instances of the "manufacture" of sand from massive sandstone to meet a scarcity of nearby supplies of natural sand, and crushed rock (Fig. 12-9) is a well-known manufactured product. Certain special sands for glass manufacture and foundry use must meet exacting specifications, and more than 90 per cent of all sand and gravel produced for commercial use requires special preparation. Moreover, because of the universal demand and the transportation expense, most of the sand and gravel is used locally. Widely distributed deposits are thus essential.

Aside from building, which is the largest use of sand and gravel combined, paving is the only other one that is at all comparable in volume (Fig. 12-10). Glass manufacture, molding (foundry), engine use, and grinding and polishing are typical uses of sand. Gravel, in addition to its use in building, is employed in paving and as railroad ballast.

Supply problems are less important in the sand and gravel picture than conservation conflicts which their exploitation brings about. Gravel

figure 12-9

Limestone quarry in Mackinac County, Mich. The product (dolomite) is used as a metallurgical flux stone by the United States Steel Corporation but is also suitable for road aggregate, agricultural lime, and many other industrial applications. The crusher plant used to reduce this stone has a capacity of 1,800 tons of crushed stone per operating hour. (Michigan Department of Conservation.)

Sandstone quarry of the Star Stone Company, at Napoleon, Mich. Stone for landscaping purposes is removed with minimum waste. (Michigan Department of Conservation.)

figure 12-10

pits are landscape scars, and seldom are they put to constructive space utilization after being worked out. Necessary washing operations and consequent siltation and gravel-waste pollution of streams have become subject to legislation in certain states. Ponds for the collection of "tailings" and finer wastes from aggregate works are in use to meet this conservation problem *of water.* Occasional efforts made to level, screen, or otherwise make gravel and sand pits eventually available for spatial use are on record. One Michigan city has a public stadium in a former gravel pit, and here and there one is used as a sanitary fill where city waste is buried and packed beyond the reach of rats, without danger to water supplies.

Other Minerals Used in Concrete Construction. As mentioned above, the natural materials used in manufacturing portland cement—the product which, with sand and gravel, supplies a vast construction industry with concrete—are limestone, cement rock,[8] clay or shale, and marl. Blast-furnace slag and fly ash are also used. These are all relatively plentiful, although not always distributed advantageously for local use. In order of volume consumed in cement manufacture, the materials rank as follows: limestone, clay, and shale combined, 72 per cent; cement rock and pure limestone, 22 per cent; blast-furnace slag and limestone, 4 per cent; and marl and clay, 2 per cent. The average weight of materials required to produce a barrel (376 pounds) or portland cement is 654 pounds, and the annual consumption amounts to about 70 million short tons. This includes small amounts of a dozen or more miscellaneous materials such as flue dust, calcium chloride, and grinding aids.

Except for reasonably full recovery and as an outlet for certain by-products of other industries, no program of conservation covers these important materials.

RESOURCES FROM WHICH LIME IS PRODUCED Because lime is cheap and widely useful and finds its greatest utility in building and in chemical and other industries, a word should be said here concerning the importance of limestone, marl, and oystershell, from which it is principally produced. As in the case of portland cement, adequate local deposits or supplies of these materials specifically available for making lime are desirable. Fourteen of the states produce the bulk of the lime sold and possess within their boundaries the largest deposits of the raw resources. Ohio, Pennsylvania, and Missouri lead in order of volume and account for more than one-half the production of manufactured lime annually. The total sold or used in the United States was more than 13.8 million short tons in 1962. Some of the uses for lime which are not generally known

---

[8] "Cement rock" is a term applied to rock containing adequate proportions of lime and other compounds for use in cement making. It is not so uniform or so "pure" as limestone.

include manufacture of glue, varnish, and rubber and the refining of petroleum, salt, and sugar. Two contributions which it makes to conservation of water are purification and prevention of pollution through treatment of sewage and trade wastes.

Clays. In addition to the common clays used in cement manufacture, which amount to 21 per cent of all clays produced, building requires a considerable proportion of the refractories (heat-resistant brick and tile), which consume 15 per cent of the clays produced, and practically all, except drain and sewer tile, of the heavy clay products such as common brick and tiles for walls, floors, and facing. (Aside from building, clays are important in pottery, rotary-drilling muds, coating paper, and filtering and decolorizing oil.) From a conservation viewpoint, clays are useful in treating scarcer natural-resource materials and in the manufacture of heavy products which may to some extent substitute for steel construction. Exploitation occasions little waste, but no particular conservation efforts are in force.

Building Stone. In their native form—unmanufactured save for shaping—sandstone, granite, marble, limestone, and slate are valuable building materials, used at one step from the natural-resource stage. Cut stones, slabs, and mill blocks (which include a small proportion of refractory stone) constitute their largest use, and their consumption amounts to more than 10 million cubic feet annually. In addition to structural efficiency, much of this stone is used for decoration and dignified effect, which no one would question as a cultural contribution, in public, religious, and business buildings and monuments.

Use of the various building stones in terms of tonnage and value and including other small-volume uses rank about as follows:

Tonnage	*Value*
1. Granite	1. Granite
2. Limestone	2. Marble
3. Sandstone	3. Limestone
4. Slate	4. Sandstone
5. Marble	5. Slate
6. Miscellaneous	6. Miscellaneous

Slate is produced in greatest volume in Vermont, Maine, New York, and Pennsylvania. Limestone for building comes from Indiana and Missouri chiefly. Granite in considerable amounts is quarried in some twenty-five states, the leading ones of which are Georgia, Massachusetts, Vermont, Pennsylvania, Maine, and North Carolina. Architectural sandstone is produced principally in Ohio, Pennsylvania, Tennessee, and New York, in the order given. Tennessee accounts for more than one-half the production of marble, followed by Arkansas, Maryland, and Colorado.

Miscellaneous building stone includes light-colored volcanic rock, mica schist, greenstone, and others, among which a large variety of local field stone is represented.

Conservation of building stone involves little that the ordinary citizen can do. On the other hand, those who quarry and merchandise this material have steadily improved exploitation practices in the general directions of *channeling*—which cuts and removes stone in shapes and sizes appropriate for use without wasteful dressing, instead of employing the older and more wasteful blasting practices—and of finding use for broken and small-sized material. The latter finds outlet as crushed stone in highway construction and in the production of concrete for many other construction purposes (Fig. 12-9). Quarrying is perhaps less likely to leave ugly landscape scars than the exploitation of sand, gravel, and other minerals; and quarries, with their clifflike walls and accumulations of water, have recreation and scenic potentialities which merit more attention from land-use planners.

ABRASIVES

An industrial nation such as the United States operates with sharp tools and minute measurements, and it could not do this without grinding, sharpening, drilling, and polishing materials. From the hand-operated grindstone of the colonial farm to the emery wheels and sanding belts and drums of today, emery, sand, other silicon-containing materials, corundum, garnet, pumice, and industrial diamonds have had to be found and prepared for abrasive duty.

Of the dozen natural abrasives produced domestically, ground sand and sandstone, pumice and pumicite (volcanic materials), and quartz lead in volume. All are abundant. Natural alumina abrasives include corundum and emery. The former is largely imported from South Africa; the latter is produced in relatively small amounts domestically, but is almost indispensable in such uses as saw sharpening. The most important natural carbon abrasive is the industrial diamond, of which the United States has no deposits but which are now being manufactured. Artificial abrasives made of silicon and aluminum compounds offer substitute possibilities. No other organized programs of conservation of the rarer abrasive materials are in force.

SALTS

Displaced ocean floors and ancient inland-lake beds have left numerous deposits of salts now considered indispensable to human welfare. Common salt, known to most people only as food seasoning; potash and phosphorus, thought of usually as fertilizing materials only; borax, "mineral-water" ingredients, and various drugs, used widely but taken for granted, form the natural-resource base for vast industries and a considerable world trade. Most of these resources are classified as "known reserves adequate" and require only brief consideration.

Common Salt. Although the world and domestic reserves of the materials from which salt is produced seem inexhaustible, the industry has its conservation problems; one of these has to do with the severe corrosion produced by salt on the metal equipment which is used in processing and in which the material is used industrially. Here it is not salt itself, but metals as natural resources, which must be conserved. Some progress is being made on the latter problem through development of corrosion-resistant linings and platings which not only conserve equipment but keep the salt solutions purer. More than 28 million short tons of salt were sold or used in the United States in 1962. Texas, Louisiana, New York, Michigan, Ohio, and California lead in production in the order given. In terms of table and household use, consumption amounts to about 5 pounds annually per capita. Industrial uses such as bleaching and the manufacture of glass and various chemicals require around 70 per cent of the total domestic production.

Salt is mined as block and granular material and pumped out as brine either natural or artificially dissolved. The brine is then evaporated and the residue refined. Some salt is recovered by pumping in and evaporating sea water. It seldom occurs without being associated with other materials such as bromine, iron, or magnesium compounds. In some countries it is used for household and table purposes with only superficial refinement.

Miscellaneous Salines. Calcium chloride, well known for its hygroscopic and antifreeze characteristics, has many uses and is produced in many domestic localities from natural brines. Demand for bromine, which also comes from natural brines, including sea water, is increasing because of its use in antiknock gasoline. Iodine, used in photographic emulsions, animal feeds, iodized salts, drugs, and dyes, is recovered from waste oil-field and other brines and may be recovered from seaweed.

Sodium carbonate and sodium sulfate, extensively used in the glass, soap, and paper industries and variously used as refining materials, are widely distributed and in adequate supply. Borax and other boron minerals, in addition to extensive household use, have become an item in the fertilizer industry and are finding increasing use in the hardening of certain metals. Reserves are adequate.

Phosphates. The United States has long been the largest producer and exporter of phosphates in various forms and has adequate supplies to meet the heavy domestic demand for phosphate fertilizer. The older Southeastern fields in Tennessee, Kentucky, South Carolina, Florida, and, farther west, in Arkansas have in recent years been supplemented by discoveries in Utah, Montana, Idaho, and Wyoming. Lately, export trade finds vigorous competition from North African producers. Western deposits are largely located on public lands and are operated under the Mineral Leasing Act of 1920. Domestic consumption occurs mostly in states east of the Mississippi. Factors of export competition and long freight haul are not too good for the phosphate-mining business but do put the brakes on wasteful exploitation. Aside from the 80-odd per cent of use for fertilizer, phosphate materials find their way into such varied uses as stock and poultry food, rodent poisons, tracer bullets, matches, and poison gases.

Much of the mining of phosphate rock in the Southeast is by open-pit methods, which results in high recovery but ruined landscapes.

Stipulations in Western Federal phosphate leases include conservation features.

Potash. Unlike phosphate, potash had to be imported into this country previous to World War I, when supplies from the rich Stassfurt fields were cut off from import. This stimulated discovery through congressional appropriation, and deep, rich deposits were found in New Mexico. It is interesting that the discoveries were made in drilling for oil. There is now a thriving American potash industry, handicapped somewhat by location distant from greatest demand but backed by resources adequate for many years ahead (Fig. 12-11). Potash is essential as a plant nutrient,

Aerial view of potash workings near Carlsbad, N.Mex. Mine head and refinery are seen just above center of picture; tailing, or waste, dumps are seen at upper left as a white area and as a darker patch adjoining storage sheds at right margin. (Photo by American Potash Institute, Inc.)

figure 12-11

and more than 90 per cent of total consumption is used for agricultural purposes. The remainder is used principally by the chemical industries.

Imports amounted in 1962 to less than 7 per cent of total consumption. Most of the domestic deposits are on Federal lands, operated under the Mineral Leasing Law of 1920, and operators are required to use conservation procedures in mining. Some production comes from natural brines from wells in private ownership.

OTHER NONMETALLIC MINERALS

Certain important nonmetallics such as feldspar, graphite, sulfur, fluorspar, mica, and asbestos defy classification and should be taken up separately.

Sulfur. Consumption of domestic native and by-product sulfur, having increased from almost zero in 1900 to 4¾ million short tons in 1954, has recently emphasized the consideration of reserve problems. Sulfur occurs in almost pure form as crystals, masses, and powders and in combination with certain metals as pyrites (sulfide). Its uses vary from chemical, fertilizers, insecticides, and pulp and paper manufacture, which account for more than three-fourths of total consumption, to such products as rubber, explosives, and paints. Much of the industrial consumption is in the form of sulfuric acid. Thus the figure for sulfur consumption for 1962 was 6.25 million long tons. Texas with three-fourths and Louisiana with one-fourth of the supply produce practically all the domestic native sulfur. Ores and by-product sulfur come from many localities. In spite of shrinking reserves the United States exports a net of almost 1½ million long tons of sulfur a year. Pyrite, a metallic-appearing sulfide mineral, has approached production of a million long tons a year and is an additional source of sulfur and sulfuric acid. As a substitute source of native sulfur, its use constitutes good conservation. By-product sulfur is recovered in the flotation treatment of copper, lead, and zinc ores and from smelter fumes and from natural gas and oil. The smelter fumes are a nuisance in smelter centers, and their treatment to produce sulfuric acid yielded a small addition to the total production in 1962. This process is not particularly profitable, but some of the cost can be charged off against prevention of damage to vegetation. Likewise, current interest in smog control will no doubt bring about by-product treatment of industrial sulfur gases from urban industries. Sulfur is also recovered in the treatment of "sour" natural gas in oil fields, from coke manufacture, and from oil-refining gases. All this by-product business amounts to conservation with some of the expenses paid and adds to the domestic sulfur reserves when industry decides the practices can be used "economically."

Fluorspar. Important in steel and glass manufacture and in the production of hydrofluoric acid, which has many industrial uses, fluorspar is mined principally in Illinois, Colorado, and Kentucky. Reserves are inadequate, and almost one-half the amount consumed in this country was imported in 1962. Some progress may be looked for in beneficiation of lean material.

Graphite. With high consumption and inadequate reserves of natural graphite, improvement in beneficiation of ores and the manufacture of artificial graphite from coal appear to be the directions which conservation must take. Uses range from foundry batteries, lubricants, and crucibles to the "lead" in the everyday pencil. Production of natural graphite in the United States in 1962 amounted to somewhat less than one-third of consumption. Imports included both natural and artificial graphite.

Asbestos. Length of fiber, which adapts it for weaving into textiles, fire resistance, and filtering value are qualities which give asbestos a wide variety of uses. Aside from insulation, the use for brake lining is perhaps best known by the average citizen. In 1962 domestic production, mainly from Vermont, California, and Arizona, supplied only about 7 per cent of the amount consumed. Canada is the principal source of imports. Lower-grade asbestos is produced in several states, and some progress is reported in developing synthetic substitutes, one project having been inaugurated at Norris, Tennessee by the Bureau of Mines. Short-fiber asbestos, consumed largely in the manufacture of asbestos cement and asphalt building materials, constitutes 97 per cent of all fiber used in 1962.

Mica. Used all the way from roofing and paint to electric insulation and Christmas-tree snow, mica has become one of the indispensable minerals. It occurs naturally in sheets which split into very thin transparent layers. Its property of nonconductivity of electricity and heat make sheet mica of special value. Unfortunately it is scarcest in this form, and domestic reserves are insignificant. Scrap mica can be used for many industrial purposes, such as manufacture of wallpaper, dusting powder, automobile tires, and the production of paints and plastics. Domestic sheet mica comes mainly from North Carolina and New Hampshire. Scrap mica, suitable for the ground product, not only comes from shop and factory wastes but is recovered from the washing of kaolin, a ceramic clay. Imports of all grades of mica are heavy and expensive. They come principally from India and Madagascar. Some progress is being made in producing a synthetic mica under the sponsorship of the Office of Naval Research.

BIBLIOGRAPHY

Annual Reports of the Secretary of the Interior, 1950–1962.

BROWN, HARRISON, JAMES BONNER, AND JOHN WEIR: The Next Hundred Years, The Viking Press, Inc., New York, 1957.

Investigation of National Resources, Hearings before Sub-Committee of Committee on Public Lands, 78th Congress, 1st Session U.S. Senate, May 15, 16, and 20, 1947.

LANDES, KENNETH K.: Petroleum Geology, John Wiley & Sons, Inc., New York, 1951.

LANDSBERG, HANS H., LEONARD L. FISCHMAN, AND JOSEPH L. FISHER: Resources in America's Future, The Johns Hopkins Press, Baltimore, 1963.

LOVERING, T. S.: Minerals in World Affairs, Prentice-Hall, Inc., Englewood Cliffs, N.J., 1943.

LYONS, BARROW: Tomorrow's Birthright, Funk and Wagnalls Company, New York, 1955.

Mineral Facts and Problems, U.S. Bureau of Mines, 1960.

Minerals Yearbook, U.S. Bureau of Mines, 1962.

NETSCHERT, BRUCE C., AND HANS H. LANDSBERG: The Future Supply of the Major Metals, Resources for the Future, Inc., Washington, D.C., 1961.

Resources for Freedom, vols. 1 and 3, Report of the President's Materials Policy Commission, 1952.

VAN HISE, CHARLES R.: The Conservation of Natural Resources in the United States, The Macmillan Company, New York, 1910.

VAN ROYEN, WILLIAM, OLIVER BOWLES, AND ELMER W. PEHRSON: Mineral Resources of the World, Prentice-Hall, Inc., Englewood Cliffs, N.J., 1952.

13 RECREATION

PERHAPS THE GREATEST single problem facing the average United States citizen today is good, socially acceptable use for his leisure time. A large amount of leisure time for everyone is a new problem that has arisen within the memory of men now living, and no sure solution has been found. However, belief is widely expressed that outdoor recreation in its many forms may contribute importantly to a solution. Outdoor recreation is the sum of many things. But it would be difficult for most people to find sport, relaxation, inspiration, and adventure—all of them experiences which are a part of outdoor recreation—without access to the basic resources of land, water, trees, grass, and the myriad forms of animal life. Reservation of land for recreational use has been a part of our past history as a nation. Such reservation will be increasingly costly in the future. Recreational reservation may mean keeping good land out of food production if nonarable land is not available. It may mean building a highway at greater expense in order to retain a less costly route for recreational use. It almost certainly entails preventing industrial plants from releasing destructive pollution into water and air. On the other hand, it may be as easy as authorization of recreational use for municipal water supply reservoirs, now often prevented by archaic laws which modern sanitary engineering has outgrown; or it may be as simple as the joint use of forests for both wood production and recreation. Quite apart from the pleasure the participant may derive from the outdoor recreation of his choice, there is almost certainly the added social value, in an increasingly urbanized culture, of his coming into contact with a variety of the basic natural resources which support the economy. Provision of ample opportunity for outdoor recreation may then be one way of helping to ensure that when the citizen sanctions or participates in projects which alter the face of the earth, he acts with an appreciation of the consequences, not in a spirit of blind and foolhardy exuberance.

Recognition of problems associated with meeting the demand for outdoor recreation led Congress in 1958 to establish the Outdoor Recreation Resources Review Commission (ORRRC).[1] This commission was directed to determine the outdoor-recreation needs of the American people from the present through the year 2000 and the resources available for the purpose and to make recommendations on how these needs can be met. The ORRRC contracted for twenty-seven separate studies to be carried out by a wide variety of public agencies, colleges and universities, private research organizations and specialists, and members of its own staff. Because of the high quality of scholarship which went into these studies, the ORRRC reports have become indispensable to agency administrators, civic groups, and all who are closely concerned with solving problems of outdoor recreation.

Some of the ORRRC findings are particularly significant: (1) By the

[1] Public Law 85-470, 72 Stat. 238, June 28, 1958.

year 2000 our population will nearly double; the over-all demand for outdoor recreation will triple; not only will there be more people, but they will have more free time, more money, and more mobility. (2) The kinds of outdoor recreation most people take part in today are relatively simple: walking and driving for pleasure, playing outdoor games and sports, swimming, sight-seeing, picnicking, fishing, bicycling, boating, and hunting. (3) What people do now for outdoor recreation is not necessarily what they want to do in the future. Many among those contacted in the survey indicated that they would like to spend more time than they were able to at present in such activities as fishing, camping, swimming, and other sports. (4) Water is a focal point of outdoor recreation. People regard water in many ways. It is something to swim in, to fish in, to boat on, to camp beside, or just to look at. (5) The recreation problem is not one of number of acres, but of effective acres. Too often areas designated for public outdoor recreation use are located at a considerable distance from major population centers. (6) People want outdoor recreation close to home, and for most people home is in the fast-growing metropolitan areas where two out of three Americans now live. (7) As mobility continues to increase, more people will continue to travel farther to enjoy outstanding scenic, wildlife, and wilderness areas. Continued improvement in methods of transportation, in incomes, and in vacation time allotments will result in increased pressure on outdoor-recreation resources. (8) There are many overlooked outdoor-recreation resources in urban areas. It is very important to develop such resources since there is tremendous demand for recreational opportunity within after-work and weekend hours.[2]

Publication of the ORRRC's findings and recommendations in 1962 gave impetus to several far-reaching actions. Among these were the creation of the Bureau of Outdoor Recreation within the Department of the Interior also in 1962; and passage by the Eightieth Congress of the Land and Water Conservation Fund Act in 1964 (Public Law 88-578). Since the fund established by this act is to run for 25 years from its effective date of January 1, 1965, its provisions deserve extended mention:[3]

The Land and Water Conservation Fund Act authorizes a program of grants-in-aid to the states for planning, acquiring, and developing needed outdoor recreation resources. About 60 per cent of the Fund will be available for State purposes and 40 per cent to certain Federal agencies for outdoor recreation needs.

[2] Action for Outdoor Recreation for America, Citizens Committee for the ORRRC Report, 1963, pp. 8–10.
[3] News Release, Office of the Secretary, U.S. *Department of the Interior*, Sept 5, 1964.

The Fund's revenues will come from nominal admission and user fees at certain Federal recreation areas, the existing motorboat fuels tax, net proceeds from the sale of Federal surplus real property, and repayable advance appropriations beginning in the third year.

In an average year during its first 10 years, the Fund is expected to make about $180 million available for State and Federal purposes. Of this amount approximately $108 million each year is expected to go to the States in 50-50 matching grants. The remainder will go for acquisition of certain needed Federal outdoor recreation areas and to help offset capital costs of Federal water development projects which are allocated to public recreation and fish and wildlife enhancement.

Under the provisions of the Act, which will be administered by the Bureau of Outdoor Recreation, entrance and admission fees may be charged only if four conditions are met. These are: (1) The area is specifically designated and posted; (2) The area is administered by a Federal agency (which excludes areas under lease to States, public, or private agencies); (3) Facilities or services for the benefit of recreation users are provided at Federal expense; (4) The area is administered primarily for scenic, scientific, historical, cultural, or other recreational purposes.

No fees of any kind may be charged under authority of the Act for use of any waters, for travel by private non-commercial vehicle through designated areas on Federal aid highways, national parkways, or roads in the national forest system, or as a Federal hunting and fishing license.

Among its activities under the act the Bureau of Outdoor Recreation develops and maintains a nation-wide plan for outdoor recreation, interprets the act, prepares instructions and guides for state participation, reviews and approves comprehensive outdoor-recreation plans submitted by the several states, and takes responsibility for final approval of financial assistance for all projects whether state or local.

A very important provision of the Land and Water Conservation Act is its requirement that each state desiring financial assistance not only match any Federal aid received on a 50-50 basis but also develop a comprehensive state-wide outdoor-recreation plan if it is to qualify for financial assistance. All state and local projects must be within the scope of the plan to merit consideration. This requirement serves two particularly important purposes: It ensures the collection and compilation "at the grass roots" of facts on both needs and the resources available to meet them; and it practically assures broad citizen participation in the planning process.

Some states and local areas have long maintained active programs for meeting outdoor-recreation needs, and in several recent instances they have expanded their own unaided activities. Since 1960, several states have embarked on new, large-scale programs for acquisition and development of outdoor-recreation lands. This trend began with New

York's program of 1960, financed by a 75-million-dollar bond issue, to support matching grants to local units of government as well as to expand state-owned facilities. Since that time, expanded programs have been undertaken by a number of states led, dollarwise, by California with a 150-million-dollar bond issue; and including New Jersey, Pennsylvania, Minnesota, Wisconsin, Ohio, Michigan, and Washington, the latter two each with 10-million-dollar bond issues.

All these actions lead to the conclusion that the population of the United States regards outdoor recreation as something for which it is willing to pay, not only through earmarking an appreciable portion of its finances for land acquisition and development but through deliberate refusal to tolerate private commercial development, on public recreation lands, of mineral or forest resources, lest irreversible damage be suffered by aesthetic features.

THE NATIONAL-PARK SYSTEM

Although Hot Springs in Arkansas was withdrawn from settlement and entry and was dedicated to the use of all people as early as 1845, that event can hardly be regarded as the start of the national-park movement, even though the area was later included in the system. It is generally agreed that the act of Congress in March, 1872, which carved Yellowstone out of the public domain as a "public park or pleasuring-ground for the benefit and enjoyment of the people" first put the national-park concept into law and served as a precedent for subsequent national-park legislation. Actually it was not until 1916 that Congress acted to establish the National Park Service within the Department of the Interior and charged it with the administration of all the national parks and most of the national monuments which had been created up to that time. Today the National Park Service administers nearly 26 million acres of land, although not all the administered units, such as Lake Mead and Glen Canyon, are parts of the national-park system.

The national-park system itself includes not only the national parks (32) and monuments (77) but also the national seashores (5) and parkways (3). It also includes many areas of essentially historic or memorial interest, such as the national historical parks, sites, and memorials (50), military parks (11), battlefields (5), battlefield parks (5), battlefield sites (3), cemeteries (10), and the national capital parks, which embrace about 38,000 acres of land in and around Washington, D.C.

Increased pressure on outdoor recreational facilities is emphasized by the fact that visits to units of the national-park system in 1964 numbered over 102 million, a gain of nearly 9 per cent over 1963.[4] Major elements

[4] *Ibid.*, May 3, 1965.

of the national-park system which exist primarily to serve outdoor recreation will be discussed briefly.

The National Parks. The location and area of the national parks are listed in Table 13-1. The largest of the national parks is Yellowstone, with an area of almost 2¼ million acres. Mount McKinley is a close second, with almost 2 million acres. Platt in Oklahoma and Hot Springs in Arkansas are the smallest, each about 1,000 acres in size. All the national parks existing prior to 1930 were created by withdrawing and dedicating land from the public domain. Both land purchase and donations to the Federal government have figured in subsequent acquisitions.

At best the national parks present the scenic masterpieces of this country (Fig. 13-1), with a spatial setting appropriate to such presentation and, indeed, a part of it. Considered in this way, such intangibles as beauty, majesty, and grandeur of the scene become natural resources subject, unless conserved, to marring and in some instances, if pressures for commercial use are not constantly resisted, to utter destruction.

The particular features of the national parks are worth summarizing as follows: mountains such as Whitney, Lassen, Rainier, McKinley, and the Great Smokies, all located in parks named after them; giant sequoia

Dream Lake, Rocky Mountain National Park. (Photo by National Park Service.)

figure 13-1

TABLE 13-1. INFORMATION RELATING TO THE
NATIONAL PARKS, JAN. 1, 1964

National parks	State	Federal land, acres
Acadia	Maine	31,692
Big Bend	Tex.	700,241
Bryce Canyon	Utah	36,010
Canyonlands	Utah	257,640
Carlsbad Caverns	N.Mex.	43,404
Crater Lake	Ore.	160,290
Everglades	Fla.	1,302,509
Glacier	Mont.	1,009,448
Grand Canyon	Ariz.	673,203
Grand Teton	Wyo.	302,454
Great Smoky Mountains	Tenn.–N.C.	510,200
Haleakala	Hawaii	17,130
Hawaii Volcanoes	Hawaii	201,007
Hot Springs	Ark.	1,032
Isle Royale	Mich.	539,347
Kings Canyon	Calif.	453,768
Lassen Volcanic	Calif.	106,126
Mammoth Cave	Ky.	51,351
Mesa Verde	Colo.	51,277
Mount McKinley	Alaska	1,939,359
Mount Rainier	Wash.	241,781
Olympic	Wash.	888,558
Petrified Forest	Ariz.	94,189
Platt	Okla.	912
Rocky Mountain	Colo.	259,956
Sequoia	Calif.	385,413
Shenandoah	Va.	193,646
Virgin Islands	U.S. Virgin Islands	10,836
Wind Cave	S.Dak.	28,059
Yellowstone	Idaho-Mont.-Wyo.	2,213,207
Yosemite	Calif.	758,132
Zion	Utah	133,956
Total		13,596,135

trees, among the oldest living plants and of majestic size and beauty, with their youngsters coming on; monoliths surrounding great glacial valleys such as those of Yosemite; caverns such as those of Carlsbad and Mammoth Cave; geologic erosion on a grand scale as at the Grand Canyon; thermal areas such as those in Yellowstone; large and relatively rare wild animals such as grizzly bear, moose, elk, alligator, eagle, swan, and buffalo; wind-carved and highly colored rock formations (Fig. 13-2); lakes of unusual depth, color, and beauty; waterfalls; great stretches of virgin hardwood and coniferous forests in various of the Western and

Southern parks; and archeological sites with structures and evidence of ancient cultures such as the prehistoric copper mines on Isle Royale and the cliff dwellings of the Southwest.

There is hardly one of the greater national parks that is free from continuing pressure for exploitation of its natural resources—water, timber, and forage for domestic animals being the ones most often coveted.

The National Park Service finds itself constantly face to face with the tough problem of making the parks widely available to the public "and [the duty] to provide for the enjoyment of same [their resources] in such manner and by such means as will leave them unimpaired for the enjoyment of future generations." This basic purpose involves very careful planning of all roads, structures, and concession quarters; protection of the forests and other resources from fire, insects, and disease, *which frequently in themselves constitute natural phenomena*; resisting constant pressure for the invasion of the parks for exploitation of timber, forage, minerals, and particularly water resources, and storage sites; resisting efforts to legislate inferior areas into the national-park family; protecting the wild-animal life, predator and prey alike, and seeing that the animal resources do not increase beyond a point where demand for food will destroy valuable cover and even deplete the animal population itself; acquiring of interior private holdings which now offer to the owners opportunity to conduct business, violate development plans, and generally ignore park policies *within* the parks; and controlling vandalism which destroys and defaces park property and natural resources.

The purpose of national parks, too, involves equitable distribution of their benefits (Fig. 13-3). Their location and relative inaccessibility make this difficult from the viewpoints of travel and expense. Ideally every citizen of the country who wants to visit a national park should be able to do so. He is one of the owners. Actually those who get into

Angel Arch, Canyonlands National Park, Utah. Note three figures below arch. (Photo by National Park Service.)

figure 13-2

figure 13-3

The Eastern national parks with their spring blossoms offer pleasant recreation on horseback. (Photo by Tennessee Valley Authority.)

the national parks each year represent less than one-tenth of the population, and this is true in spite of heroic effort for years upon the part of the National Park Service to promote and build roads to and within the parks and to bring about the availability of reasonably priced and comfortable subsistence and lodging accommodations.

The problems raised by the purposes in the foregoing account are not easy to solve. The National Park Service, which is just 50 years old, struggles doggedly with the principal conservation problem, the conflict between heavy use and maintenance of the "unimpaired" condition. Some sacrifices of such condition must be made at the areas of concentrated use and in order to have the parks at all accessible to large numbers of people. Development plans are carefully worked out, and constant study is carried on to achieve harmony between man-made facilities and the natural scene (Fig. 13-4).

Methods of extinguishing and preventing man-caused fires are highly developed in the national parks, and expert talent is employed. The same is true in protecting the park forests from insects and disease, with full cooperation of the appropriate bureaus of the Department of Agriculture. The National Park Service must depend largely upon the conservation and scientific societies to back it up in its everlasting insistence that the commercially important natural resources within the parks are not to be exploited for private gain. Unless these defenses are continually active, artificial emergencies can be pleaded "in the national interest" and away will go majestic forests, towering waterfalls, natural meadows, and even mineral deposits, with all the disfigurement which accompanies their exploitation. It is to be hoped that the American people will never

figure 13-4

A ranger naturalist conducts a hike in Yellowstone National
Park, Wyoming. (Photo by National Park Service.)

sacrifice the character of the national parks to prevent a tremor of delay
in the satisfaction of their mounting demands for material comforts
and convenience.

Wild-animal life in the national parks is not easy to manage since its
increase cannot legally be harvested. It must be protected, but it is deliberately *unmanaged* in the technical sense, the only check on its increase being the presence of predators and death from natural causes.
However, predators are present in inadequate numbers to keep elk populations in balance with winter feed, for example. Therefore, unless elk in
the Yellowstone and Grand Teton Parks are fed in winter and surplus
numbers are removed by hunters just outside the park boundaries or
by park employees within, not only would many animals starve outright
in winter, but the entire herd would deteriorate in condition and appearance while wreaking havoc to the range, itself a valuable attribute of
the parks. Reduction of the herd by firearms may sound cruel, but it is
surely less cruel to the individual animal than slow starvation and results
in greatly improved conditions for the survivors.

Small appropriations are available each year for acquiring privately
owned tracts within the parks, but progress is slow. Nothing short of
complete ownership will assure compliance with national-park policy.

The goal of fair distribution of park benefits appears to people of
certain localities to indicate that they should have a national park
nearby. Pressure for inclusion of unimpressive areas is still strong and is
aggravated by ignorance on the part of the general public concerning
national-park specifications. Watchful scientific societies and conservation organizations play an important role in leading opposition to legislation which is often introduced to accomplish these ends.

There is no one answer to the problem of making a national park visit available to every citizen who wants one and who helps pay for the system. There is, of course, a limit to the amount of use the parks can support. This use continues to climb: between 1952 and 1962 the number of visits increased by 87 per cent. But since the principal activities of park visitors appear to be camping, hiking, going on conducted nature walks, and attending organized campfire programs and lectures, it may be assumed that most visitors appreciate what the parks are for and how they should be used.[5]

National Monuments. Sixty-five of the seventy-seven national monuments have been set aside by presidential proclamation under the Act for the Preservation of American Antiquities, passed in 1906. The act included the setting aside not only of "historic landmarks, historic and prehistoric structures" but of "other objects of historic or scientific interest." This brought into the system not only Cabrillo in California of less than a single acre, Yucca House in Colorado of less than 10 acres, and Mound City Group in Ohio of 67½ acres, but Glacier Bay and Katmai in Alaska, each covering more than 2¼ million acres. The remaining eighteen monuments, not set aside by the act, were established by specific acts of Congress. Ordinarily the national monuments are much less impressive than the national parks, but they attract amateur adventurers, budding archaeologists, and many sightseers. Some of the national parks have first been set aside as national monuments. The conservation problems are similar to those of the national parks (Fig. 13-5).

National Parkways and Seashores. These categories of areas established within the national-park system tend to serve narrower and more specialized interests than the national parks themselves. Examples are the Blue Ridge National Parkway, planned to fully exploit the scenic features of these mountains over a span of nearly 500 miles; and the Padre Island National Seashore, along the Gulf Coast of Texas (Fig. 13-6), designed to protect the public's right of entrance to and use of many miles of ocean beach and shifting sand dunes.

National Forests. The national forests were established primarily for the growing of timber and protection of watersheds. Other uses and resources were not emphasized in the law of 1897 which outlined objectives and purposes of the "forest reserves." Local people had long made modest use of the national forests for hunting, fishing, and camping. But large-scale recreation has been more or less thrust upon the national forests because it, like grazing, has become big business. A generous program of road-building had been a part of the early planning to insure that the forests would be accessible for commercial logging operations.

---

[5] *Annual Report of Secretary of the Interior*, 1961, p. 360.

figure 13-5

Devil's Postpile National Monument, California. View of the Postpile itself, with great accumulation of broken basaltic rock fragments at its base. (Photo by Ralph H. Anderson, National Park Service.)

figure 13-6
Beachcombing on Padre Island National Seashore, Tex. (Photo by W. E. Dutton, National Park Service.)

figure 13-7
Opening Day on Spruce Knob Lake, Monongahela National Forest, West
Virginia. (Photo by United States Forest Service. Courtesy of American
Forests.)

The carrying out of those plans has depended not only upon special appropriations but upon return of a part of the revenue from timber sales
and grazing to the local counties and to special road- and trail-building
funds. However, this same ready accessibility beckoned to the growing
army of outdoor recreationists; and today millions seek the national
forests not only for day use, fishing (Fig. 13-7), and inexpensive camping trips but for the hunting and trapping permitted here but banned in
the national parks. Having an ample share of scenic attractiveness (Fig.
13-8) and being widely distributed over the entire country, the national
forests offer outdoor recreation somewhat closer to the urban dweller's
concept of "roughing it" (Fig. 13-9) than the more highly developed
parks. Although wilderness travel is common in both types of reserva-

One may get a sense of space and distance from many na-
tional-forest scenes. View of canyon in Gallatin National
Forest, Montana.

figure 13-8

397

figure 13-9

Hikers backpacking through Three Sisters Wilderness Area, Willamette National Forest, Oregon. (Photo by Leland J. Prater, United States Forest Service.)

tion, the best canoeing water is found in national forests, and much of the extended horseback travel, aside from that of organized Western mountain clubs, penetrates the dedicated wilderness areas of the national forests (Fig. 13-10).

Organization camps representing everything from farm youth to young-people's church groups operate in national forests on an area-rental basis. Resorts of various specifications, usually informal and using the guest-cabin plan, may also operate under area permit. Winter-sports areas and day-use areas for picnicking were built in considerable numbers by various public work agencies during the 1930s, and many of these persist, sometimes now under the operation of local communities.

Recreation visits to the national forests have increased by 240 per cent in the last 10 years.[6] General enjoyment of the forest environment, picnicking, fishing, hunting, winter sports, and camping are the most popular activities. The Forest Service maintains no naturalist service for interpreting the country and its resources to visitors and, except on very heavily used public campgrounds and day-use areas and at winter-sports areas, assigns no officer exclusively to the duty of serving recreation

[6] Recreation in Small Watershed Projects, Soil Conservation Service, U.S. Department of Agriculture, PA 610, February, 1964.

users. On the other hand, while merging field duties with the general activities on national forests, specialists in the Washington office staff of the Forest Service and in most of the ten regional office staffs are employed both in wild-animal-life management and in recreational use other than hunting and fishing.

Conservation problems on the national forests are continually arising. Among them, the reconciling of recreation use with such pressing demands as timber growing and harvesting, grazing of domestic livestock, mining, and commercial occupancy of land for stores, sawmills, and mining installations constitute the most serious. The term *multiple use* implies a kind of planning, supervision, and judgment in administration which is not easy and for which manpower is not always available. Furthermore, the mere policing of heavily used areas to keep them uninjured, clean, and well serviced with water, shelter, and sanitary facilities is anything but automatic. Distributing the users and on rare occasions charging them a small fee have been the subject of recent experimentation and may prove to be the answer to guaranteeing fairness to all who seek recreation. Along the same line, the equity of renting summer-home sites and thus assigning monopolistic use of choice areas may be questioned as increasing demand for mass use appears.

Efforts to conserve the recreation resources of national forests include planning of recreation developments in order best to serve the public and to make use of the scenic and sport resources; definite protection of developed areas from invasion by permitted livestock; bringing water

Trail riding in the Goat Rock Wild Area, Washington. Since 1933, several hundred of these 10- to 12-day horseback trips have been arranged by the American Forestry Association. (Photo by James P. Gilligan.)

figure 13-10

supplies to dry but attractive areas; requiring strict adherence to sanitary standards from those who have land under permit; assisting state officers in the enforcement of fish and game regulations; studying and understanding and increasing the fish and other wild-animal resources; and resisting constant pressures to invade wilderness country, dedicated and potential, with roads, reservoirs, airplane landing fields, and other developments which would dilute the quality of recreation areas. As in the national-park picture, various organizations with scientific and conservation objectives are active in defending the recreation resources of the national forests.

RECREATION ON NON-FEDERAL PUBLIC LAND

Development and maintenance of parks, parkways, and other outdoor-recreation facilities has never been a monopoly of the Federal government. States, counties, municipalities, and other local units of government including legally established, regional recreational authorities, have long provided such facilities. State- or local-government developments are close to the local user and, beyond this, traditionally draw more distant users who add their contribution to the local economy.

State Parks. It may be noted that between 1950 and 1959 visits to state parks increased by 123 per cent although their acreage increased only 22 per cent. By comparison, in 1960 the national parks had five times as many acres as state parks but only one-third as many visits. Thus, in a sense, density of use of state parks was fourteen times that of national parks.[7] Public use at this level of density clearly points to intensive day use for picnics (Fig. 13-11), swimming, and the like. Many state parks are quite large and have as much true wilderness character as their national counterparts. For example, the Adirondack Forest Preserve, a part of the New York State park system, embraces over 2¼ million acres maintained largely as wilderness. Michigan's Porcupine Mountains State Park of over 50,000 acres drew national attention in the late 1950s when authorities were asked to issue a permit for copper-ore exploration within its boundaries. Public resistance was awakened on a nation-wide scale, and the potential threat to wilderness was averted.

As indicated earlier (page 388) many states are acting to greatly increase both state and local park facilities, and new sources of revenue are being sought to meet the mounting demand. Many states have long charged moderate fees for entrance to parks and for use of special services within, such as firewood, camp sites, electrical or water connections, or parking space. Concession contracts often go to the bidder who offers the highest proportion of his profit for park maintenance.

[7] *Outdoor Recreation for America*, ORRRC, Washington, D.C., January, 1962, p. 49.

figure 13-11

A picnic at Gold Head Branch State Park in Florida, Lake Jackson in background. (Photo by Florida Board of Forestry.)

Parkways. The survey of the recreational wants and needs of the American people made for ORRRC indicated that in 1960 "driving for pleasure" was the single most popular outdoor recreational activity. More than half the population over twelve years of age indicated a preference for this form of recreation.[8] These people enjoy the scene, and they like change and variety, even though they do not enter or explore wild lands. For these the elongated park characterized by a limited-access road, located to give the best views and following a belt of relatively wild country, is a satisfying facility. The spatial use of land as a natural resource thus comes close to those who may live in crowded communities. The term parkway is commonly applied to these areas. Such areas may include small rest and picnic spots, beaches, canoe ports, winter-sports facilities, and fishing-access sites. Wild-animal resources are particularly attractive to the motorist. For example, in many parts of the country localized heavy populations of waterfowl attract more attention from sightseers than from hunters. The same thing is true where populations of large ungulates such as elk and deer are abundant. Here the motorist's progress is enlivened by highway signs reading "deer crossing" placed not so much to spot actual deer trails as to keep him reminded of the ever-present visual thrill—and safety hazard—posed by these animals. Space, water, and vegetative cover thereby become involved as recreation resources, not only for themselves but as habitat for wild-animal life; and their conservation for exclusive recreation use becomes increasingly important. Among the distinctive conservation problems

[8] Trends in American Living and Outdoor Recreation, *ORRRC Rept.* 22, Washington, D.C., 1962, p 49.

involved is that of reconciling heavy use in terms of traffic and effect on soil, cover, and animal life with the continuing need to maintain a natural and unlittered scene. Not the least problems are acquiring enough land to keep the parkways attractive and to prevent vandalism.

RECREATION RESOURCES IN PRIVATE OWNERSHIP

Not all land devoted to recreation is in public ownership, and, indeed, the people of this country would be hard pressed if this were so. Hunters and fishermen, particularly in the heavily populated farming regions, depend largely for their sport upon consent or purchased privilege to enter private property. Hunting clubs with their own headquarters must frequently lease adjoining lands or waters if they hope to use such resources exclusively. Proprietors of many resorts and camps may themselves own only small strategically located tracts of land and depend upon a hinterland in public ownership for the use of the guests they house and feed. Inland-river and lake shores and even the shores of the Great Lakes and the oceans have passed largely into private ownership, and only by recapturing or leasing them can the general public share the sort of thing available to the cottage or estate owner or the frequenter of the resort or club.

This situation poses two knotty problems for the landowner to face: (1) To what extent should he allow the general public to use his land for recreation either with or without charge? (2) How can he conserve the natural resources involved without systematic policing of the area and the users? On the part of the recreation seeker the question may be asked, "Are we not entitled to outdoor recreation, and where shall we get it if not on farms and private estates?" (Fig. 13-12.)

Frequently the latter questions can be answered only by such rejoinders as, "Buy yourself a piece of land." "Join a rod and gun club with its own land." "Prove to me beforehand that you will clean up your picnic area, abstain from shooting my cow, close gates after you, obey the fish and game laws, be careful with fire, leave some of the flowers, and maybe pay me a moderate fee for the day." "There's a resort up the road, why don't you go there?" or "The state park is only 20 miles from here, and you can swim in the lake there."

On the other hand, a considerable block of the recreation-seeking public is taken care of on private land which they own or which is made available to them by the owner. Among the more heavily used of these lands are beaches, summer-cottage colonies, clubs, summer and winter resorts, youth camps, and farms.

Traditionally popular with hunters of upland game, farms are developing broader recreational appeal for the whole family. A hundred years ago many New England farmers "kept summer boarders." The

figure 13-12

*Hunters arrange with the owner of a farm for a day's rec-
reation. They agree to be careful around buildings and
stock. (Michigan Department of Conservation.)*

up-country farm offered adventure for urban youngsters, restful quiet
for their parents, and the bounty of a country kitchen and relief from
the city's heat for the whole family—and at a cost within the means of
many who felt "priced out" of the commercial resorts of that era. Now,
tastes have come a full circle and once again farm-based vacations are
growing in popularity. Under authority of the Food and Agriculture
Act of 1962 the U.S. Department of Agriculture offers assistance to
farmers and ranchers who wish to develop outdoor-recreation facilities
for profit. Speaking in support of this act before a congressional committee in 1962, Secretary of Agriculture Orville L. Freeman pointed to
estimates that by 1980 food and fiber needs of a human population of
245 million would be met by production from 51 million acres less than
the acreage currently classed as cropland.[9] The Department of Agriculture lists four primary reasons for its interest in farm-based outdoor
recreation: (1) It offers a chance to provide additional income to farmers

[9] Rural Recreation: A New Family-farm Business, U.S. Department of Agriculture,
September, 1962, p. 1.

and associated businesses, and, at the same time, enables farmers to stay on their farms; (2) it can aid in diverting cropland to a more remunerative use for the owner which can later, if and when needed, be returned to cultivation; (3) it provides an urgently needed service; and (4) it helps stabilize the local economy and strengthen social institutions without removing land from private ownership or reducing the tax base.[10]

In a sense the return to popularity of the farm vacation may represent a subconscious desire to return to an earlier and presumably simpler way of life. What future turns the nation's outdoor recreation tastes may take is anyone's guess (and such guessing is an increasingly popular enterprise with professional recreationists). There are signs that hunting and fishing—the so-called blood sports—may be winning new and eloquent opponents.[11] And, in fact, these and related diversions are of comparatively recent origin as far as the majority of the "solid middle class" of this country is concerned. Up until the time of World War I hunting and fishing were often thought of as reserved for the wealthy, the ne'er-do-well, and the young. For the majority of people leisure was used in simply doing nothing—in resting from arduous physical labor characterized by long working days and weeks. With growth of the view that recreation is not only enjoyable but may contribute to improved health and work efficiency, the Puritan ethic is mollified. But it would be risky to predict that the year 2000 will see twice as many or half as many people participating in the pastimes which led in the ORRRC surveys.

Perhaps as human populations grow and occupy more land with their gainful activities, people will grow more intellectual and will be able to find necessary relaxation by turning inward with their own thoughts—an activity that would require only a square yard of space per individual. That time, however, seems far in the future. Most people seem still to feel a strong attraction for woods and waters, and on their annual vacations and as much oftener as they can arrange it, they set out in search of the solitude which grows ever more difficult to find.

[10] *Ibid.*
[11] Justin W. Leonard, Moral, Ethical and Fiscal Aspects of Wildlife Management, *Trans. Twenty-ninth North Amer. Wildlife Conf.*, 1965.

BIBLIOGRAPHY

Action for Outdoor Recreation for America, Citizens Committee for the ORRRC Report, 1963.
Annual Reports of the Chief of the Forest Service, 1949–1963.
Annual Reports of the Secretary of the Interior, 1949–1963.
Areas Administered by the National Park Service, U.S. Department of the Interior, 1964.

Great Lakes Park Institute, Proceedings of the Fifth Annual Meeting, Indiana University, Department of Recreation, Bloomington, Ind., 1951. (Mimeographed.)

LEONARD, JUSTIN W.: Moral, Ethical, and Fiscal Aspects of Wildlife Management, *Trans. Twenty-ninth North Amer. Wildlife Conf.*, 1965.

MCKAYE, BENTON The New Exploration, Harcourt, Brace and Company, Inc., New York, 1928.

Michigan Conservation, monthly magazine of the Michigan Department of Conservation, Lansing, Mich., 1949–1965.

News Releases, Office of the Secretary, U.S. Department of the Interior, September 5, 1964 and May 3, 1965.

Outdoor Recreation for America, ORRRC, Washington, D.C., January, 1962.

People and Timber, Forest Service, *U.S. Dept. Agr. Misc. Publ.* 721, 1956.

Recreation in Small Watershed Projects, Soil Conservation Service, U.S. Department of Agriculture, PA 610, February, 1964.

Rural Recreation: A New Family-farm Business, U.S. Department of Agriculture, September, 1962.

SHANKLAND, ROBERT: Steve Mather of the National Parks, Alfred A. Knopf, Inc., New York, 1950.

SMITH, GUY-HAROLD, ed.: Conservation of Natural Resources, John Wiley & Sons, Inc., New York, 3d ed., 1965.

THOREAU, HENRY DAVID: Walden, The Macmillan Company, New York, 1929.

Trends in American Living and Outdoor Recreation, *ORRRC Rept.* 22, Washington, D.C., 1962.

WELLS, GEORGE, AND IRIS WELLS: The Handbook of Wilderness Travels, Harper & Row, Publishers, Incorporated, New York, 1956.

14 HUMAN POWERS AS NATURAL RESOURCES

BECAUSE THE USE of human beings for the benefit of themselves and other human beings is a use of services which flow from human powers, the term *human powers* will be used in this discussion rather than the more common term *human resources*. From man's own viewpoint the greatest of all natural resources are the human powers developed during the long course of the evolution which has elevated him above the lower animals and made him master of all he surveys.

There is nothing to indicate that early man or his immediate primate ancestors made impossible demands of the resources which supported them. Drought and famine may have caused both distress and death within circumscribed localities, just as they do today. But man survived because, while his mental capacity increased as he climbed the ladder of evolution, his physical anatomy remained comparatively nonspecialized. The combination has enabled him either to seek out or create for himself an acceptable environment, whereas animals attaining greater physical specialization have been doomed to extinction by drastic environmental change. Long before the dawn of recorded history man was securely established from the Tropics to the Arctic, from desert to forest, and from sea level to timberline.

Perhaps man's greatest physical endowments were his opposable thumb, making possible the tool-using hand; the ability to assume a permanently upright, bipedal stance, which freed the hands from duties of locomotion; and certain anatomical features which facilitated articulate speech. Whether man's enormous brain capacity would have evolved without these concomitant anatomical attributes is a question biologists still ponder. It seems safe to conclude, however, that manual dexterity, coupled with speech which allowed the development of symbolization and the transmission of knowledge from one generation to the next, gave man his dominion over the earth. Another gift of evolution, man's innate aggressiveness toward his fellow man, may, of course, in this nuclear age, cause his extinction more rapidly than natural causes wiped out trilobites and dinosaurs in past geological ages.

Man, of course, assumes that he is the lord of creation and that all other elements or resources of nature are for his benefit. He may object to the very natural urge of the coyote to prey upon his sheep, but actually he uses his own powers and those of others to prey upon the coyote and even, perhaps, to use its hide for a garment. Other of his powers and those of his fellows are used for more sophisticated purposes, such as maintaining the health of his family, moving natural-resource materials about in commerce, educating his children, striving to better understand his environment, and, on occasion, even attempting to save from extinction some of the wild animals with which he shares the earth.

Human powers are a favorite topic for human inquiry and speculation, and they have been classified, categorized, and defined in too many ways to review here. Ely[1] has regrouped the basic physical and mental attributes just mentioned into powers of the body and powers of the spirit and has subdivided the latter into moral and intellectual powers. An economist might class human powers as roughly equivalent to the second of the three traditionally recognized forms of capital—private, human, and social.[2] In this view human capital refers to those human qualities which are developed by investments in education and training, health improvement, and recreational and aesthetic experiences. Human capital is, in essence, created by the transfer of new and old information, itself a form of social capital, into individual minds.

A moment's thought will suggest that some human powers can easily get out of hand as far as the good of mankind is concerned, and certainly the way in which the material resources of the earth have been handled is an example of this. Moreover, the powers themselves are somewhat analogous to material natural resources in the sense that they may be wasted, depleted, and reduced in productivity and may frequently be inequitably distributed in terms of talent needed at varying times, places, and by different groups. Examples suggest themselves: a skilled and promising scientist drafted as a private in fighting forces; an overstaffed enterprise during a time of scarcity of man power, or a surplus of labor for one industry and scarcity in another requiring different skills, side by side; disease and unsafe working conditions cutting down the producing power of a training or manufacturing force; and lack of medical and teaching services in a fast-growing pioneer community with poorly paid and irregularly employed medical and teaching talent in older, larger communities.

On the positive side, human powers may be analogous to material natural resources because they are subject to efficient use through proper training and allocation, with minimum waste; to improvement in skill and output through training, supplying with proper tools, and guiding in the expenditure of effort; to redistribution through planning, forecasting need, and possibly decentralizing certain industries; and to better distribution in a social sense, by such procedures as extension courses in centers away from main educational plants, group hospitalization, traveling and decentralized service forces for widely used mechanical devices, and forecasting the need for training workers in new fields.

FACTORS WHICH WASTE AND DEPLETE HUMAN POWERS

Human powers may be reduced, wasted, or depleted by a variety of factors, both external and internal. Despite the promise of these powers,

[1] Richard T. Ely, Ralph K. Hess, Charles K. Lieth, and Thomas Nixon Carver, *Foundations of National Prosperity*, The Macmillan Company, New York, 1923, p. 48.

[2] Lee H. Martin, Social Capital and Living Standards, *A Place to Live, Yearbook of U.S. Dept. Agr.*, 1963, pp. 210–216.

during his early history as a species man probably made no greater demands on his supporting resources than did the lower animals and his numbers were held in check by the same external factors which limited theirs—famine, disease, and predation, the latter progressing from individual attack through small raiding parties to large-scale organized warfare. Such internal depleting factors as dishonesty, idleness, and vice loom larger in the United States today than external factors, although war remains an ever-present threat.

Disease. Undoubtedly human powers are being greatly enhanced by the conquest of disease—not merely the killers such as pneumonia and septicemia, but, also the chronic weakeners such as malaria and hookworm and the cripplers such as poliomyelitis. However, the battle is far from won, and human powers continue to be sapped or destroyed by cancer, kidney ailments, heart and circulatory diseases, and arthritis, among others. Loss of time from employment due to the common cold still runs to astronomical figures.

Accidents. Few reforms get more publicity or put out more effort than accident prevention, and yet figures compiled by the National Safety Council for 1963 indicate a total of 101,000 deaths by accident, of which 43,600 were caused by motor vehicles, 29,000 occurred in homes, 17,500 were caused by nonmotor public vehicles, and 14,200 were occupational. (Figures are rounded approximations, and duplication between motor-vehicle, occupational, and home accidents is eliminated in the total.) Wage losses from motor-vehicle-accident injuries alone in 1963 reached 2 billion dollars, and medical expense amounted to 450 million dollars. It is hardly likely that this depleter of human powers can be reduced in the face of the mania for greater speed and more power and the economic limitations observed in employment of safety-engineering talent and physical improvements, to say nothing of the effectiveness of legislation and law enforcement. Much of this record appears to be an inevitable accompaniment to the standards of production and living which Americans demand.

Vice and Crime. Although there is probably a great degree of natural rebelliousness and of battle against frustration in mankind as a whole, and although vice is superficially defined as meanness by those who suffer as a result of it, vice is somewhat of a corollary to substandard health and living conditions and to boredom. Vice, therefore, as a depleter of human powers, overlaps disease and idleness. Aside from the waste and destruction of economic goods occasioned by theft, arson, and general racketeering, for example, it is well to remember that the talents of otherwise valuable members of society are frequently turned to use for the planning and executing of crime. Again, the vast army of persons required to police and care for criminals, captured and at large, requires the use of human powers in disproportionate volume. This may not appear to be waste when the necessity for maintaining order and protecting society is considered. However, the number of people required to achieve such results is appalling.

Idleness. There has been a good deal of talk throughout the ages of the pleasure of having nothing to do. The sluggard of Biblical times represents one extreme. The talented individual of the modern world who has the means to live without working and chooses to do so represents the other. Between the two there are vast resources of human powers unused either voluntarily or necessarily because there is no opportunity for employing them. By far the greater depletion occurs, of course, among those individuals who choose to be idle. Their talents, or powers, are frequently more valuable than those of the "unemployables," be the latter diseased, unskilled, disadvantageously located, imprisoned, or incurably lazy.

In an excellent essay, Carver[3] reduces this situation to a matter of ideals and interests, both of which may be influenced by training and education. He draws attention to an Indiana farmer who apparently gets his satisfaction out of life by producing economic goods. The goods he produces are hogs. As one observes his operation, it seems to go something like this: The sale of his hogs brings in more money than he needs to live on, and so he spends the surplus for more land, upon which he raises corn to feed more hogs, which brings in more profit, which he spends to buy more land to grow more corn to feed more hogs—and so on far into the twilight along the Wabash. By this time, the observer—an intellectual, no doubt, who likes his bacon for breakfast—begins to smile and feel that something is wrong. But the fact remains that the farmer is producing economic goods.

The intellectual retires to his study and starts thinking about Michelangelo, who worked feverishly and persistently throughout his life, not only in art but in other fields. His total accomplishment for the spiritual satisfaction of his fellowmen is almost beyond human comprehension. He also was a producer whose satisfaction came through creative effort.

Slowly the following diagram begins to take form:

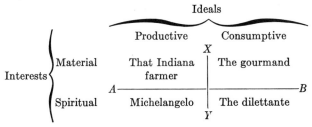

[3] Ely and associates, *op. cit.*, p. 295.

Under the consumptive ideals in this picture appears the gourmand or glutton, who apparently lives to eat and drink. He would be in a tough spot if it were not for the producer to his left. Below him is the dilettante, who dabbles with art and science but only for amusement. Probably he rationalizes his program by assuming that he inspires the producer of art by serving as a consuming audience.

This diagram is not reproduced to belittle artistic and scientific achievement or, in other words, to compare material and spiritual production. It *is* useful to demonstrate that the line XY, which separates the voluntarily idle and unproductive possessor of powers from the voluntarily occupied producer, regardless of the quality of his powers, is important. The line AB on the other hand is not so important. The world has not yet suffered too much for lack of consumers of really essential economic goods. But the strike of the producer, either on the part of labor or management, has frequently caused suffering.

This is a long argument to indicate that idleness is a depleter of human powers, but it should also be pointed out that mankind has not courageously faced the problem of making it simple for all who want to work to be employed constructively.

Dishonesty. Credit, safety of property and person, peace among men, organizations, and nations are all founded upon adherence to standards of honesty as well as on signed legal agreements with penalties prescribed for violation. There is no complete substitute for the will to keep one's word even to his hurt. Dishonesty, therefore, with its chance to disrupt order and safety is a depleter not only of the powers of the liar but of those of his fellow men to whom he is untrue. In this connection the conservation of natural resources and of human powers requires courageous facing of the dangers surrounding the modern code of dishonesty from which may be extracted such passages as, "The end (always) justifies the means." "The crime consists of getting caught." "If I don't take it somebody else will." "What he doesn't know won't hurt him." And perhaps (with a warped meaning), "God helps the man who helps himself." Perhaps mankind was endowed with the power to rationalize so that he could maintain a sense of validity in a turbulent world, but he still has an obligation to strive for intellectual honesty.

War. Regardless of the mental and moral gymnastics by which war is rationalized and of the total positive results of war in the development of a civilization, war does destroy in vast measure the resource consisting of human powers. Moreover, the quality of human powers destroyed is high in terms of vigor, courage, and potential contribution to the good of society. It is not the old, worn-out, or unemployable surpluses of population or human powers that go to battle. It is a select group, often the

figure 14-1

*Testing for gas after a blast. The safety-lamp flame changes color
if methane is present. (Bituminous Coal Institute.)*

best, particularly in terms of health, intelligence, and strength. What
this expenditure purchases must also be charged with the destructive use
of vast quantities of treasure and natural resources with minimum recovery. One of the developments that is to be hoped for and worked for
is a program of waging peace with somewhere near the energy with
which nations wage war.

Disasters. Floods, earthquakes, hurricanes, and other natural phenomena which constitute disasters are dramatic and persistent. And although
they are relatively unimportant in the total picture of the depletion of
human powers, it is defeatist to say that these as well as the disasters
caused by mankind—wrecks, fires, mine disasters—cannot be attacked
and their depletion of human powers reduced (Fig. 14-1). The reader is
referred back to the discussions of flood control on pages 137–141 and
mine safety on pages 320 and 418.

Overpopulation. One human power that has concerned a number of
recent writers and thinkers in connection with conserving natural resources is mankind's power to reproduce. Theoretically reproduction

413

brings about a continuing flow into the world's reservoir of human powers. Actually it may add to populations which are ill fed and proportionately unproductive. Even in a great democracy such as the United States, with a relatively small percentage increase of population annually, there are sections in which disproportionate population increase is accompanied by irregular and inadequate food supply and living conditions generally. Increase in numbers of people, therefore, does not necessarily mean increase in the total resource of human powers.

Almost all the voices raised in behalf of population control are speaking of world population, and although the United States faces a less immediate population problem than other countries, her food-producing resources will be increasingly called upon to help the vast portion of the globe which is now inhabited by undernourished people. By similar token the rapidly expanding and space-requiring advances in her technology will lessen, rather than increase, her own self-sufficiency. In a sense, therefore, to talk of world-population problems is to talk of this country's conservation and production problems and of the demand for an increasing supply of human powers. For any who wish to confine their thinking to the United States alone, it is well to bear in mind that each 24 hours we have about 6,600 more mouths to feed. This figure is net and is derived from the subtraction of 1.8 million deaths in 1963 from 4.1 million births.

The 1965 world population of over 3 billion includes one-third, at least, of such a number who are undernourished, and those inhabiting almost two thirds of the area of the globe account for an annual increase in population ranging from 1.25 to 3 per cent a year. At a rate of 1 per cent a year, the population would double in two generations; and the present world rate is approximately 1.7 per cent. Some examples will make this figure even more startling: Haiti, with a population of 4.5 million on 10,000 square miles of badly abused land, has doubled its population in 30 years. Italy increased its numbers 50 per cent in 50 years. World population is likely to increase at a rate of at least 1.7 per cent per year for the next decade, but the growth in the rate of human food consumption world wide is averaging about 3 per cent per year. And although developed countries may keep up the rates of growth in food production and imports adequate to keep pace with population growth, many of the low-income countries are not raising their food-production rates fast enough and, consequently, are faced with serious prospects.[4]

On the whole then it appears that simply increasing population may well amount eventually to decrease rather than increase of human powers.

[4] Robert D. Stevens, Population, Income, and Food, *Farmer's World, Yearbook of U.S. Dept. Agr.,* 1957, pp. 53–57.

CONSERVING HUMAN POWERS

Because a harvest of human powers, or even an inventory, cannot be expressed in tons, board feet, or kilowatts, the means of conserving such powers must also differ from those used to conserve material natural resources. On the other hand, the items of (1) use with minimum waste, (2) increase in productivity, and (3) equitable distribution are still subject in some degree to control. The over-all cure is made up largely of research, education, and sounding out a positive, if qualified, answer to the old inquiry, "Am I my brother's keeper?" One of the most dramatically affirmative answers of our times lies in the Peace Corps. This program, founded by President John F. Kennedy in 1961, has fired the imaginations of young people with its promise of an outlet, in the cause of peace, for those traits of self-sacrifice, purposefulness, and service to others so characteristic of war.[5] The achievements of the Peace Corps' dedicated members are already great, perhaps more for intangible results than for the very real contributions to the material betterment of many people in many lands. Specifically, society has a number of tough jobs on its hands.

Disease. This yields remarkably to the application of the results of long-drawn-out, and patient research. More than a score of associations and foundations are active in promoting and supporting research, prevention, and treatment of as many important diseases. The following are examples of research, educational, and action programs which deserve mention: Tuberculosis, long the great killer, especially of youth, claimed only 9,311 lives in 1963. This was a 40 per cent reduction over the previous 8 years. About fifty thousand new cases are reported each year, most of them detected by wholesale chest X-ray examination conducted by health agencies. Much of this work is financed by the National Tuberculosis Association from proceeds of the sale of Christmas Seals. Funds allocated to state, county, and city units are also used partially for education. Steady and promising research on the origin and treatment of cancer has long been under way and has recently been accelerated in the field of atomic energy. The American Cancer Society declares that the number of lives saved from cancer can be doubled if people see their doctors earlier and if doctors become more familiar with known means of detection and treatment. The society conducts an aggressive educational campaign using a variety of communications media.

The National Foundation, which supported development of the Salk and Sabin poliomyelitis vaccines through the March of Dimes, is now able, because of these vaccines' dramatic success, to expand its program to combat arthritis and birth defects.

[5] The Peace Corps, Pauline Madow, ed., *Reference Shelf*, vol. 36, no. 2, the H. W. Wilson Company, New York, 1964, p. 9.

Other groups organized to work for the prevention and treatment of disease include associations and foundations concerned with heart ailments, diabetes, leprosy, rheumatism, muscular dystrophy, and eye banks for sight restoration.

While the above are somewhat spectacular, the quiet and persistent work of thousands of physicians, nurses, research workers, visiting nurses, mental-hospital workers, and good neighbors forms an effective attack on suffering and disease.

Alleviation of human suffering depends not only upon advances in medical knowledge and skills but on the ability of all our citizens to receive the benefit of these advances regardless of economic status. Health insurance plans are a common fringe benefit of the actively employed and are generally available to those able to pay the premiums. However, such protection remains beyond the means of many people, means of providing medical care for such people have provoked heated discussions in Congress and elsewhere. A solution adequate to the philosophy, is being sought in Medicare, a plan for health and hospital insurance tied in with Social Security.

Idleness. Idleness, particularly involuntary idleness, poses a problem for society in general which can be met. In the Great Depression following the Crash of 1929, employment was furnished to millions on a vast public-works program. Sarcastic and bitter criticism was leveled at many of these public enterprises, but large public-works programs have been the classic palliative for unemployment since the building of the pyramids of Egypt. Despite the jibes hurled at some of the best citizens in the country who found themselves employed by WPA and other agencies, these people showed little evidence of "making a career of being publicly supported." For as recovery developed, these same involuntarily unemployed left the public rolls as fast as they could obtain private employment. Normally, the unemployed in the United States do not represent any great proportion of the workers, and frequently the "unemployables" comprise a considerable part of the number. Here, as well as in a general situation, education to equip and allocate workers in all fields has no substitute. Although it is hardly true that "the world owes me a living," it may very well be true that "democracy owes me *the opportunity, as a good citizen,* to earn a living." Today retraining programs go hand-in-hand with the growth of automation and cybernetics. A Federal program of this sort is the Job Corps, created in 1964. Under this program, camps are operated in national parks, forests, wildlife refuges, and other federally owned areas. Young men recruited into these camps not only perform much needed conservation work but also gain new skills and new confidence to improve their employability.

The problem of the school dropout involves many people and agencies in attempted solutions. Efforts to combat delinquency and unemployability of insufficiently trained youth are exemplified by a variety of programs, among them youth rehabilitation camp programs geared to conservation projects in which healthful outdoor exercise is coupled with learning the advantages of teamwork and cooperation and gaining new outlooks and occupational skills (Fig. 14-2).

One direction in which too little progress has been made is that of according respect to a conscientious and productive worker in *any* useful occupation. Let the poet respect the charwoman and the statesman the garbage man or let the "self-made" businessman tolerate the professor, and vice versa (see diagram, page 411).

Vice and Crime. It has been pointed out that vice and crime are often results of substandard conditions of health and living and are certainly stimulated by boredom resulting from having nothing interesting to do in leisure hours. A part, if only a small one, therefore, of the remedy is in the hands of society. And when slums are replaced by decent housing, or racial discrimination is dispensed with in employment, or playgrounds

417

are furnished at public expense, they need not be considered failures if at first they seem to be unappreciated and if the first decent wages of the tenants are spent for a showy automobile. The reconditioning of embittered youth may take several generations, but it is worth working at. Education can also do much to lessen tendencies to crime. There is a long way to go in prison reform.

Dishonesty. Just how *honest* one can be and still make a living is a question that bothers many a possessor of considerable human powers. Unfortunately such a person often concludes that "virtue is its own (read 'only') reward" and that this is not enough. Or he may conclude, as did the lad trying to remember the Sunday School text, that "a lie is an abomination unto the Lord, but a very present help in time of trouble." But because the keeping of one's word is so important in human and even international relations, a radical change in the present-day habits of adults who set an example for their children is one of the few hopes for the emergence of an honest generation.

Accidents. These command the attention of the newspapers, police, hospitals, and the National Safety Council, and there is a healthy pre-occupation with accident prevention. The two approaches, safer gadgets and relentless education, both pay off. The potentialities of wise legislation have not yet been fully realized. Safety measures in coal mining are more fully discussed on page 320 (Fig. 14-1).

War. War is regarded by some scholars as a biological phenomenon. In any event, it is unlikely to go out of style unless its causes can be recognized and eliminated. The United Nations bids fair to make steady, if irritatingly slow, progress in this direction. Poison gas was not used in World War II, but this was because of its "inefficiency" and not for humanitarian reasons. The hydrogen bomb does not suffer from "inefficiency," and if it should be used in another world war, the results will be quick and terrible.

Disasters. These overlap accidents but are due to natural phenomena. Research, legislation, and planned or restricted occupancy of flood plains and lake shores offer some hope of forecasting and escaping.

Overpopulation. Increase in numbers of people was given only one alternative by Malthus whose thesis was that population tends to outrun the means of subsistence. That alternative was moral restraint. Since then, alternatives of new-land discovery, improvement in crop production, food from the sea, development of synthetics, and general natural-resource conservation have been offered on the positive side. These possibilities are not yet exhausted, but their use is not too encouraging on a global basis. On the restrictive, or negative, side, birth control is generally advocated by the "neomalthusians,' as the recent writers have been called. So great is interest in this alternative that the well-known planned-parent-hood movement is prospering. Furnishing of birth-control information and the establishment of clinics are increasingly common in many lands. Eugenics has still far to go. A new approach to it, however, is being hinted at in the growing understanding of deoxyribonucleic acid (DNA) and the fundamental genetic material of the cell. The dream (or threat) of artificially controlled inheritance is moving a step closer to reality.

Education and the Future. In the foregoing discussion, education has been frequently mentioned. It is a broad term and should be so understood. Education occurs both in and out of school. There is no substitute for that obtained in either way. The tools of communication, measurement, reasoning, and analysis are perhaps best acquired in school. Attitudes, habits, viewpoints, and, unfortunately, prejudices build up outside school—in family, gang, club, and business. An educated man should be informed, know where to acquire needed facts, and have ability to reason out a healthy sense of values. On the vocational side it is no discredit to education to say that he should have mastered certain skills even if some of them are only manual. These are releasers and maintainers of human powers. But today's complex world needs men who are interested in knowing not only *how to do it* but *why*. Unless democracy learns to discipline its beliefs so that unusual intelligence, as well as the ordinary run, is capitalized through special education, there is bound to be a continuing shortage of qualified social and political leaders, scientists, and engineers. A higher level of education than ever before is required to conserve those resources which we think of as *natural* and which constitute the foundations of national prosperity. Yet existing educational facilities are being outgrown faster than they are being expanded (Fig. 14-3). Beyond this we have a civilization to maintain and improve and a universe to explore. President Lyndon B. Johnson's proclamation of "The Great Society," with its declaration of war on poverty and its plans for urban redevelopment, for beautification of the countryside, for expanded educational facilities, for improved care and opportunity for the disadvantaged, crystallizes a growing national awareness of today's human powers. Their continued conservation will give reality to our dreams.

BIBLIOGRAPHY

Annual Report of Resources for the Future, Washington, D.C., 1957.
Annual Report of the Secretary of Health, Education, and Welfare, 1957.
BROWN, HARRISON, JAMES BONNER, AND JOHN WEIR: The Next Hundred Years, The Viking Press, Inc., New York, 1957.
CAIN, STANLEY A.: A Second Look at Mathus's Principle of Population, in Resources and Policy: Current Issues in Conservation, Lee S. Greene and René de Visme Williamson, eds., reprinted from *J. Politics*, vol. 13, pp. 315–324, August, 1951.

figure 14-3
The population explosion hits the campus. (Photo, University of Michigan.)

COLE, CHARLES C.: Encouraging Scientific Talent: A Report to the National Science Foundation, College Entrance Examination Board, New York, 1955.

ELY, RICHARD T., RALPH K. HESS, CHARLES K. LIETH, AND THOMAS NIXON CARVER: Foundations of National Prosperity, The Macmillan Company, New York, 1923.

KELLOGG, CHARLES E.: Opportunities for World Abundance, in Resources and Policy: Current Issues in Conservation, Lee S. Greene and René de Visme Williamson, eds., reprinted from *J. Politics*, vol. 13, pp. 325–344, August, 1951.

LEONARD, JUSTIN W.: People and Land, *New York State Conservationist*, vol. 15, no. 4, pp. 2–4, 37, 1961.

MADOW, PAULINE, ED.: The Peace Corps, *Reference Shelf*, vol. 36, no. 2, The H. W. Wilson Company, New York, 1964.

MATHER, KIRTLEY F.: Enough and to Spare, Harper & Row, Publishers, Incorporated, New York, 1944.

MUMFORD, LEWIS: The City in History, Harcourt, Brace & World, Inc., New York, 1961.

News Releases, U.S. Department of the Interior, 1960–1965.

THOMAS, WILLIAM L., ED.: Man's Role in Changing the Face of the Earth, The University of Chicago Press, Chicago, 1956.

VOGT, WILLIAM: Road to Survival, William Sloane Associates, New York, 1948.

World Almanac, New York World-Telegram and The Sun, New York, 1965.

INDEX